Phillip A. Walter
RR 5 BOX 232
GOSHEN IND
46526

Workers Setting in Place One of the Many Beams That Go into a Structure.
Each Beam Must Be Carefully Designed To Support Its Load
Courtesy of Standard Oil Co. (N.J.). Photo by Libsohn

ELEMENTARY
Structural Design

By CHARLES O. HARRIS, B.S., M.S., Sc.D.

Head of Department of Applied Mechanics, Michigan State University

Formerly Professor of Engineering Mechanics, University of Notre Dame

Formerly Assistant Professor of Mechanics, Illinois Institute of Technology

Author of

STRENGTH OF MATERIALS *and* SLIDE RULE SIMPLIFIED

Illustrated

AMERICAN TECHNICAL SOCIETY • CHICAGO, U. S. A.

FIRST EDITION

1st Printing, 1951
2nd Printing, 1958 *(Amended)*
3rd Printing, 1962
4th Printing, 1964
5th Printing, 1966
6th Printing, 1969
7th Printing, 1972

LIBRARY OF CONGRESS NUMBER 51-649
ISBN 0-8269-0520-X

PRINTED IN THE UNITED STATES OF AMERICA

PREFACE

This book is a systematic, detailed presentation of the elements of structural engineering. It is intended for use by engineering and technical students, building trades apprentices, and by people in industry who wish to learn structural engineering by home study.

The organization has been worked out with great care to make learning easy. Each chapter begins with a statement of purpose. The student is told *what* he is going to learn, *why* he should learn this material, and *how* the structural engineer uses it in actual work. Then each topic is explained in a series of short steps with several illustrative examples and a set of practice problems to which answers are given. There is a summary near the end of each chapter, followed by a set of review questions and a set of review problems. Teachers will find the review questions and problems useful in checking students' grasp of the material. Those who study alone should complete the problems and questions before going on to the next chapter.

The mathematics used in the book is limited to very simple algebra and trigonometry. Throughout the book, emphasis is placed on understanding formulas rather than deriving them; therefore, very few derivations are presented. Formulas are stated and explained, and the methods of using them are explained in many short, detailed steps.

The choice and treatment of material in the book are novel, and they reflect the views developed by the author during many years of teaching and through many experiences using this material in practice.

The first chapter includes such fundamental topics as force, components of a force, and moment of a force. These topics are vital prerequisites to the study of structural engineering. They are included here not only for the benefit of those who may not have had the opportunity to study them before, but also because it is the author's experience as a teacher that nearly all students who have studied these topics before need to review them at this point.

Next, there is one chapter each on the subjects of equilibrium, centroid, and moment of inertia. These subjects are also prerequisite to structural engineering. They are to be studied thoroughly by people who have not studied them earlier, and they should be reviewed by those who have.

Review of previous material is emphasized throughout the book, especially in Chapters VI and XI, where the first part of the chapter is a review of material which was covered in the earlier part of the book and is to be used again in the particular chapter.

One chapter is devoted to beams of standard section because most beams used in structures are of this type. Tables are included which give the properties of many standard sections, and full explanations are given for the use of these tables, enabling the reader to find the properties of a section and design a beam of standard section. There are three tables of standard steel sections and one table of standard wood sections.

The subject of deflection of a beam, often difficult for the student, is presented in a novel manner which is easily mastered. A table of formulas is given which with any beam deflection can be simply calculated with an accuracy of two per cent. Formulas are explained thoroughly, and their use is shown by illustrative examples.

Special attention is paid to showing the student how to recognize a statically indeterminate beam. Then formulas are given and explained for the bending moments, shearing forces, and reactions on a number of examples of statically indeterminate beams. The examples chosen include those statically indeterminate beams likely to occur in simple structural work.

One chapter is devoted to the reinforced concrete floor slab because of the wide use of this structural element. First there is an explanation of what concrete is, and then the procedure of designing a reinforced concrete floor slab is presented in a number of simple steps.

The subject of structural connections is so important that it is presented in a separate chapter. The common types of riveted and welded connections are explained in detail, and procedures are given for designing them.

Charles O. Harris

FOREWORD TO THE STUDENT

This book provides you with an efficient aid to learning structural engineering. Now it is up to you to do your part by studying with care and diligence. Here are a few suggestions that will help.

Study systematically and learn one subject at a time—master each article before you go on to the next.

Study with paper, pencil, and slide rule at hand, and write out the illustrative examples. Check the calculations with your slide rule, and see if the answers are in agreement—don't consider it a mistake if you obtain an answer of 4,670 when the book gives 4,680. That isn't a mistake, but it is just the difference in the way two people read the slide rule.

Work the practice problems at the end of each article, check your answers, and be sure that you understand each problem.

There is a summary at the end of the new material in each chapter. Study this summary carefully before going on to the review questions and problems. Don't go on to the next chapter until you have done this, for you need to know the first part of the book in order to understand the last part.

Use the slide rule as often as possible in working the problems. It will save you much time and effort, and you will make fewer mistakes than if you work out the calculations longhand.

Be sure to work the problems. You cannot possibly learn this subject without working many problems. The problems have been chosen with great care to help you in learning, and the more you work, the more you will learn.

CONTENTS

CHAPTER I

FUNDAMENTALS

PURPOSE OF THIS CHAPTER. In this study of *Elementary Structural Design*, the subject of strength of materials is the medium, or tool, by means of which we solve the various problems involved in designing structural members, and, also, in designing complete structures. The study of this subject will become easier when you have a clear understanding of the principle and importance of design.

Several fundamentals will be studied in this chapter, since they are involved in nearly every problem which must be solved when finding the strength of a material. These fundamentals include: *force*, *components of force*, and *moment of a force*. You will have to learn, first, what these forces are and how they are calculated, so you can understand the methods used in solving the problems in later chapters. Time will not be taken now to explain *force*, but it will be explained later.

1-1. What Elementary Structural Design Is.

In this study of *Elementary Structural Design*, you will learn how to calculate the strength of a material used for a structural member; that is, how to find how strong a material is, and how to design a structural member made from that material, so that it will be strong enough to support the loads placed upon it. For example, you will learn how to design the beams which support a floor so that the beams will be strong enough to carry the loads which will be placed on the floor.

Also, in *Elementary Structural Design*, you will learn how different materials, such as wood, concrete, and steel, react when loads are applied to them. You will have to learn, also, just how strong different materials are.

1-2. Why You Should Study Strength of Materials.

In a study of *Elementary Structural Design*, it is important that you study strength of materials, because a knowledge of strength of materials is the basis for all structural design. Since certain formulas and procedures are used in design, it is not only necessary to learn these formulas and procedures but, also, to learn how they are used.

1-3. How Strength of Materials Is Used in Structural Design.

It is necessary to know the strength of any material used, when designing each member, or piece, of a structure. (To *design a member* means to decide of what material it is to be made; also, what its shape and dimensions are to be.) The structural design of a building usually starts at the top. You will get an idea of how the design proceeds by looking at Fig. 1, which shows some of the structural members in a building. The first member to be designed is the *roof slab* followed by the *roof beams* which support the roof slab. The *columns* (posts) which support the roof structure are then designed. The next structure

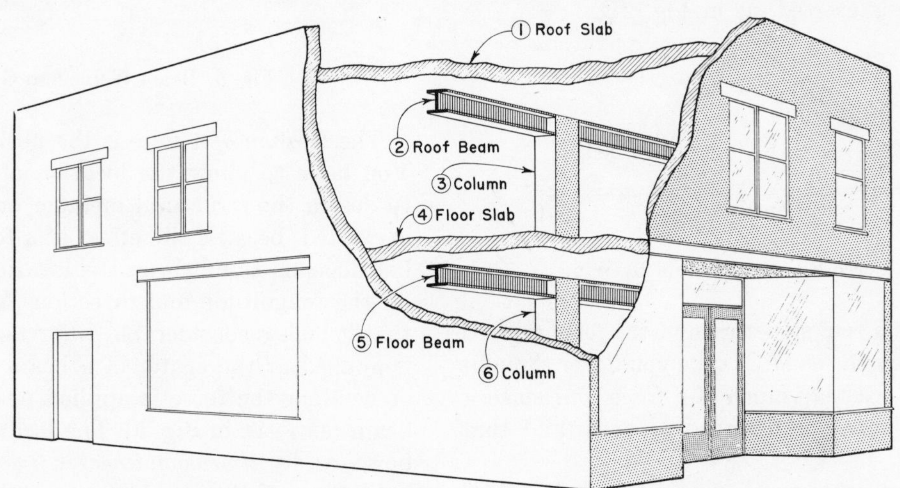

Fig. 1. Cutaway View of Building To Show Structural Members

member to be designed is the *floor slab for the top floor* followed by the *floor beams for the top floor*. Next are the *columns which support the top floor*. This procedure is continued right on down to the basement until all of the structural members of the building have been designed.

The same formulas and methods used in finding the strength of materials are used, also, in the design of all structural members, whether these members are floor slabs, roof slabs, beams, or columns. The architect designs one member at a time and applies his knowledge of strength of materials to calculate the size of the member so that it will be strong enough to carry its load.

1-4. Force.

Force is one of the factors you will have to work with in every problem in *Elementary Structural Design*, therefore, it is important to know what it is. A *force* is a push or a pull which is exerted by one object upon another and is represented by an arrow. For example, Fig. 2*A* shows the force which rolls of paper stored in a warehouse exert against the floor.

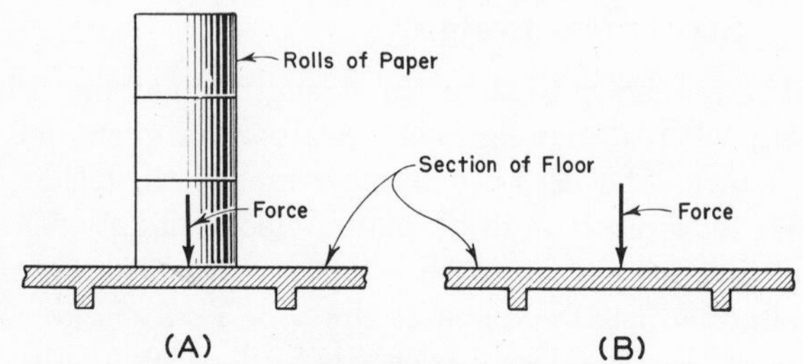

Fig. 2. Force Exerted on Warehouse Floor by Rolls of Paper

The rolls of paper are shown in Fig. 2*A* so that you can see why there is a force exerted on the floor. In working problems, draw only the force and the object upon which it is exerted, as in Fig. 2*B*.

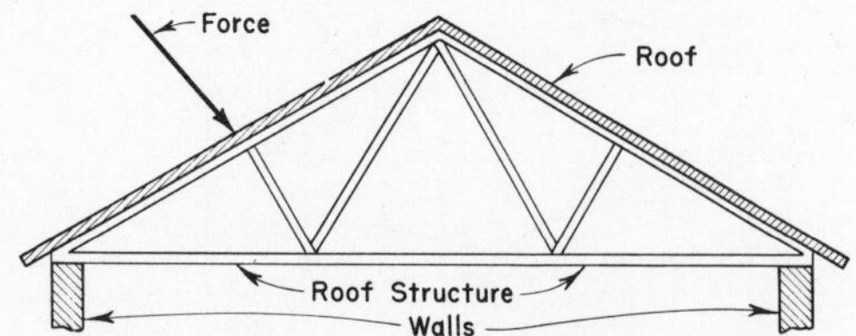

Fig. 3. Force Exerted on Roof by Wind

Fig. 3 shows a roof structure and the *force* exerted upon the roof by the *wind*. Maybe you never thought of the wind as exerting much of a force, but since it does, the roof must be designed to withstand that force.

Force is usually measured in *pounds* and structural engineers often use the *symbol* # for pounds. Thus, 1,000 pounds is 1,000 #, and 2,600 pounds is 2,600 #. In large structures, the forces are large and it is convenient to use the *kip* as the unit of force. A *kip* is equal to 1,000 pounds; therefore, 30,000 pounds equals 30 kips, and 1,000,000 pounds equals 1,000 kips. The size or amount of a force is usually called the *magnitude of the force*.

Force has *direction* as well as *magnitude*. You have to know the direction of a force in order to design the structure to which the force is applied. Since the force tends to push in the same direction as it is applied, you must make sure that the structure can withstand this force. The best way to show the direction of a force is to make a sketch and show the angle which the force makes with a horizontal line.

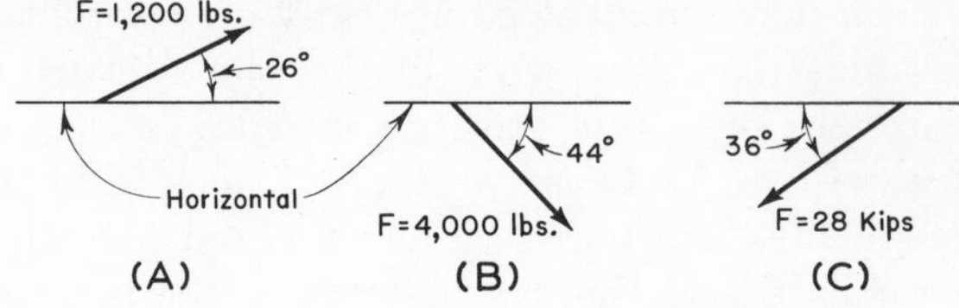

Fig. 4. Directions of Force

Force is represented by the letter *F*. Fig. 4*A* shows a force of 1,200 pounds which is directed upward to the right at an angle of 26° with the horizontal. Fig. 4*B* shows a force of 4,000 pounds which is directed downward to the right at an angle of 44° with the horizontal. Fig. 4*C* shows a force of 28 kips (28,000 pounds) which is directed downward to the left at an angle of 36° with the horizontal.

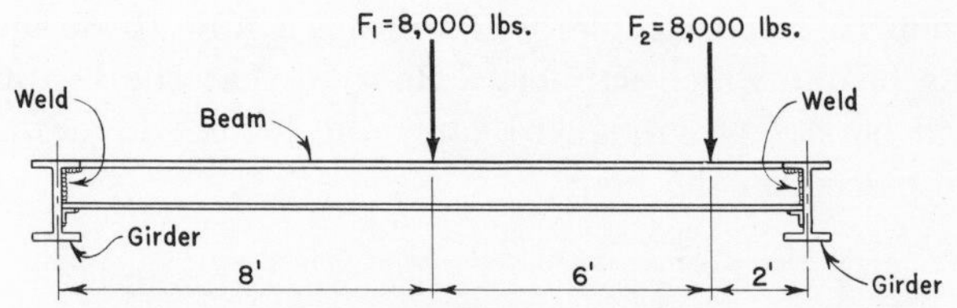

Fig. 5. Beam Welded to Girders

The *location of a force* is the position of the force. You have to know the location of a force in order to design the structural member on which the force is exerted, because the effect of a force on the member depends as much on the location of the force as on the magnitude and direction. You will see later that it makes considerable difference whether a force is applied at the center of a beam (as F_1 in Fig. 5) or whether the force is applied near the end of the beam (as F_2 is, in Fig. 5). The location of a force can be shown by *dimension lines* such as you see in Fig. 5.

In some of the problems you will draw a force to scale so that the length of the force represents the magnitude or amount of the force. Fig. 6 shows an example. The force of 2,000 pounds is laid off to a scale of 1,000 pounds per inch, hence, the arrow is 2 inches long.

1-5. Components of a Force.

A *component* is one of two forces which may replace a given force. Components will be studied at this time because they are used later in the solution of many problems which are made easier by replacing a force

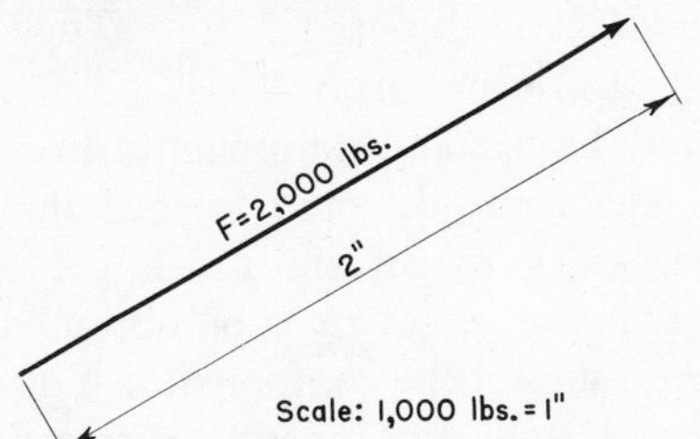

Fig. 6. Force Laid off to Scale

by its components. Begin with the force F in Fig. 7*A*. The force is laid off to scale so that the length of the arrow represents the magnitude of the force, and the force is at an angle θ (Greek letter *theta*) with the horizontal. Then draw the right triangle in Fig. 7*B* in which the force F is the hypotenuse, and in which one leg of the triangle is *horizontal* and one leg is *vertical*. The horizontal and vertical legs of the triangle represent components of the force F; that is, forces which can replace the force F. One of the components is horizontal and one is vertical. This is the most useful set of components, as you will see later. The triangle could be drawn with sides in any direction, but then the components of the force would be in these directions. The triangle must have one horizontal and one vertical leg to give components which are horizontal and vertical.

The horizontal leg of the triangle in Fig. 7*B* represents the horizontal component of the force (also called the x component) and we write is as F_x (read as F sub x). Now, you should remember from trigonometry that the cosine of the angle θ is equal to the horizontal leg of the triangle divided by the hypotenuse, and, in this case

$$\frac{F_x}{F} = \cos \theta$$

Multiply each side of this equation by F, to get

$$\frac{F_x}{F} \times F = F \cos \theta$$

Cancel F on the left side of the equation and you will have

$$F_x = F \cos \theta$$

This last equation states that the x component of the force is equal to the product of the force and the cosine of the angle which the force makes with the horizontal. You can look up the cosine of an angle in a *trig* table, or get it from your slide rule. The multiplication can easily be made with the slide rule.

Illustrative Example 1. Calculate the x component of the 3,600-lb. force in Fig. 8.

Solution:

1. The force F is 3,600 lbs.
2. The angle θ is 40°
3. The x component is

$$F_x = F \cos \theta = 3{,}600 \cos 40°$$

The cosine of 40° is 0.768, so

$$F_x = 3{,}600 \times 0.768 = 2{,}770 \text{ lbs.}$$

Back in Fig. 7*B*, the vertical leg of the triangle represents the vertical component (also called the y component) of the force and we write it as F_y (read as F sub y). From trigonometry, the sine of the angle

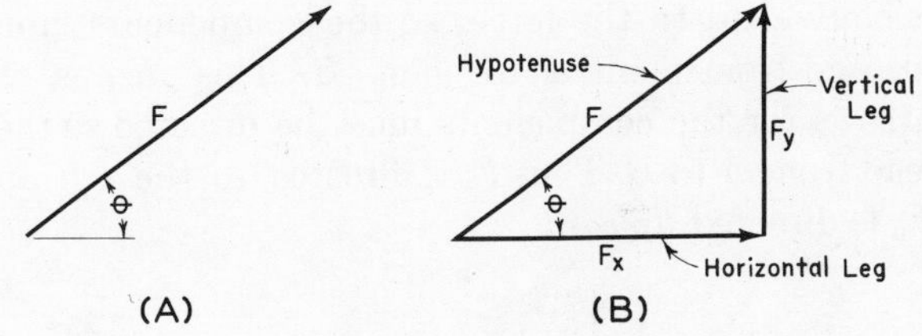

Fig. 7. Components of a Force

θ is equal to the vertical leg of the triangle divided by the hypotenuse. Here, this gives

$$\frac{F_y}{F} = \sin \theta$$

Multiply each side of the equation by F. This gives

$$\frac{F_y}{F} \times F = F \sin \theta$$

Cancel F on the left side of the equation and you will have

$$F_y = F \sin \theta$$

This equation states that the y component of the force is equal to the product of the force and the sine of the angle which the force makes with the horizontal.

Illustrative Example 2. Find the y component of the 3,600-lb. force in Fig. 8.

Solution:

1. The force F is 3,600 lbs.
2. The angle θ is 40°
3. The y component of the force is

$$F_y = F \sin \theta = 3{,}600 \sin 40°$$

The sine of 40° is 0.643, so

$$F_y = 3{,}600 \times 0.643 = 2{,}310 \text{ lbs.}$$

Study the triangle in Fig. 9A. Here the hypotenuse of the triangle represents a force F which is directed upward to the left. The horizontal leg of the triangle represents the horizontal component of the force (F_x) and the vertical leg of the triangle represents the vertical component of the force (F_y). Notice that the force F goes from point A to point B in Fig. 9A. The components can replace the force; that is, the pair of components is equivalent to the force; so the components must also go from point A to point B. This means the arrows for the components must be directed so they lead from A to B. Thus F_x is directed to the *left* and F_y is directed *upward.*

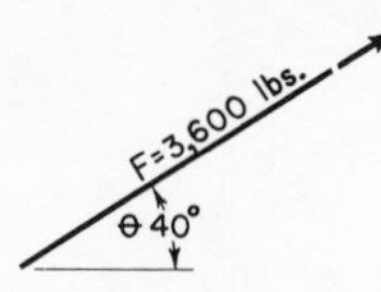

Fig. 8. Force in Example 1 (Art. 5)

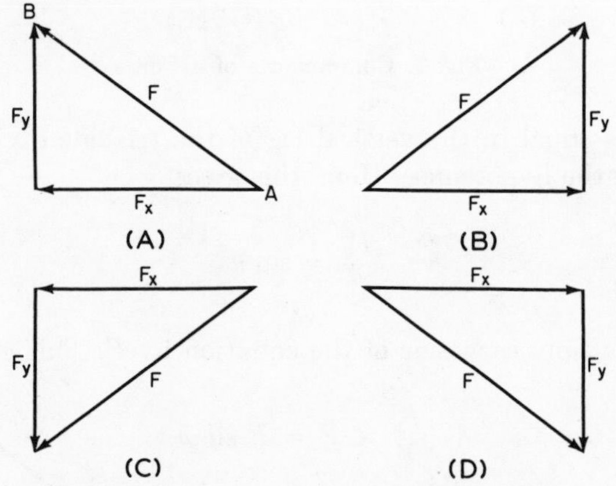

Fig. 9. Components of Force in Example 2 (Art. 5)

The same procedure can always be used to determine whether the x component of a force is directed to the right or left, and whether the y component is directed upward or downward. Thus, in Fig. 9B, you can see that F_x is directed toward the right and F_y is directed upward. In Fig. 9C, F_x is directed toward the left and F_y is directed downward. Then, in Fig. 9D, F_x is directed toward the right and F_y is directed downward.

An x component is *positive* if it is directed toward the right, and *negative* if it is directed toward the left; also, a y component is *positive* if it is directed upward, and *negative* if it is directed downward. In later problems we may have some components directed toward the right, and some directed toward the left and it will be necessary to get the net effect of the components. This net effect may be obtained by taking the algebraic sum of the components. You can always tell which way each component is directed by looking at the force; each component is then given the proper algebraic sign.

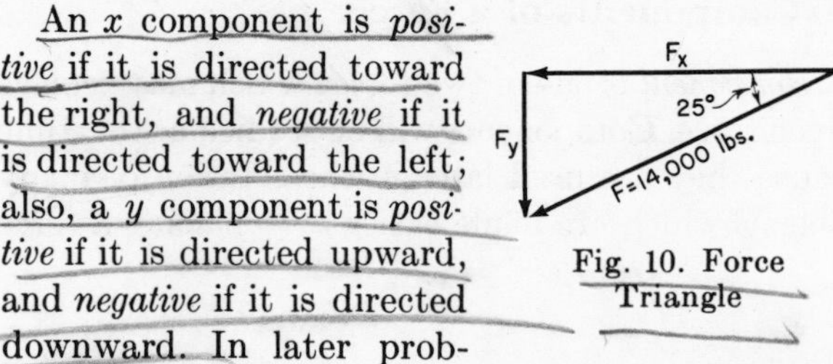

Fig. 10. Force Triangle

Illustrative Example 3. Find the x and y components of a force of 14,000 lbs. which is directed downward to the left at an angle of 25° with the horizontal.

Solution:

1. Fig. 10 shows the force triangle.
2. The force F is 14,000 lbs.
3. The angle θ is 25°
4. The x component of the force is *negative* because it is directed toward the left, so

$$F_x = -F \cos \theta = -14{,}000 \cos 25°$$
$$= -14{,}000 \times 0.907$$
$$= -12{,}700 \text{ lbs.}$$

5. The y component is *negative* because it is directed downward. Then,

$$F_y = -F \sin \theta = -14{,}000 \sin 25°$$
$$= -14{,}000 \times 0.423$$
$$= -5{,}930 \text{ lbs.}$$

Practice Problems (Art. 1-5).[1] Practice finding the components in the following problems. This knowledge will be useful in later work. Calculate each of the x and y components of each of the forces described in these problems.

---

[1] To check your answers to *Practice Problems*, refer to the section entitled *Answers to Problems*, at the back of this book.

1. A force of 6,800 lbs. which is directed upward to the right at an angle of 60° with the horizontal.
2. A force of 390 lbs. which is directed upward to the left at an angle of 48° with the horizontal.
3. A force of 21,600 lbs. which is directed downward to the left at an angle of 18°30′ with the horizontal.
4. A force of 1,640 lbs. which is directed downward to the right at an angle of 54°40′ with the horizontal.
5. The 3,200-lb. force in Fig. 11.
6. The 5,400-lb. force in Fig. 11.
7. The 2,400-lb. force in Fig. 11.
8. The 4,360-lb. force in Fig. 11.

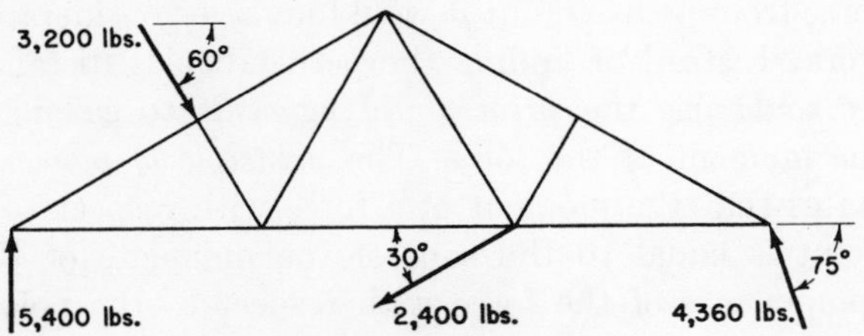

Fig. 11. Forces on Roof Truss

1-6. Moment of a Force.

The moment of a force has to be calculated in most problems of structural design. *The moment of a force with respect to a point is equal to the product of the force and the pependicular distance of the force from the point.* For example, Fig. 12 shows a force F which is at a perpendicular distance d from point O. Here, the moment of F with respect to point O is Fd, and we usually write such a moment as

$$M_o = Fd$$

Here the symbol M_o (read M sub O) means the moment of the force with respect to point O. The point O is called the *moment center* and the distance d the *moment arm*.

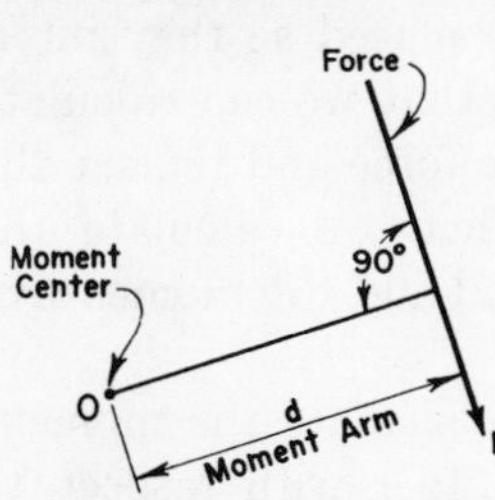

Fig. 12. Moment of a Force

The importance of a moment with respect to a point is that the moment of a force represents the tendency of the force to turn or tip an object about the point. Fig. 13 shows a small derrick of the type used to lift material to the top of a building; here the 400-lb. force is the weight of the material being lifted. The moment of the 400-lb. force with respect to point O represents the tendency of the force to tip the derrick about point O.

Illustrative Example 1. Calculate the moment of the 400-lb. force with respect to point O in Fig. 13.

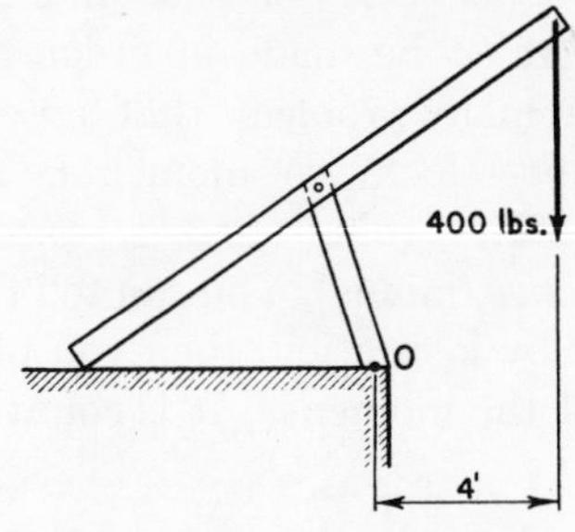

Fig. 13. Small Derrick

Solution:

1. The force is 400 lbs.
2. The perpendicular distance is 4 ft.
3. The moment is

$$M_o = 400 \times 4 = 1{,}600 \text{ lb. ft.}$$

Notice how the answer is expressed in this problem; it is in units of pound feet because a force in pounds was multiplied by a distance in feet. Both the magnitude of the force and its distance from the moment center are used in calculating the moment. These are the important factors in the tendency to tip, so it is easy to see how the moment of the force represents the tendency to tip.

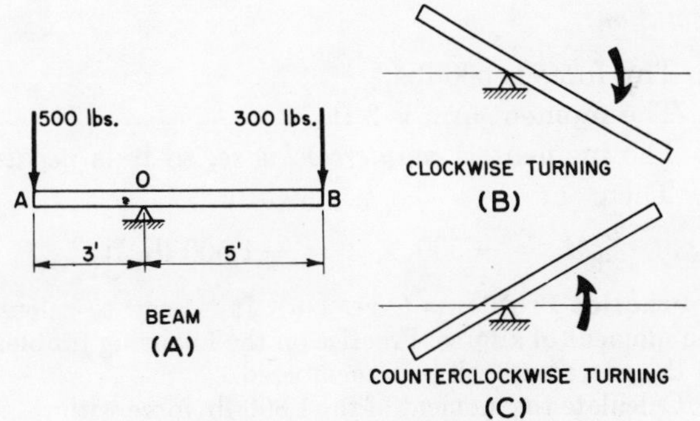

Fig. 14. Positive and Negative Moments

Fig. 14A shows a beam balanced on a pivot at O. The 300-pound force tends to push the end B down and the end A up. This would be a clockwise (the way the hands of a clock turn) turning or rotation of the beam as in Fig. 14B, and so we say that the moment of the 300-pound force is *clockwise* with respect to point O. Also, you can see that the 500-pound force tends to push the end A down and the end B up. This would be a counterclockwise (opposite to the way the hands of a clock turn) rotation of the beam as in Fig. 14*C*, and so the moment of the force is *counterclockwise* with respect to point *O*.

A distinction between *clockwise* and *counterclockwise* moments must be made in order to represent the net effect in many problems that have both clockwise and counterclockwise moments. A *clockwise* moment is *positive* (plus) and a *counterclockwise* moment is *negative* (minus). You can tell the direction of the moment by inspection; then you place a minus sign in front of the moment if it is counterclockwise.

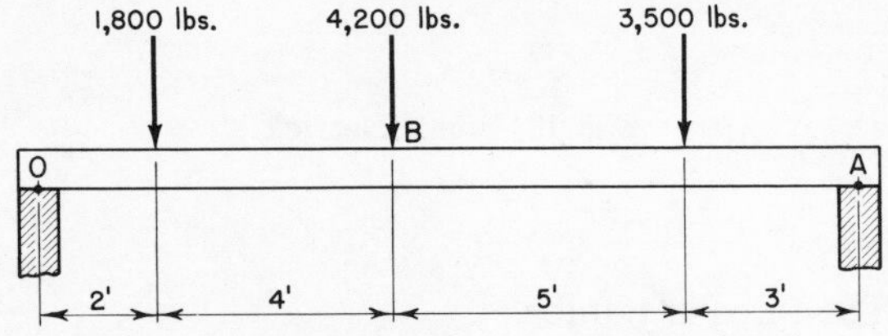

Fig. 15. Forces on a Beam

Illustrative Example 2. Calculate the moment of the 300-lb. force in Fig. 14, with respect to point *O*.

Solution:

1. The force is 300 lbs.
2. The moment arm is 5 ft.
3. The moment is *clockwise*, so it is *positive*, and is

$$M_o = 300 \times 5 = 1{,}500 \text{ lb. ft.}$$

Illustrative Example 3. What is the moment of the 500-lb. force with respect to point *O* in Fig. 14?

Solution:

1. The force is 500 lbs.
2. The moment arm is 3 ft.
3. The moment is *counterclockwise*, so it is *negative*. Then,

$$M_o = -500 \times 3 = -1{,}500 \text{ lb. ft.}$$

Practice Problems (Art. 1-6). It is easy to calculate the moment of a force. Practice on the following problems, so the procedure will be remembered.

1. Calculate the moment of the 1,800-lb. force with respect to point *O* in Fig. 15.
2. Find the moment of the 3,500-lb. force with respect to point *A* in Fig. 15.
3. What is the moment of the 4,200-lb. force with respect to point *A* in Fig. 15?
4. Find the moment of the 3,500-lb. force in Fig. 15 with respect to point *O*.
5. Calculate the moment of the 1,800-lb. force with respect to point *B* in Fig. 15.
6. What is the moment of the 4,200-lb. force in Fig. 15 with respect to point *O*?

1-7. Principle of Moments.

The principle of moments is: *The moment of a force with respect to a point is equal to the sum of the moments of the components of the force with respect to the point, providing the components are placed so they intersect on the force.* This principle leads to an easy way of doing problems in which it would be difficult to calculate the moment arm of a force. For example, Fig. 16*A* shows the line drawing of a roof truss on which a 3,000-pound force acts. Now suppose we want to calculate the moment of the 3,000-pound force with respect to point *O*. We could use trigonometry to find the perpendicular distance of the force from point *O*, but it would involve considerable work. Instead of finding the perpendicular distance we *could* use the *principle of moments* to calculate the moment of the force. The *principle of moments* states that the moment of a force with respect to a point is equal to the sum of the moments of the components of the force with respect to the point,

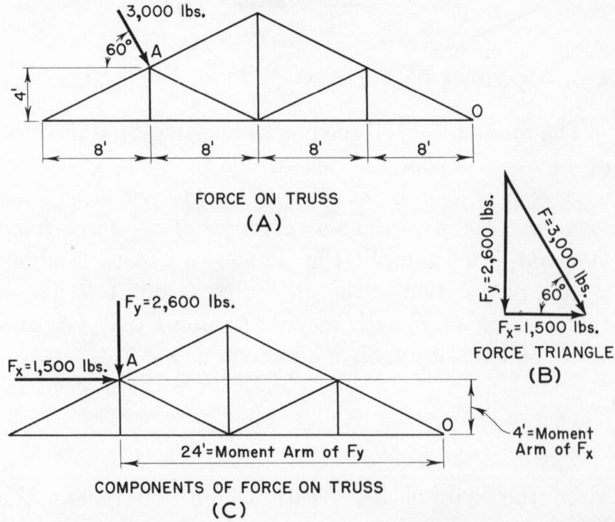

Fig. 16. Force and Components of Force on Roof Truss

providing the components are placed so they intersect on the force. This means that we can calculate the x and y components of the force and replace the force by the components. Then we calculate the moment of each component and add the moments of the components.

Illustrative Example 1. Calculate the moment of the 3,000-lb. force in Fig. 16*A* with respect to point *O*.

Solution:

1. The first step is to find the components of the force which you already know how to do. Draw the force triangle as in Fig. 16*B*. Notice the components F_x and F_y.

a) The x component is equal to the product of the force and the cosine of the angle which the force makes with the horizontal. You can see that the x component is directed toward the right, so it is *positive*.

$$F_x = 3{,}000 \cos 60° = 3{,}000 \times 0.5 = 1{,}500 \text{ lbs.}$$

b) The y component is equal to the force times the sine of the angle which the force makes with the horizontal. The y component is downward, so it is *negative*.

$$F_y = -3{,}000 \sin 60° = -3{,}000 \times 0.866 = -2{,}600 \text{ lbs.}$$

Fig. 16*C* shows the components of the force at point *A* where the force is applied to the truss. The 3,000-lb. force has been replaced by its components.

2. The moment arm of F_x is the perpendicular distance from F_x to *O*. We extend F_x to the right to get this distance, which is 4 ft.
3. The moment of F_x is *clockwise* with respect to point *O*, so it is positive. The amount of the moment is

$$1{,}500 \times 4 = 6{,}000 \text{ lb. ft.}$$

4. The moment arm of F_y is the perpendicular distance from F_y to *O*. This is 24 ft.

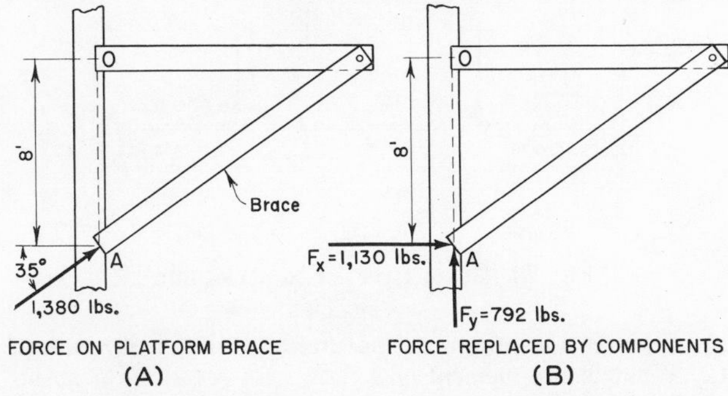

Fig. 17. Force Replaced by Components on Platform Brace

5. The moment of F_y with respect to point *O* is *negative* because it is *counterclockwise*, and it is

$$-2{,}600 \times 24 = -62{,}400 \text{ lb. ft.}$$

6. The moment of the 3,000-lb. force with respect to point *O* is equal to the sum of the moments of the components of the force; that is, it is the sum of 6,000 lb. ft. and −62,400 lb. ft., so

$$M_o = 6{,}000 - 62{,}400 = -56{,}400 \text{ lb. ft.}$$

The *negative sign* for the answer shows that the moment is *counterclockwise*.

It is important to remember in using the principle of moments to place the components of the force so they intersect on the force. Then calculate the moment of each component and add the moments of the components.

Illustrative Example 2. Fig. 17*A* shows a platform supported by a brace and a wall. A force of 1,380 lbs. acts on the brace at *A* to support the brace and platform. Calculate the moment of this force with respect to point *O*.

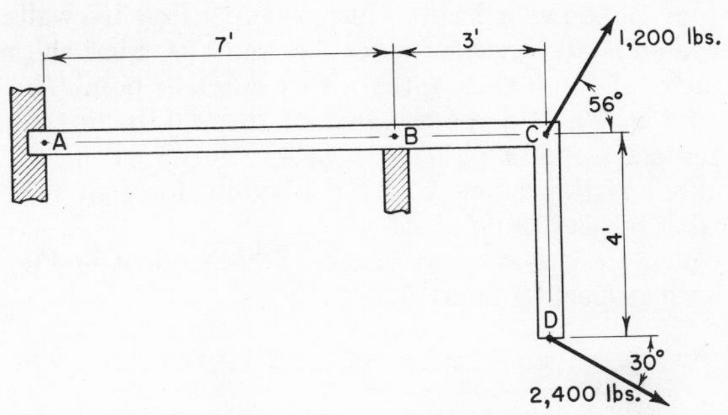

Fig. 18. A Bent Member

Solution:

1. First we find the components of the force.
   a) $F_x = 1{,}380 \cos 35° = 1{,}380 \times 0.819 = 1{,}130$ lbs.
   b) $F_y = 1{,}380 \sin 35° = 1{,}380 \times 0.574 = 792$ lbs. The force is directed upward to the right in Fig. 17*A*, so F_x is directed toward the right and F_y is directed upward. Fig. 17*B* shows the components at point *A*. We have replaced the force by its components.
2. The moment arm of F_x is 8 ft., Fig. 17*B*.
3. The moment of F_x is equal to the product of F_x and its *moment arm*. This moment is *counterclockwise*, so it is *negative*. The amount is

$$-1{,}130 \times 8 = -9{,}040 \text{ lb. ft.}$$

4. The moment arm of F_y is *zero* because F_y goes through point *O*. Thus the moment of F_y with respect to point *O* is

$$792 \times 0 = 0$$

(You probably learned in algebra that when you multiply any number by *zero*, the result is *zero*.)

5. Now we add the moments of the components to find the moment of the 1,380-lb. force with respect to point *O*. This is

$$M_o = -9{,}040 + 0 = -9{,}040 \text{ lb. ft.}$$

Practice Problems (Art. 1-7). It will help you to learn the *principle of moments* if you do these problems for practice.

1. Fig. 18 shows a bent, structural member which is supported by walls at A and B and which is subjected to forces at C and D. Calculate the moment of the 1,200-lb. force with respect to point A.
2. In Fig. 18, find the moment of the 2,400-lb. force with respect to point B.
3. What is the moment of the 1,200-lb. force in Fig. 18 with respect to point D?
4. Calculate the moment of the 2,400-lb. force in Fig. 18 with respect to point C.
5. Fig. 19 shows a beam which is supported by walls at the ends and by the braces AB and CD. Find the moment of the 900-lb. force with respect to point E.
6. In Fig. 19, find the moment of the 900-lb. force with respect to point C.
7. What is the moment of the 1,500-lb. force in Fig. 19 with respect to point E?
8. Calculate the moment of the 1,500-lb. force in Fig. 19 with respect to point A.

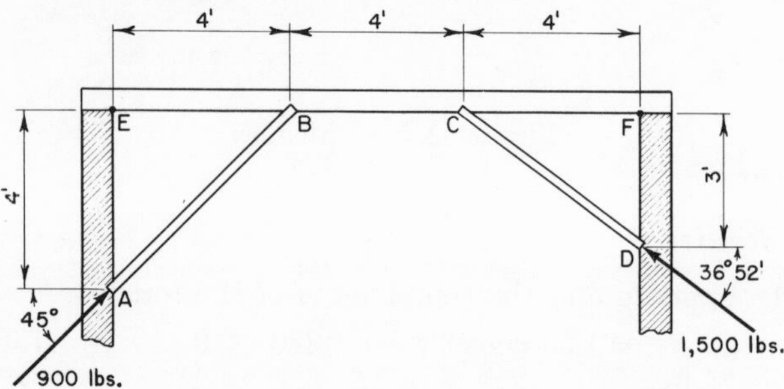

Fig. 19. A Beam Supported by Walls and Braces

SUMMARY OF CHAPTER I

Here is a summary of the main points in this chapter.

1. *Elementary Structural Design* deals with the strength of objects which are subjected to force and with the methods used to design structural members.
2. It is necessary to study strength of materials to learn the formulas and methods which are used in designing structural members.
3. *A force is a push or a pull exerted by one body on another.*
   a) *A force has magnitude*, which is usually expressed in pounds.
   b) *A force has direction*, and the direction is usually expressed as the angle which the force makes with the horizontal.
   c) *A force has location.*
4. *A component of a force is one of two forces which may replace the force.*
   a) The x component of a force is equal to the product of the force and the cosine of the angle which the force makes with the horizontal. Thus,

$$F_x = F \cos \theta$$

   The y component is *positive* if directed toward the right, and *negative* if directed toward the left.
   b) The y component of a force is equal to the product of the force and the sine of the angle which the force makes with the horizontal. Thus,

$$F_y = F \sin \theta$$

   The i component is *positive* if directed upward and *negative* if directed downward.
5. The *moment of a force with respect to a point* is equal to the product of the force and the perpendicular distance from the force to the point.
   a) *A clockwise moment is positive.*
   b) *A counterclockwise moment is negative.*
   c) *Moment is usually expressed in lb. ft.*
6. The principle of moments is: *The moment of a force with respect to a point is equal to the sum of the moments of the components of the force with respect to the point, providing the components are placed so they intersect on the force.*

Review Questions

These review questions will test your knowledge of the information given in this chapter. You should be able to answer the questions without looking at the preceding pages.

1. What is *Elementary Structural Design?*
2. How is strength of materials used in structural design?
3. What is a *force?*
4. What is the *magnitude of a force?*
5. In what units can the magnitude of a force be expressed?
6. What is a *kip?*
7. What is a *component of a force?*
8. How is the x component of a force calculated?
9. How is the y component of a force calculated?
10. When is an x component of a force *positive* and when is it *negative?*

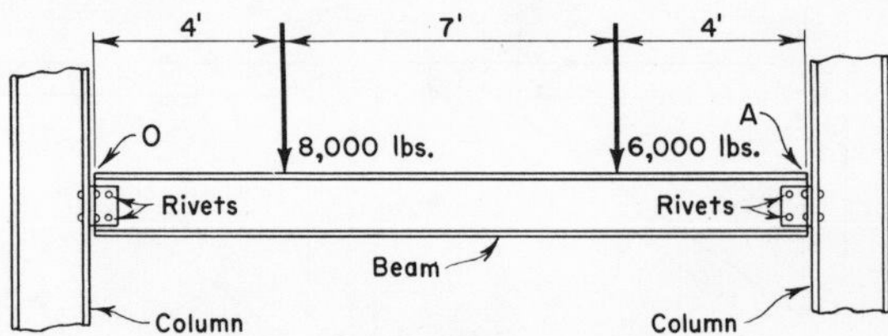

Fig. 20. Beam Riveted to a Column

11. When is a y component *positive* and when is it *negative?*
12. What is the *moment of a force with respect to a point?*
13. In what units can the *moment of force* be expressed?
14. When is a moment *positive* and when is it *negative?*
15. Why is moment important?
16. State the *principle of moments.*

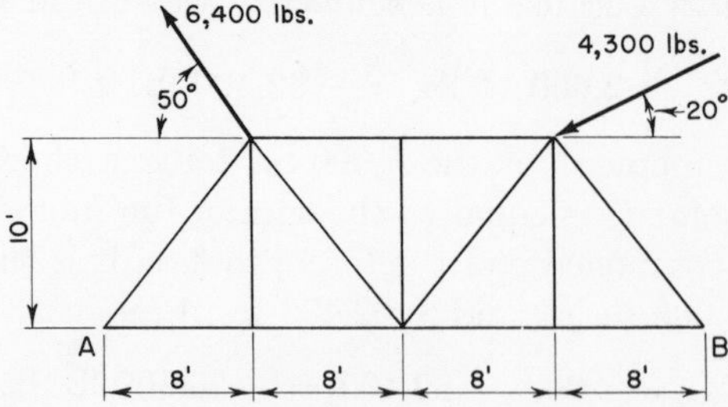

Fig. 21. Forces on Roof Truss in Review Problem 6

Review Problems[2]

To make sure you really know the material presented in this chapter, work the following problems.

1. A force of 16,800 lbs. is directed upward to the right at an angle of 70° with the horizontal. Find the x and y components of the force.
2. Find the x and y components of a force of 960 lbs. which is directed downward to the right at an angle of 34° with the horizontal.

[2] To check your answers to the *Review Problems*, refer to the section entitled *Answers to Problems*, at the back of this book.

3. Fig. 20 shows a beam which is supported by riveted connections to columns at the ends. Calculate the moment of the 8,000-lb. force with respect to point O.
4. In Fig. 20, what is the moment of the 6,000-lb. force with respect to point O?
5. In Fig. 20, find the moment of the 8,000-lb. force with respect to point A.
6. Fig. 21 shows a line drawing of a roof truss. Find the moment of the 6,400-lb. force with respect to point A.
7. In Fig. 21, calculate the moment of the 4,300-lb. force with respect to point A.
8. In Fig. 21, what is the moment of the 6,400-lb. force with respect to point B?

Chapter II

EQUILIBRIUM

Purpose of This Chapter: The purpose of this chapter is to show you how to find all of the forces acting on a structural member. At the beginning of the problem, some of the forces called *loads* are known; for example, the forces of 4,000 pounds and 6,000 pounds on the beam in Fig. 1. These loads tend to push the beam down. The walls which support the beam exert forces on the beam to hold it up. The forces exerted by the walls are unknown at the start of the problem and are called *reactions; reactions* are forces exerted on a beam or any other structural member by the objects which support it.

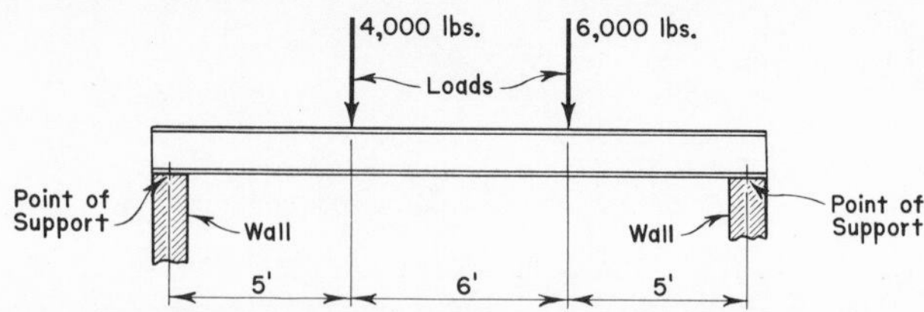

Fig. 1. Beam Supported on Walls

You will also learn how to find the reactions on a beam or other structural member so you will know all of the forces exerted on the member. The calculation of the reactions is always the first step in the design of a structural member. Learn how to find reactions now so you can design a beam later.

2-1. What Equilibrium Is.

Equilibrium is a state of balance between the forces acting on an object. Each force which acts on the object tends to move it, but the tendency of one force is balanced by opposing tendencies of other forces, so that the object remains at rest. For example, Fig. 2 shows the forces acting on a roof truss, the x components of the inclined forces which are applied at A, B, and C are directed toward the right;

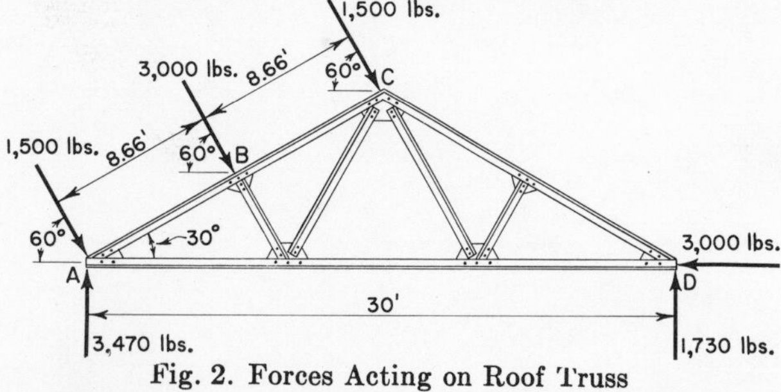

Fig. 2. Forces Acting on Roof Truss

and these x components tend to push the truss to the right. However, the 3,000-pound force at D is directed toward the left and tends to push the truss to the left. Thus, the tendency of some x components to cause motion is balanced by other x components so that the truss remains at rest. We can express the balance of the x components in an equation as,

$$\Sigma F_x = 0$$

where the symbol Σ (Greek letter *sigma*) stands for *summation* and the equation is read, as: *The sum of the x components of the forces is equal to zero.*

The x components which are directed toward the right are *positive* and the x components directed toward the left are *negative* in applying this equation.

Write out the equation, $\Sigma F_x = 0$, for the forces in Fig. 2. We need the x component of each force to do this, but you learned to calculate x components in Chapter I. For each of the 1,500-pound forces at A and C, the x component is

$$1{,}500 \cos 60° = 1{,}500 \times 0.5 = 750 \text{ lbs.}$$

The x component of the 3,000-lb. force at B is

$$3{,}000 \cos 60° = 3{,}000 \times 0.5 = 1{,}500 \text{ lbs.}$$

and the x component of the 3,000-lb. force at D is

$$-3{,}000 \text{ lbs.}$$

Now, by combining all the forces, you have

$$\Sigma F_x = 2 \times 750 + 1{,}500 - 3{,}000 = 0$$

$$3{,}000 - 3{,}000 = 0$$

$$0 = 0$$

Also, in Fig. 2, you can see that the y components of the inclined forces at A, B, and C are downward, and the vertical forces at A and D are upward. The tendency of the y components of the inclined forces at A, B, and C to push the truss down is balanced by the tendency of the vertical forces at A and D to push the truss up. This balance of the y components is written as the equation

$$\Sigma F_y = 0$$

We read the equation as: *The sum of the y components of the forces is equal to zero.* Here we take y components which are upward as *positive* and y components which are downward as *negative.*

Think about the moment of a force as we look at Fig. 2. You know that the moment of a force, with respect to a point, is equal to the product of the force and the perpendicular distance from the force to the point, and that the *moment* represents the tendency of the force to turn the object about the point. You can see that the inclined forces at B and C have clockwise moments about point A, and this means that these forces tend to turn the truss in a clockwise direction about point A. However, the 3,000-pound force at D has a counterclockwise moment about A so the 3,000-pound force tends to turn the truss in a counterclockwise direction about A. The tendency to turn clockwise is balanced by the tendency to turn counterclockwise and the moments are balanced. The equation which expresses the balance of the moments is

$$\Sigma M_A = 0$$

and this equation is read as: *The sum of the moments with respect to point A is zero. Clockwise* moments are taken as *positive* and *counterclockwise* moments as *negative* in this equation. Actually, the sum of the moments of the forces is *zero* with respect to any other point, too, if the truss is in equilibrium, so we could write

$$\Sigma M_B = 0; \quad \text{or } \Sigma M_C = 0; \quad \text{or } \Sigma M_D = 0$$

You can think of a force as tending to do any or all of three things to the object it acts on:

(1) Push the object in a horizontal direction.
(2) Push the object in a vertical direction.
(3) Turn or tip the object.

The x component of a force represents the tendency of the force to push the object in a horizontal direction, but when an object is in equilibrium, the x components of all of the forces are in balance. One x component cancels another. Also, the y components are balanced and the moments are balanced. Now, in order for the forces to be balanced, so there is no tendency remaining for the body to move, the three equations

$$\Sigma F_x = 0; \quad \Sigma F_y = 0; \quad \text{and } \Sigma M = 0$$

must be true. These equations are called the *equations of equilibrium*, and will be used to find the unknown forces on structural members.

2-2. Free-Body Diagrams.

A *free-body diagram* is a picture of an object showing all of the forces exerted upon the object. You draw the free-body diagram at the beginning of the problem. All of the forces, known and unknown, which act on the body are shown. You now have all of the forces necessary to work the problem.

In a free-body diagram it is not necessary to show all of the details of a structural member; often a line to represent the member is enough. For example, look at the picture of the beam in Fig. 3*A;* Fig. 3*B* shows the free-body diagram of the beam, where the heavy line AB represents the beam. The first step in drawing the free-body diagram is to draw this line. The second step is to put in the known forces or loads, namely, the force of 6,000 pounds and the force of 10,000 pounds as shown in Fig. 3*A*. The last step in drawing the free-body diagram is to put in the reactions (we represent the reactions by R_1 and R_2), which are the forces exerted on the beam by its supports. You can see in Fig. 3*A* that the beam is supported at points A and B, where it is welded to

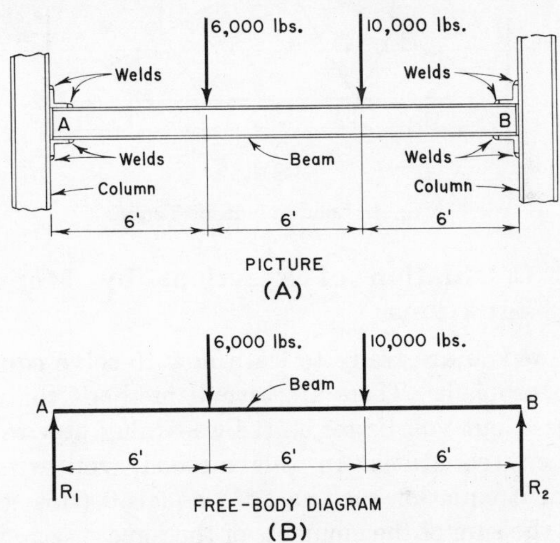

Fig. 3. Beam Welded to Columns

the columns. The columns must exert forces on the beam at A and B to balance the loads and hold up the beam. The forces exerted by the supports are called reactions and one of your problems is to learn how to find reactions. The reactions on a beam are vertical when the loads are vertical, and are shown as R_1 (at A) and R_2 (at B) in Fig. 3*B*. The drawing of the reactions completes the free-body diagram of the beam.

Another free-body diagram, Fig. 4*A*, shows a roof truss; the loads at A, B, C, D, and E represent the weight of the roof. The truss is supported by walls at A and E. Fig. 4*B* shows the free-body diagram of the roof truss. First you make the line drawing, then you draw the loads, and, last, the reactions at the supports. The reactions are R_1 (at A) and R_2 (at E).

Now you have an idea of what a free-body diagram is. You will learn more about free-body diagrams as you study equilibrium problems, because the free-body diagram will be drawn for each problem. Do not neglect this first and most important step in the problem.

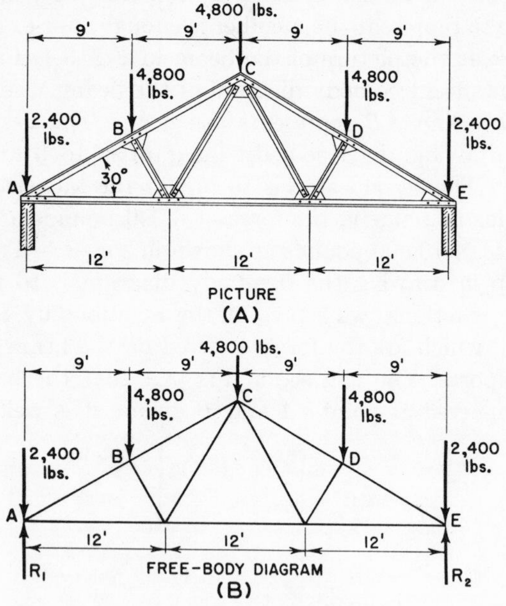

Fig. 4. Loads on Roof Truss

2-3. Calculation of Reactions by Moment Equations.

Now you are ready to learn how to solve equilibrium problems. There are several methods that can be used but you better start by learning how to use moment equations. In this method, you write a moment equation such as ΣM_A equals 0 (this states that the sum of the moments of the forces is *zero* with respect to point A) and solve the equation for an unknown force or reaction. The best way to demonstrate the process is by example.

Illustrative Example 1. Fig. 5A shows a rectangular wood beam ABC which is supported by walls at A and C, and which carries the end of another beam D at B. The beam D pushes down on ABC with a force of 2,000 lbs. Find the reactions of the walls on the beam ABC.

Solution:

1. The free-body diagram is shown in Fig. 5B.
   a) The heavy line ABC is drawn to represent the beam.
   b) The load of 2,000 lbs. is drawn at B. This force is exerted by the beam D upon the beam ABC.
   c) The reactions R_1 and R_2 are drawn at A and C, which are the forces the walls exert on the beam ABC.
2. We write the moment equation $\Sigma M_A = 0$. The moment of the 2,000-lb. force with respect to point A is 2,000 × 5, since the moment of a force with respect to a point is equal to the product of the force and its perpendicular distance from the point. The moment of the force R_2 is $-12R_2$ (minus because it is counterclockwise). The moment of the force R_1 is *zero* because R_2 goes through A. This is why A was chosen as a moment center.

$$\Sigma M_A = 2{,}000 \times 5 - 12R_2 = 0$$

We can transpose the term 12 R_2 to get

$$12\ R_2 = 2{,}000 \times 5 = 10{,}000$$

Then, dividing by 12

$$R_2 = \frac{10{,}000}{12} = 833 \text{ lbs.}$$

3. We write the moment equation $\Sigma M_C = 0$. The moment of the force R_1 with respect to C is 12 R_1, the moment of the 2,000-lb. force is $-2{,}000 \times 7$ (remember a counterclockwise moment is *negative*). The moment of the force R_2 is *zero* because R_2 goes through C. Then,

$$\Sigma M_C = 12\ R_1 - 2{,}000 \times 7 = 0$$

Now we transpose the term $-2{,}000 \times 7$ and

$$12\ R_1 = 2{,}000 \times 7 = 14{,}000$$

$$R_1 = 1{,}167 \text{ lbs.}$$

Study this example for a minute. Notice that point *A* was chosen as the moment center for the first equa-

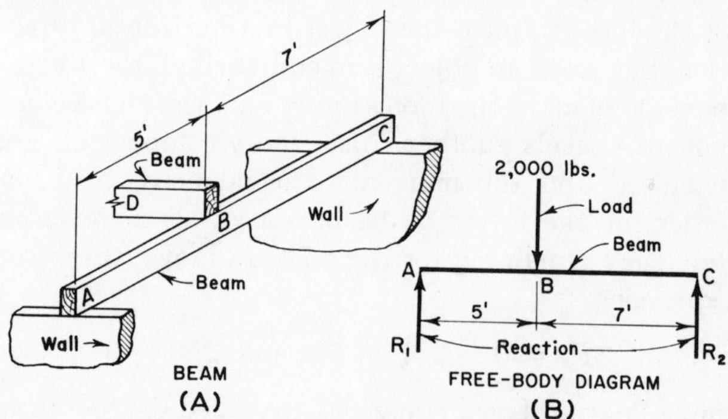

Fig. 5. Rectangular Wood Beam

tion, because the force R_1 goes through A and, therefore, has no moment about A. Then the unknown force R_1 does not appear in the equation. The only unknown force in the equations is R_2 and we can solve for it easily.

Notice also that we chose point C as the moment center for the second equation because the force R_2 goes through C. Then R_2 does not appear in this equation and we can solve the equation for R_1 without any trouble.

You can see that it is a good idea to choose a moment center at the point where an unknown force is applied. Remember this when working all of your problems.

Illustrative Example 2. Fig. 6 shows the free-body diagram of a beam which is supported at A and B, and is subjected to three loads. Calculate the reactions R_1 and R_2.

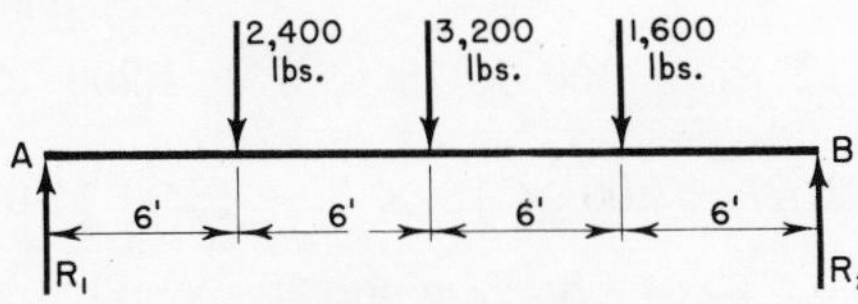

Fig. 6. Free-body Diagram of Beam Subjected to Three Loads

Solution:

1. The first step is to write the moment equation $\Sigma M_A = 0$. The moment of the 2,400-lb. force with respect to point A is $2{,}400 \times 6$, the moment of the 3,200-lb. force is $3{,}200 \times 12$ and the moment of the 1,600-lb. force is $1{,}600 \times 18$. The moment of the force R_2 is $-24\ R_2$, so

$$\Sigma M_A = 2{,}400 \times 6 + 3{,}200 \times 12 + 1{,}600 \times 18 - 24\ R_2 = 0$$

Transpose the term 24 R_2 and we have

$$24\ R_2 = 2{,}400 \times 6 + 3{,}200 \times 12 + 1{,}600 \times 18$$

$$= 14{,}400 + 38{,}400 + 28{,}800 = 81{,}600$$

$$R_2 = 3{,}400 \text{ lbs.}$$

2. The second step is to write the moment equation $\Sigma M_B = 0$. The moment of the force R_1 with respect to point B is 24 R_1. The moment of the 2,400-lb. force is $-2{,}400 \times 18$, the moment of the 3,200-lb. force is $-3{,}200 \times 12$ and the moment of the 1,600-lb. force is $-1{,}600 \times 6$. Then,

$$\Sigma M_B = 24\ R_1 - 2{,}400 \times 18 - 3{,}200 \times 12 - 1{,}600 \times 6 = 0$$

We transpose all of the terms in this equation except the term 24 R_1 and

$$24\ R_1 = 2{,}400 \times 18 + 3{,}200 \times 12 + 1{,}600 \times 6$$

$$= 43{,}200 + 38{,}400 + 9{,}600 = 91{,}200$$

$$R_1 = 3{,}800 \text{ lbs.}$$

It often happens that a beam supports a weight or object which is distributed over some length, and so the load is not concentrated at a single point. For example, the beam in Fig. 7*A* supports a floor slab which weighs 600 pounds for each foot of length along the beam. This is a load which is uniformly distributed. We represent it by the cross-hatched rectangle in the free-body diagram in Fig. 7*B* and the amount is written as 600 pounds per foot.

The total force of a uniformly distributed load is equal to the amount in *pounds per foot* times the *length in feet*. Thus in a uniformly distributed load of 600 pounds per foot for a length of 16 feet, the total force is

$$600 \times 16 = 9{,}600 \text{ lbs.}$$

The moment arm for a uniformly distributed load is the distance from the center of the load to the moment center. The moment of the load with respect to the moment center is equal to the *product* of the *total force* and the *moment arm*. In Fig. 7*B*, the moment arm of the uniformly distributed load with respect to point A is 8 feet and the moment of the load with respect to point A is

$$M_A = 9{,}600 \times 8 = 76{,}800 \text{ lb. ft.}$$

We could also write this as,

$$M_A = 600 \times 16 \times 8 = 76{,}800 \text{ lb. ft.}$$

Here we have: (1) the amount of the uniformly distributed load in pounds per foot, *times* (2) the length of the load in feet, *times* (3) the *distance* from A tc the center of the load.

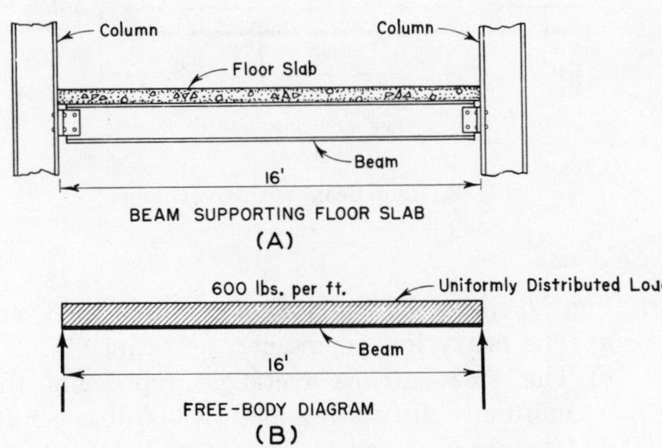

Fig. 7. Beam with Uniform Load

Illustrative Example 3. Find the reactions for the beam in Fig. 7.

Solution:

1. We write the moment equation $\Sigma M_A = 0$.

$$\Sigma M_A = 600 \times 16 \times 8 - 16\ R_2 = 0$$

$$16\ R_2 = 600 \times 16 \times 8 = 76{,}800$$

$$R_2 = 4{,}800 \text{ lbs.}$$

2. We write the moment equation $\Sigma M_B = 0$.

$$\Sigma M_B = 16\ R_1 - 600 \times 16 \times 8 = 0$$

$$16\ R_1 = 600 \times 16 \times 8 = 76{,}800$$

$$R_1 = 4{,}800 \text{ lbs.}$$

Illustrative Example 4. The beam in Fig. 8*A* supports a roof which weighs 300 lbs. per foot of length of the beam and a concentrated load of 1,200 lbs. The beam is supported by a wall at *A* and a post at *B;* and overhangs a loading platform. Find the reactions at *A* and *B*.

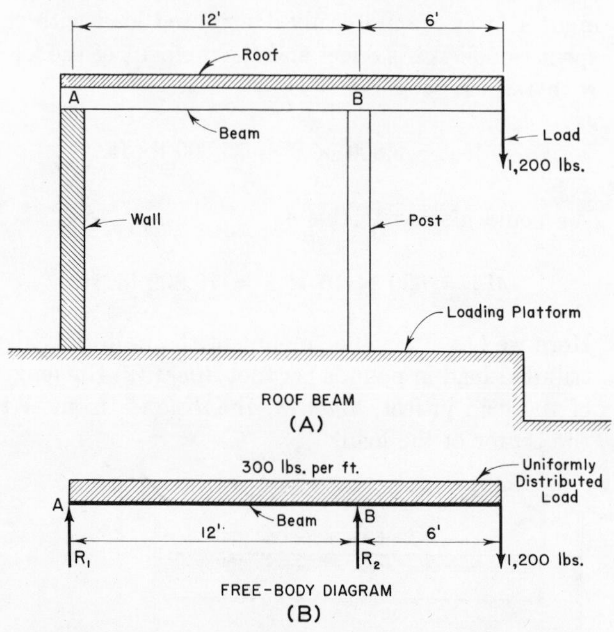

Fig. 8. Roof Beam with Overhang

Solution:

1. Fig. 8*B* shows the free-body diagram of the beam
   a) The heavy line represents the beam
   b) The cross-hatched rectangle represents the uniformly distributed load of 300 lbs. per ft.
   c) The concentrated load of 1,200 lbs. is shown at the right end of the beam.
   d) The reactions R_1 and R_2 are shown at *A* and *B*.
2. We can find the reaction R_2 by writing the moment equation $\Sigma M_A = 0$. The total force of the uniformly distributed load is 300 × 18, and the distance from *A* to its center is 9 ft., so

$$\Sigma M_A = 300 \times 18 \times 9 - 12\ R_2 + 1{,}200 \times 18 = 0$$

$$12\ R_2 = 300 \times 18 \times 9 + 1{,}200 \times 18$$

$$= 48{,}600 + 21{,}600 = 70{,}200$$

$$R_2 = 5{,}850 \text{ lbs.}$$

3. We can find the reaction R_1 by writing the moment equation $\Sigma M_B = 0$ (because R_2 goes through *B*). The distance from *B* to the center of the uniformly distributed load is 3 ft. Then,

$$\Sigma M_B = 12\ R_1 - 300 \times 18 \times 3 + 1{,}200 \times 6 = 0$$

$$12\ R_1 = 300 \times 18 \times 3 - 1{,}200 \times 6$$

$$= 16{,}200 - 7{,}200 = 9{,}000$$

$$R_1 = 750 \text{ lbs.}$$

Practice Problems (Art. 2-3). Practice carefully on the following problems, so you will remember how to use moment equations to find reactions.

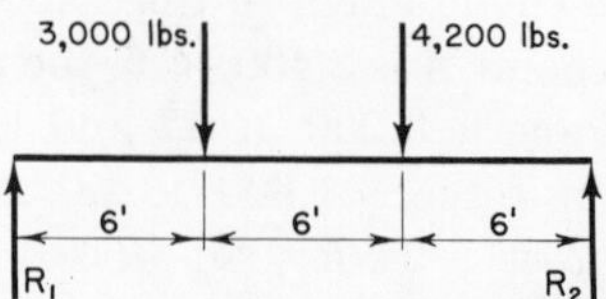

Fig. 9. Beam for Problem 1 (Art. 3)

1. Fig. 9 shows the free-body diagram of a beam which is supported at the ends and which carries two loads. Find the reactions R_1 and R_2.

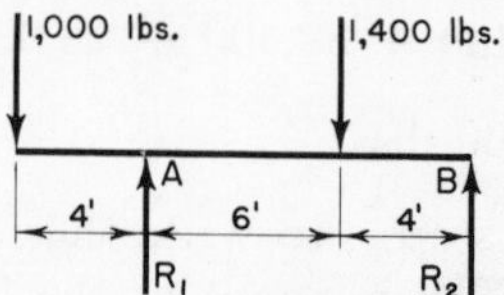

Problem 2 Fig. 10. Beam for (Art. 3)

2. Fig. 10 shows the free-body diagram of a beam which is supported at *A* and *B*. Find R_1 and R_2.

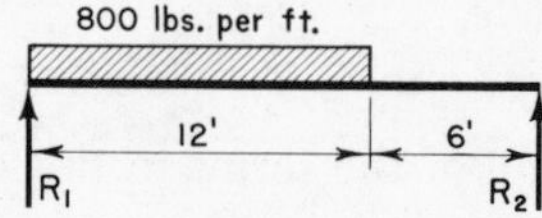

Fig. 11. Beam for Problem 3 (Art. 3)

3. Fig. 11 shows the free-body diagram of a beam which carries a uniformly distributed load over part of its length. Find R_1 and R_2.

4. Fig. 12 shows the free-body diagram of a beam which is supported at A and B. Find the reactions R_1 and R_2.

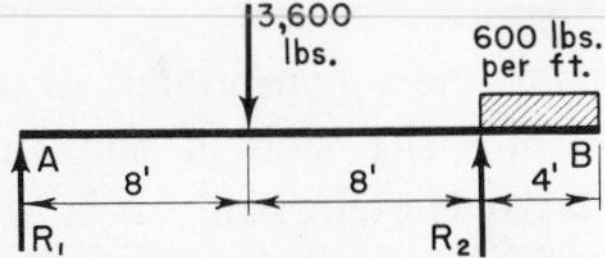

Fig. 12. Beam for Problem 4 (Art. 3)

5. The beam in Fig. 13 is supported by columns at A and B. Two smaller beams push downward on the beam with a force of 1,800 lbs. at C, and two other beams push downward with a force of 2,200 lbs. at D. Find the reactions at A and B.

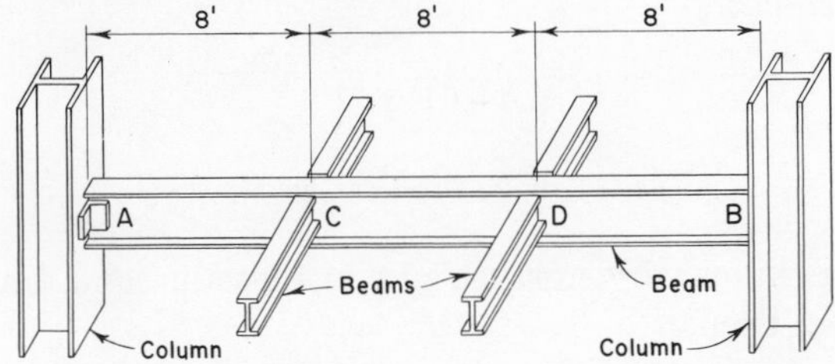

Fig. 13. Beams and Columns for Problem 5 (Art. 3)

6. The beam in Fig. 14 is supported at the ends and supports a chain hoist. Find the reactions on the beam at A and B.

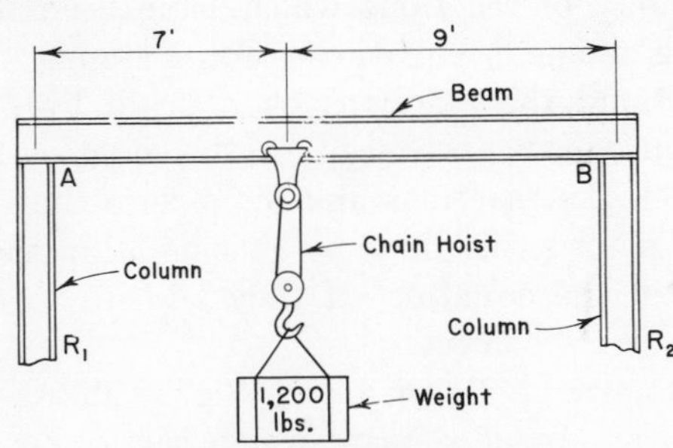

Fig. 14. Beam for Problem 6 (Art. 3)

7. Fig. 15 shows a beam which is supported by walls at A and C. The beam carries a floor slab which is cut out from B to C for a stair well. From A to B, the weight of the floor slab is 600 lbs. per ft. of length of the beam, and from B to C it is 300 lbs. per ft. Find the reactions of the walls on the beam.

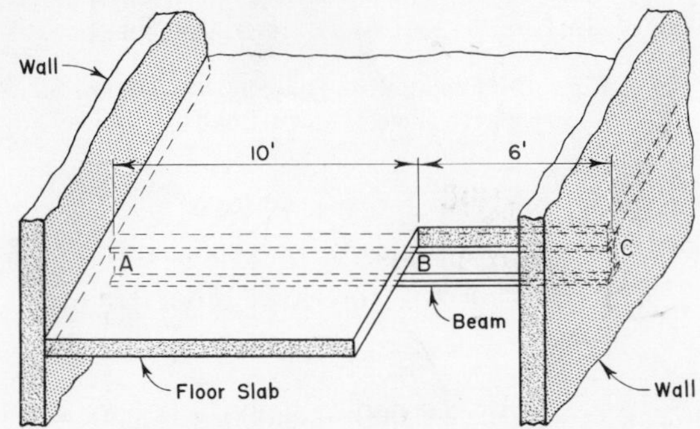

Fig. 15. Beam and Floor Slab for Problem 7 (Art. 3)

8. The beam in Fig. 16 supports a floor slab which weighs 400 lbs. per ft. of length of the beam and a machine which weighs 1,600 lbs. Find the reactions on the beam at A and B.

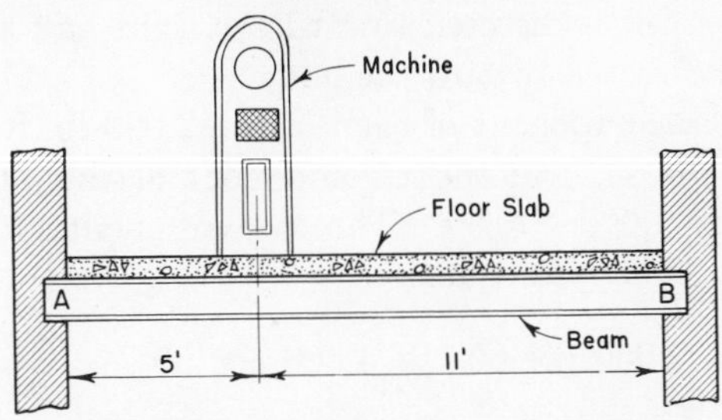

Fig. 16. Beam and Machine for Problem 8 (Art. 3)

2-4. How to Use Reactions for the Sum of Components.

The next step is to learn to use the equations for the sum of the components of forces; $\Sigma F_x = 0$ and $\Sigma F_y = 0$. The first of these equations states that the sum of the x components of the forces acting on the body is *zero* and the second equation states that the sum of the y components of the forces acting on the body is *zero*. We can use these equations to find unknown forces or reactions. The procedure is to draw the free-body diagram of the beam or other member and then to write one of these equations, in which an unknown force will appear. The equation will have to be solved for this unknown force.

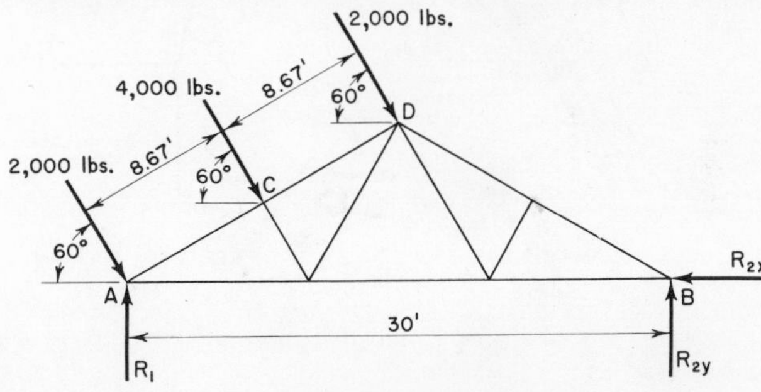

Fig. 17. Free-body Diagram for a Roof Truss Showing Effect of Wind Loads

Illustrative Example 1. Fig. 17 shows the free-body diagram of a truss under wind loads. The known forces at A, C, and D represent the effect of the wind on the roof which the truss supports. The truss is supported at A and B. The support at A exerts the vertical reaction R_1 and the support at B exerts a reaction R_2 which is represented in Fig. 17 by its components R_{2x} and R_{2y}. (You remember from Chapter I that we can always represent a force by two components.) Find the force R_{2x}.

Solution:

We can find R_{2x} by writing the equilibrium equation $\Sigma F_x = 0$. Here we must include the x component of every force which acts on the truss. (You should remember that the x component of a force is equal to the force *times* the cosine of the angle which the force makes with the horizontal. An x component is *positive* if it is directed toward the right and *negative* if it is directed toward the left.)

The x component of each of the 2,000-lb. forces is 2,000 cos 60° and the x component of the 4,000-lb. force is 4,000 cos 60°. The x component of R_{2x} is $-R_{2x}$. Then the equation is

$$\Sigma F_x = 2{,}000 \cos 60° + 4{,}000 \cos 60° + 2{,}000 \cos 60° - R_{2x} = 0$$

We can transpose the R_{2x} to get

$$R_{2x} = 2{,}000 \cos 60° + 4{,}000 \cos 60° + 2{,}000 \cos 60°$$

$$= 2{,}000 \times 0.5 + 4{,}000 \times 0.5 + 2{,}000 \times 0.5$$

$$= 1{,}000 + 2{,}000 + 1{,}000 = 4{,}000 \text{ lbs.}$$

The foregoing example illustrates the solution of problems with one unknown force. The following problem will illustrate the solution of problems involving two unknown forces.

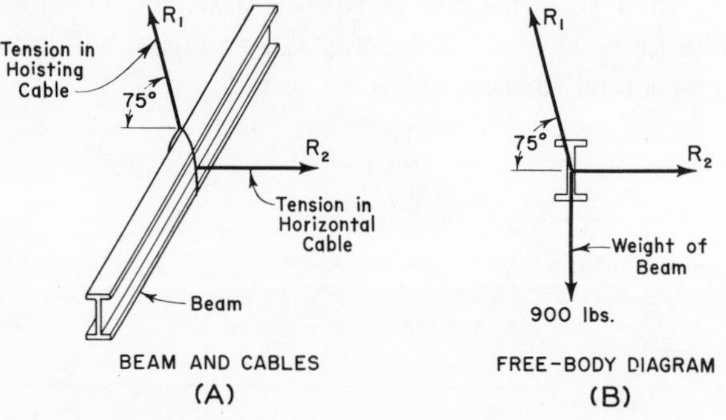

Fig. 18. Hoisting Problem

Illustrative Example 2. Fig. 18*A* shows a beam which is being hoisted by means of a cable. The lifting cable is at an angle of 75° with the horizontal and exerts the tension R_1 on the beam. Another cable is horizontal and exerts the force R_2. The beam weighs 900 lbs. Find R_1 and R_2.

Solution:

1. Fig. 18*B* shows the free-body diagram of the beam. The 900-lb. force is the weight of the beam, and R_1 and R_2 are the cable tensions.
2. The force R_1 is found by writing the equilibrium equation

$$\Sigma F_y = 0$$

Thus,

$$\Sigma F_y = R_1 \sin 75° - 900 = 0$$

(Remember that the y component of a force is equal to the force *times* the sine of the angle which the force makes with the horizontal. A y component is *positive* if directed upward and *negative* if directed downward.) Transpose the term containing R_1 and

$$R_1 \sin 75° = 900$$

$$0.966\ R_1 = 900; \quad R_1 = 932 \text{ lbs.}$$

3. The force R_2 is found by writing the equilibrium equation

$$\Sigma F_x = 0$$

$$\Sigma F_x = -R_1 \cos 75° + R_2 = 0$$

R_1 is known by now, so put in its value and transpose. Then,

$$R_2 = 932 \cos 75° = 932 \times 0.259 = 242 \text{ lbs.}$$

Another important use of equations for the sum of components, especially $\Sigma F_y = 0$, is for checking the values of reactions which have been found by writing moment equations. For instance, after we have found the reactions on a beam by means of moment equations, we can use the equation $\Sigma F_y = 0$ to check the reactions and make sure they are correct. This is easily done by placing all of the known forces in the equation. If they add up to *zero*, the reactions are correct.

Illustrative Example 3. Fig. 19 shows the free-body diagram of a beam which carries two known forces of 6,000 lbs. and 8,000 lbs. The reactions, as found by moment equations, are $R_1 = 9{,}170$ lbs. and $R_2 = 4{,}830$ lbs. Are the reactions correct?

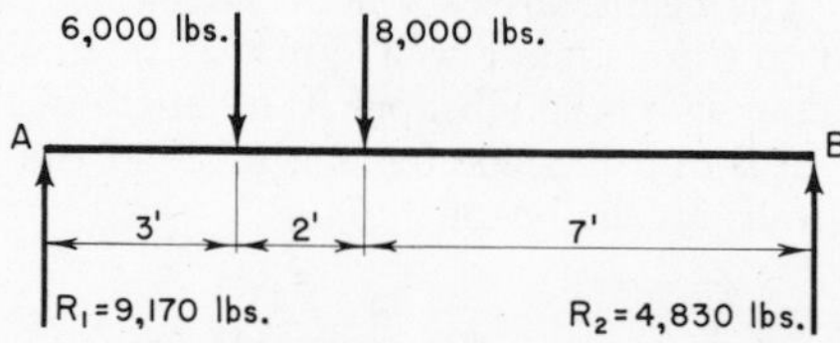

Fig. 19. Free-body Diagram of Beam with Two Known Loads

Solution:

Check the reactions by writing the equation $\Sigma F_y = 0$. Taking the forces in order from left to right

$$\Sigma F_y = 9{,}170 - 6{,}000 - 8{,}000 + 4{,}830 = 0$$

The sum of 9,170 and 4,830 is 14,000. Also, the sum of 6,000 and 8,000 is 14,000. So the equation becomes

$$14{,}000 - 14{,}000 = 0$$

$$0 = 0$$

The equation checks, so the reactions are *correct.*

Practice Problems (Art. 2-4). The best way to learn *Elementary Structural Design* is by working problems. Try these and be sure to draw your own free-body diagram for each problem.

1. The steel beam in Fig. 20 weighs 3,200 lbs. and is lifted by cables which exert the forces R_1 and R_2. Find R_1 and R_2.
2. Fig. 21 shows the forces in a joint of a roof truss of the type shown in Fig. 4, of this chapter. These forces are in equilibrium. Find F_1 and F_2.

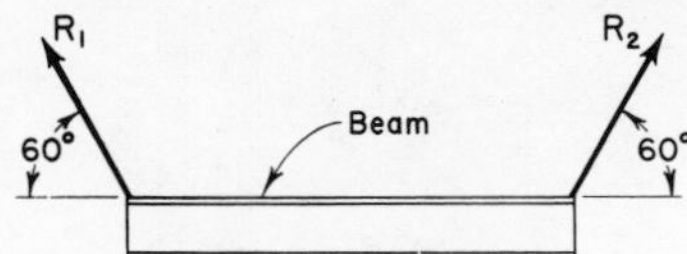

Fig. 20. Beam for Problem 1 (Art. 4)

Fig. 21. Beam for Problem 2 (Art. 4)

3. Fig. 22 shows a wood beam which is supported by posts at A and B. The beam carries two concentrated loads and a uniformly distributed load over part of the length. Find the reactions at A and B by moment equations and check them by writing $\Sigma F_y = 0$.

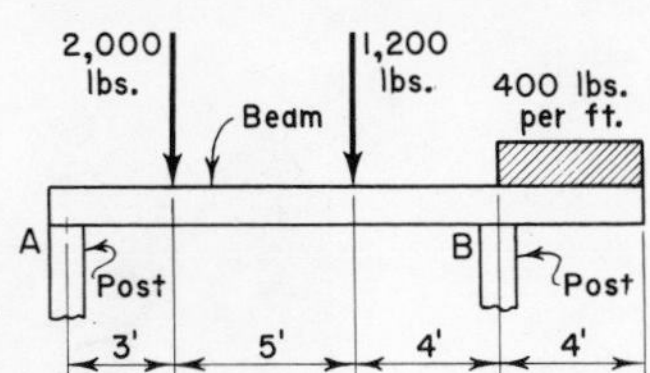

Fig. 22. Beam for Problem 3 (Art. 4)

4. The small derrick in Fig. 23 consists of the two posts AB and BC. Find the reactions R_1 and R_2.

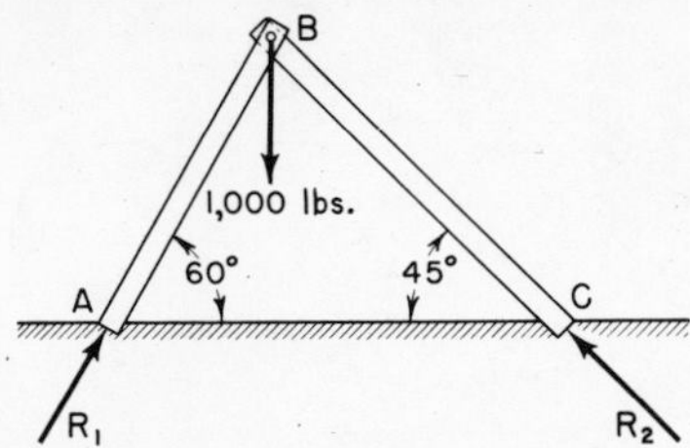

Fig. 23. Derrick for Problem 4 (Art. 4)

5. Fig. 24 shows the free-body diagram of a beam which is subjected to a uniformly distributed load of 1,000 lbs. per ft. over part of the length and a uniformly distributed load of 500 lbs. per ft. over the remainder. The reactions shown were calculated by moment equations. Are the reactions correct?
6. Find the reactions R_1 and R_2 on the bracket shown in Fig. 25.

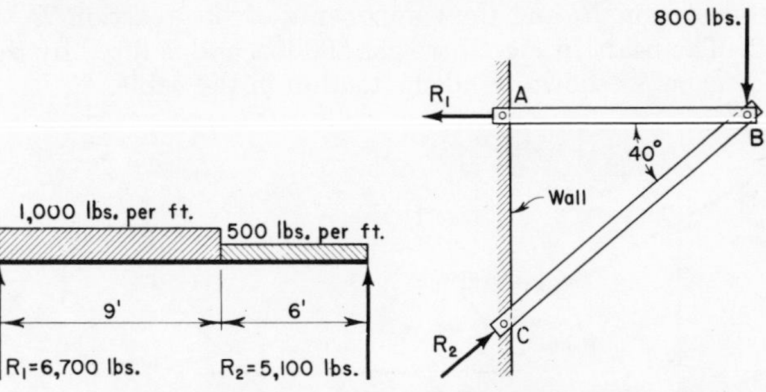

Fig. 24. Beam for Problem 5 (Art. 4)

Fig. 25. Bracket for Problem 6 (Art. 4)

SUMMARY OF CHAPTER II

Here is a summary of the main points in this chapter.

1. *Equilibrium is a state of balance between forces.* The conditions of equilibrium can be expressed as the equations

$$\Sigma F_x = 0; \quad \Sigma F_y = 0; \quad \text{and } \Sigma M = 0$$

2. *A free-body diagram is a picture of an object showing all forces acting on the object,* both known forces and unknown forces. The free-body diagram should be drawn for every equilibrium problem.
   a) A known force is called a *load.*
   b) An unknown force is called a *reaction.*
3. The object of an equilibrium problem is to find the unknown forces or reactions.
4. The reactions on a beam can be found most easily by writing moment equations.
   a) The best way is to choose the moment center at the left reaction in order to find the right-hand reaction.
   b) Then the moment center should be chosen at the right-hand reaction in order to find the left reaction.
5. The equations $\Sigma F_x = 0$ and $\Sigma F_y = 0$ are useful in finding reactions when the forces are not parallel.
   a) The equation $\Sigma F_y = 0$ can also be used to check the reactions on a beam after they have been found by moment equations.

Review Questions

Test your knowledge of this chapter by answering these questions. Do it without looking at the preceding pages.

1. What is *equilibrium?*
2. What are the *equations of equilibrium?*
3. What does the equation $\Sigma M_o = 0$ mean?
4. What does the equation $\Sigma F_y = 0$ mean?
5. What is a *free-body diagram?*
6. Why should you draw the free-body diagram for each problem?
7. What forces are shown in a free-body diagram?
8. What is a *load?*
9. What is a *reaction?*
10. How do y u use a moment equation to find a reaction on a beam?
11. What can the equation $\Sigma F_y = 0$ be used for?

Review Problems

You can review the chapter by working these problems. Be sure to draw free-body diagrams.

1. Fig. 26 shows a beam which is supported by a wall at the left end and by a cable at the right end. Find the reaction R_1 and the components of the reaction R_2.
2. The beam in Fig. 27 weighs 600 lbs. and is lifted by the cable as shown. Find the tension in the cable.

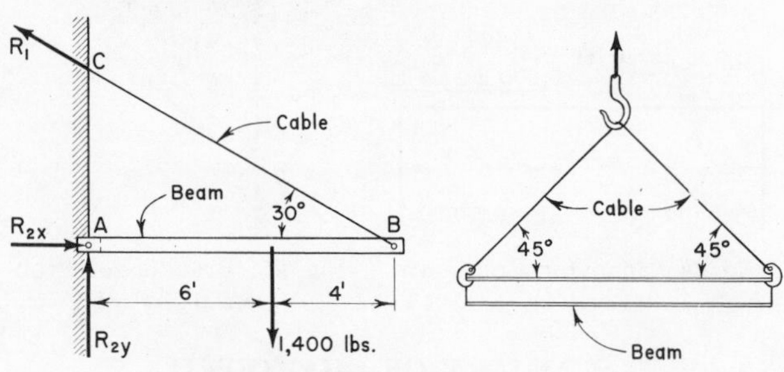

Fig. 26. Beam and Cable for Problem 1 (Review Problems)

Fig. 27. Beam and Cable for Problem 2 (Review Problems)

3. Fig. 28 shows a man on a scaffold. The man weighs 160 lbs. and the plank on which he stands weighs 8 lbs. per ft. Find the reactions on the plank at A and B, and check the values of the reactions.
4. The beam in Fig. 29 is part of a garage structure. The beam is supported by columns at A and B. The floor weighs 80 lbs. per ft. of length of the beam, and the automobile exerts a downward force of 1,200 lbs. at C

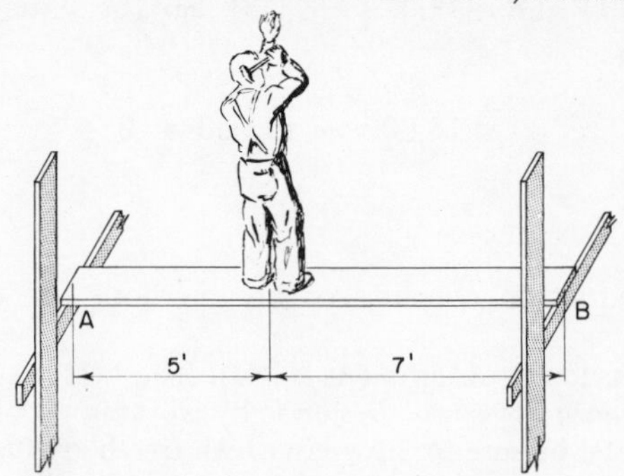

Fig. 28. Man on Scaffold—Problem 3 (Review Problems)

and a downward force of 1,600 lbs. at D. Find the reactions of the columns on the beam and check them.

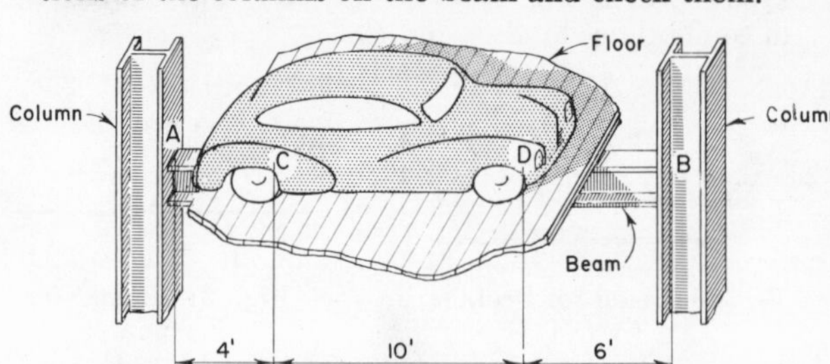

Fig. 29. Beam in Garage Structure—Problem 4 (Review Problems)

Chapter III

CENTROID OF AN AREA

Purpose of This Chapter. This chapter will define the *centroid* of an area and show how to find it.

The centroid of an area is taken up at this point because it is used in later chapters when designing structural members, such as beams and columns. For the present concentrate on what the *centroid* is.

3-1. What the Centroid Is.

The *centroid* of an area is a particular point in the area that has a special property. In Fig. 1 is shown a circular area of 3″ radius; notice that the x and y axes are shown because they make convenient reference lines. The special property of the *centroid* is that the distance of the centroid from any axis (say the x axis) is equal to the average distance of the area from that axis. You can see in Fig. 1 that the average

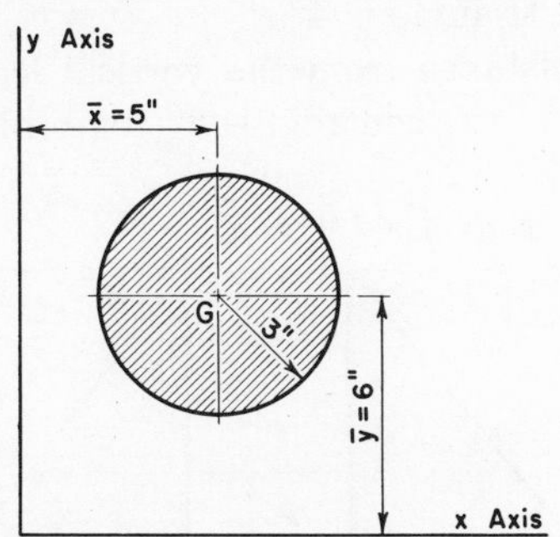

Fig. 1. Circular Area

distance from the x axis to the circular area is equal to the distance from the x axis to the center of the circle. This distance is 6″ in Fig. 1 and is designated by the symbol $\bar{y}$ (pronounced *y bar*). The centroid

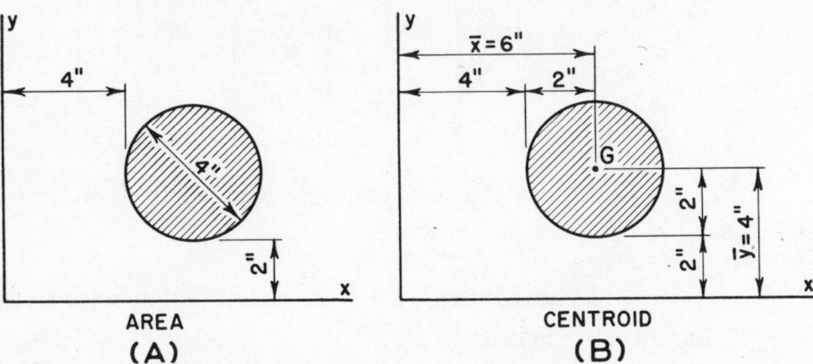

Fig. 2. Centroid of a Circular Area

of a circular area is always at the center of the circle and is designated by the letter G.

Also in Fig. 1, it is shown that the distance from the y axis to the centroid of the area is 5″. This distance is designated by the symbol $\bar{x}$ (read *x bar*).

When the two distances $\bar{x}$ and $\bar{y}$ are known, the location of the centroid is also known, and $\bar{x}$ and $\bar{y}$ may be regarded as co-ordinates of the centroid.

The *centroid* is a point in the area, so located that its distance from any axis is equal to the average distance of the area from that axis.

You may wonder what controls the position of the x and y axes. In each of the beginning problems, the axes will be placed in the locations that will make it easiest to learn to find a centroid. Later on you will be required to place the axes.

3-2. Centroids of Simple Areas.

The next step is to learn the locations of the *centroids* of simple areas such as *circles, rectangles,* and *triangles.* Later, go on to more complicated areas.

Illustrative Example 1. Locate the centroid of the circular area in Fig. 2A.

Solution:

The diameter of the circle is 4″, so the radius is 2″, one half of the diameter. Work from Fig. 2B, in which point G (at the center of the circle) is the *centroid.*

1. To find $\bar{x}$
   a) The distance from the y axis to the left edge of the area is 4″
   b) The distance from the left edge of the circle to the center is 2″
   c) Then, $\bar{x} = 4 + 2 = 6$
2. To find $\bar{y}$
   a) The distance from the x axis to the lower edge of the circle is 2″
   b) The distance from the lower edge of the circle to the center is 2″
   c) Then $\bar{y} = 2 + 2 = 4$

Fig. 3 shows a rectangular area. Notice that the width is designated as b and the altitude as h. The centroid is at G, above the base by a distance of one half the altitude, and is to the right of the left edge by a distance of one half the base. The *centroid of a rectangle* is always located in this manner. In other words the *centroid is at the center of the rectangle.*

Illustrative Example 2. Where is the centroid of the rectangular area in Fig. 4A?

Solution:

Fig. 4*B* gives all the information required to find the centroid of an area.

1. To find $\bar{x}$
   a) The distance from the y axis to the left edge of the rectangle is 2″
   b) The distance from the left edge of the rectangle to the center is 3″ (one half of the 6″ width)
   c) Then, $\bar{x} = 2 + 3 = 5''$.

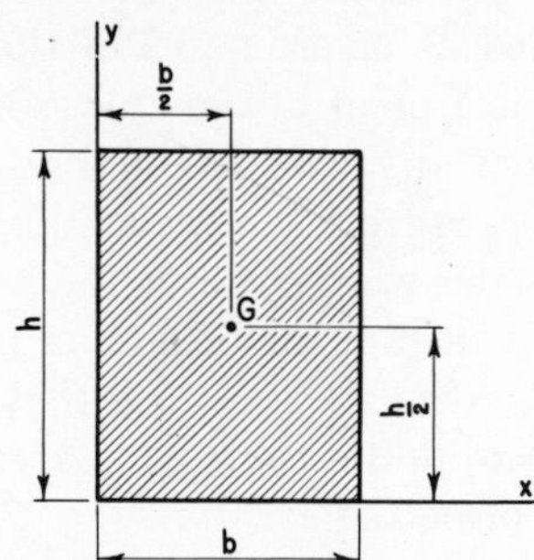

Fig. 3. Rectangular Area

2. To find $\bar{y}$
   a) The distance from the x axis to the base of the rectangle is 4″
   b) The distance from the base of the rectangle to the center is 1.5″ (one half of the 3″ altitude)
   c) Then, $\bar{y} = 4 + 1.5 = 5.5''$

Another figure that will be used often is the right triangle. Fig. 5 shows a right triangle of width b and altitude h. The centroid is at G, the distance from the vertical leg of the triangle to the centroid is $\frac{b}{3}$ (one-third of the width); also, the distance from the horizontal leg of the triangle to the centroid is $\frac{h}{3}$ (one-third of the altitude). The location of the centroid of a triangle will not be proven but the foregoing method may always be used.

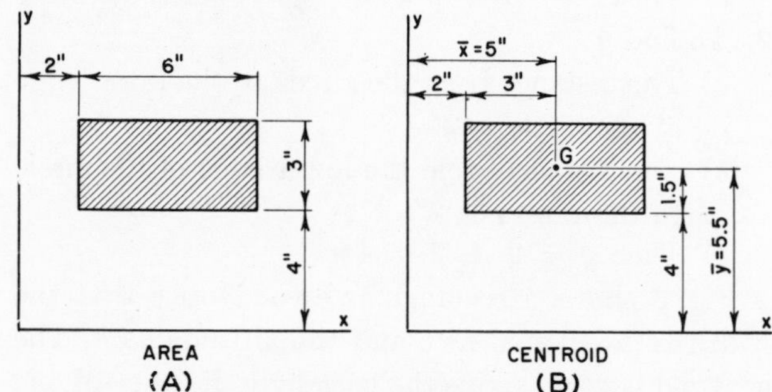

Fig. 4. Centroid of a Rectangular Area

Fig. 6 illustrates other solutions in working with triangles; notice the different positions in which the triangle may be turned. Study each triangle and make sure that you realize, in each case, the distance from the vertical leg to the centroid is one-third of the width and the distance from the horizontal leg to the centroid is one-third of the altitude.

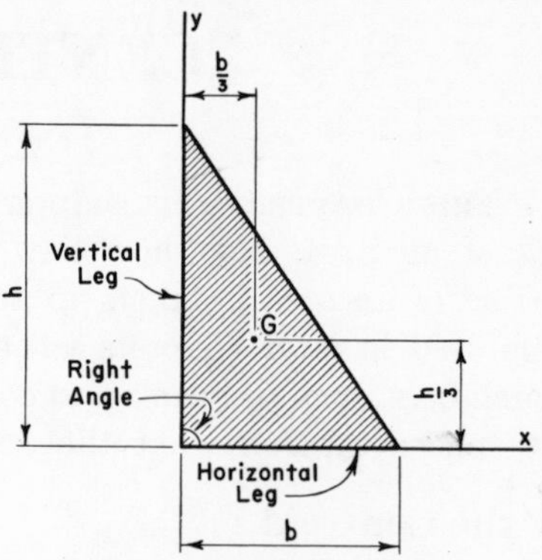

Fig. 5. Right Triangle

Illustrative Example 3. Locate the centroid of the triangular area in Fig. 7*A*.

Solution:

Fig. 7*B* is a good figure from which to work.

1. (*A*) To find $\bar{x}$
   a) The distance from the y axis to the vertical leg of the triangle is 4″
   b) The distance from the vertical leg of the triangle to the centroid is 2″ (one-third of the 6″ width).
   c) Then, $\bar{x} = 4 + 2 = 6''$

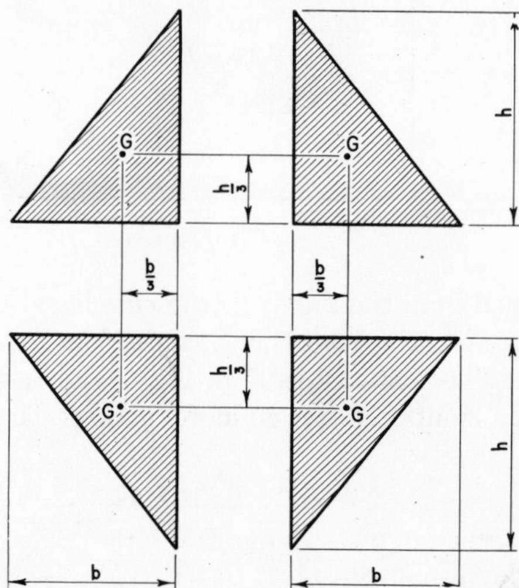

Fig. 6. Different Ways a Triangle May Be Turned

2. To find $\bar{y}$
   a) The distance from the x axis to the horizontal leg of the triangle is 8″
   b) The distance from the horizontal leg of the triangle to the centroid is 1″ (one-third of the 3″ altitude). Notice that the centroid is *below* the horizontal leg.
   c) Then, $\bar{y} = 8 - 1 = 7''$

There is one more point to consider in this topic

of simple areas. Study Fig. 8 and notice the plus and minus signs; you should remember from algebra that you took x as *positive* (plus) when it was measured

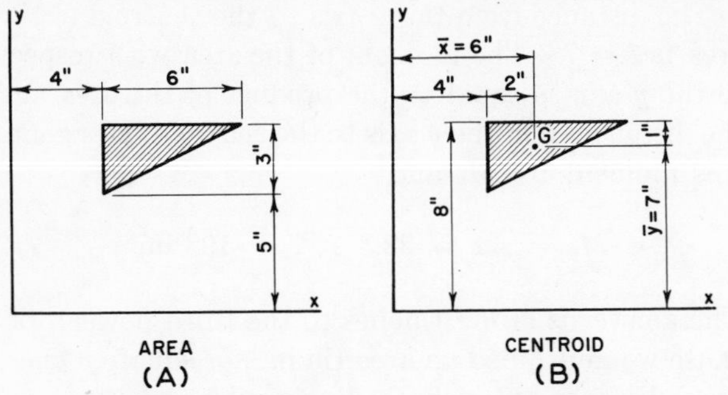

Fig. 7. Centroid of a Triangular Area

to the right of the origin 0, and *negative* (minus) when it was measured to the left; also, that you took y as *positive*, when measured upward, and *negative*, when measured downward. The same procedure will be followed here, and will mean that $\bar{x}$ is *positive* when the

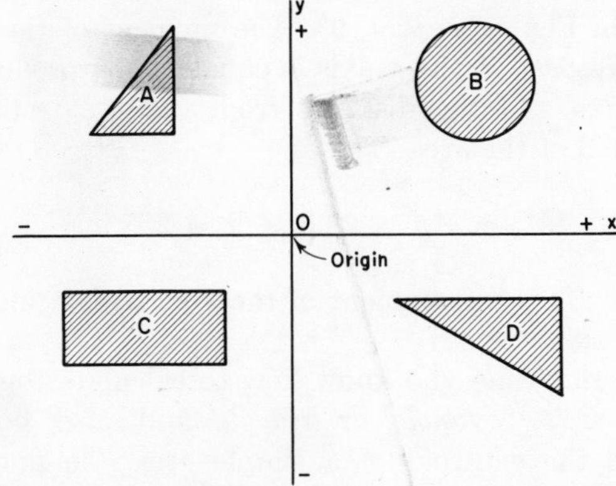

Fig. 8. Positive and Negative Values of $\bar{x}$ and $\bar{y}$

centroid of the area is to the right of the y axis and *negative* when the centroid is the left. The distance $\bar{y}$ is *positive* when the centroid of the area is above the x axis and *negative* when the centroid is below the x axis.

The triangle A in Fig. 8 is to the left of the y axis so $\bar{x}$ is *negative*. The triangle is above the x axis so $\bar{y}$ is *positive*.

The circle B in Fig. 8 is to the right of the y axis so $\bar{x}$ is *positive*, and the circle is above the x axis so $\bar{y}$ is *positive*.

The rectangle C in Fig. 8 is to the left of the y axis so $\bar{x}$ is *negative*. The rectangle is below the x axis so $\bar{y}$ is *negative*, too.

The triangle D in Fig. 8 is to the right of the y axis so $\bar{x}$ is *positive*, and the triangle is below the x axis so $\bar{y}$ is *negative*.

Illustrative Example 4. Locate the *centroid* of the triangular area in Fig. 9A.

Solution:

Work from Fig. 9B.

1. To find $\bar{x}$
   a) The distance from the y axis to the vertical leg of the triangle is $-5''$. (The minus sign is used because the distance is measured to the left from the y axis)

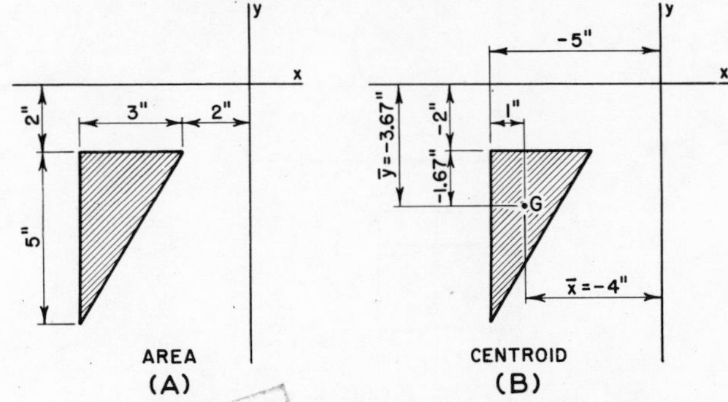

Fig. 9. Centroid of a Triangular Area

   b) The distance from the vertical leg of the triangle to the centroid is $1''$ (we take this as *positive* because the centroid is to the right of the vertical leg)
   c) Then, $\bar{x} = -5 + 1 = -4''$
2. To find $\bar{y}$
   a) The distance from the x axis to the horizontal leg of the triangle is $-2''$ (*negative* because it is measured downward)

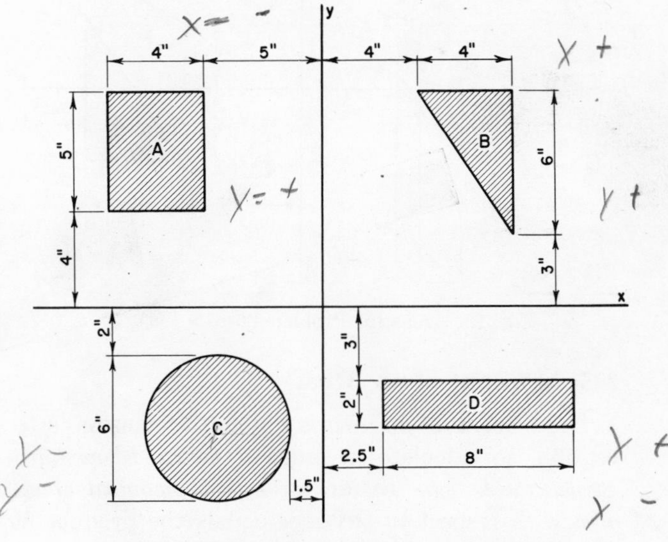

Fig. 10. Areas for Problems 1 to 4 (Art. 2)

   b) The distance from the horizontal leg of the triangle to the centroid is $-1.67''$ (one-third of 5 is 1.67 and it is *negative* because the centroid is below the horizontal leg)
   c) Then, $\bar{y} = -2 - 1.67 = -3.67''$

Practice Problems (Art. 3-2). Locate the centroid of each of the following areas.

1. The rectangle A in Fig. 10.
2. The triangle B in Fig. 10.
3. The circle C in Fig. 10.
4. The rectangle D in Fig. 10.

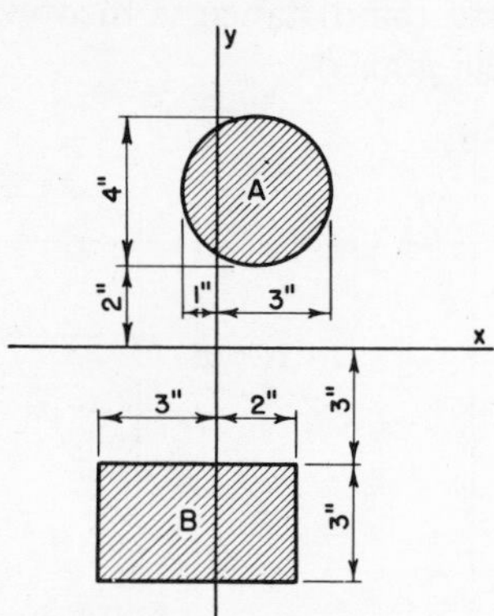

Fig. 11. Areas for Problems 5 and 6 (Art. 2)

5. The circle A in Fig. 11.
6. The rectangle B in Fig. 11.
7. The triangle A in Fig. 12.
8. The triangle B in Fig. 12.
9. The rectangle C in Fig. 12.

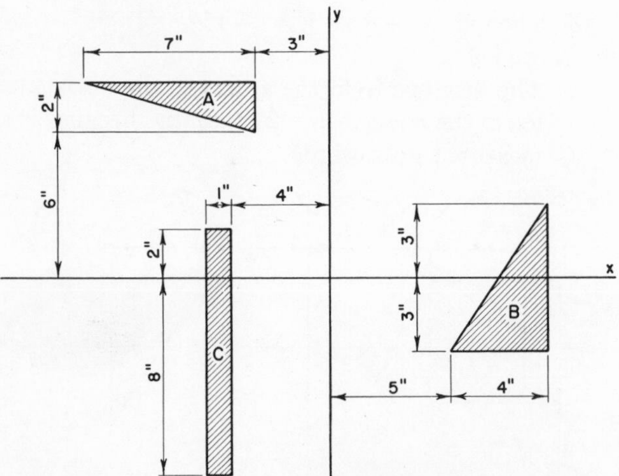

Fig. 12. Areas for Problems 6 to 9 (Art. 2)

3-3. Moment of an Area.

The *moment of an area* is a quantity you have to be able to calculate in order to learn *Elementary Structural Design*. By definition, the *moment of an area* with respect to any axis equals the product of the area (in square inches) and the distance (in inches) from the axis to the centroid of the area. The circular area in Fig. 13 will be used to illustrate. Notice that d is the diameter of the circle, and $d = 6''$.

The area A of the circle is

$$A = \frac{\pi}{4} d^2 = \frac{\pi}{4} (6)^2 = 28.3 \text{ sq. in.}$$

(You should remember that $A = \frac{\pi}{4} d^2$ from previous studies.)

The distance from the y axis to the centroid of the area is $\bar{x} = 7''$. The moment of the area with respect to the y axis is equal to the product of the area and the distance from the y axis to the centroid. Designate this moment by M_y and

$$M_y = A\bar{x} = 28.3 \times 7 = 198 \text{ in.}^3$$

The answer is in in.^{3} (inches to the third power), because we multiplied an area (in in.^{2}, or square inches) by a distance (in inches). You could write

$$\text{in.}^2 \times \text{in.} = \text{in.}^3$$

just as you used to write when you studied algebra

$$x^2 \times x = x^3$$

The distance from the x axis to the centroid of the area in Fig. 13 is $\bar{y} = 9''$. The moment of the area with respect to the x axis is equal to the product of the area and the distance from the x axis to the centroid of the area. This is

$$M_x = A\bar{y} = 28.3 \times 9 = 255 \text{ in.}^3$$

where M_x is the moment of the area with respect to the x axis.

By this time you know how to calculate the area of a *circle*, *rectangle*, or *triangle*, and, also, how to locate the centroid of a simple area. To find the moment of the area with respect to an axis simply multiply the area by the distance from the axis to the centroid of the area.

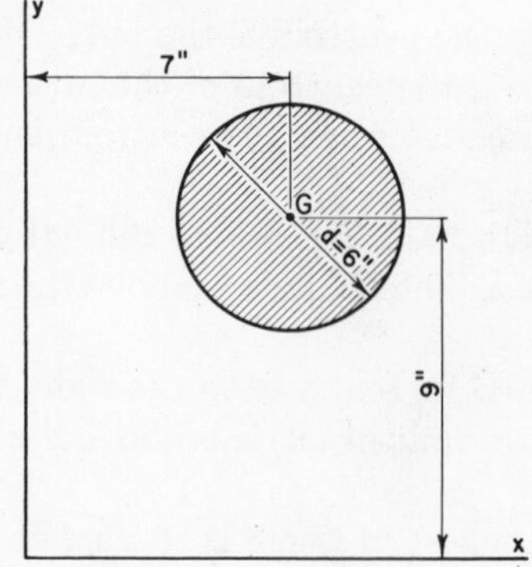

Fig. 13. Circular Area—Positive

Sometimes the distance $\bar{x}$ is positive and sometimes it is negative. If you multiply a *positive area* by a *positive distance*, the result is *positive*. For example,

$$(+10) \times (+3) = +30$$

However, if you multiply a *positive area* by a *negative distance*, the result is *negative*. For instance,

$$(+20) \times (-2) = -40$$

(This is something you learned when you studied algebra.) The distance from an axis to the centroid is *positive* in some cases and *negative* in others, so sometimes the moment of an area is positive and sometimes it is negative. You can always tell whether it is positive or negative by following the rule that the *product of two positive numbers is positive*, and *the product of a positive number* and a *negative number* is *negative*.

Illustrative Example 1. Calculate the moment of the triangular area in Fig. 14*A* with respect to the x axis and with respect to the y axis.

Solution:

Fig. 14*B* illustrates all that is necessary to locate the centroid of the area.

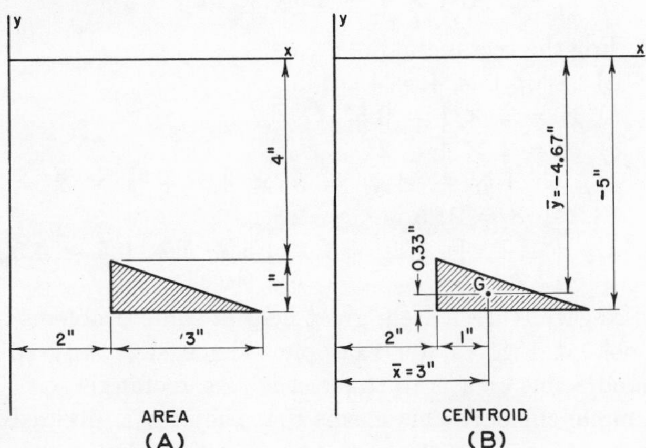

Fig. 14. Moment of an Area

1. To find $\bar{x}$
   a) The distance from the y axis to the vertical leg of the triangle is 2″
   b) The distance from the vertical leg of the triangle to the centroid is 1″ (one-third of the 3″ width)
   c) Then $\bar{x} = 2 + 1 = 3''$
2. The area of the triangle is equal to one half the product of the width and altitude. Thus,

$$A = \tfrac{1}{2} \times 3 \times 1 = 1.5 \text{ sq. in.}$$

3. The moment of the area with respect to the y axis is

$$M_y = A\bar{x} = 1.5 \times 3 = 4.5 \text{ in.}^3$$

4. To find $\bar{y}$
   a) The distance from the x axis to the horizontal leg of the triangle is $-5''$ (*negative* because it is downward)
   b) The distance from the horizontal leg of the triangle to the centroid is 0.33″ (one-third of the 1″ altitude). Notice that this distance is measured upward from the horizontal leg.
   c) Then, $\bar{y} = -5 + 0.33 = -4.67''$.

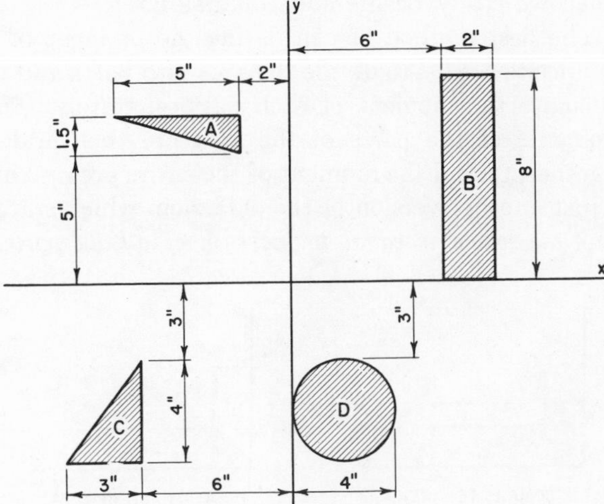

Fig. 15. Areas for Problems 1 to 4 (Art. 3)

5. The moment of the area with respect to the x axis is

$$M_x = A\bar{y} = 1.5 \times (-4.67) = -7 \text{ in.}^3$$

Practice Problems (Art. 3-3). Find the moment of each of the following areas with respect to the x and y axes.

1. The triangle A in Fig. 15.
2. The rectangle B in Fig. 15.
3. The triangle C in Fig. 15.
4. The circle D in Fig. 15.

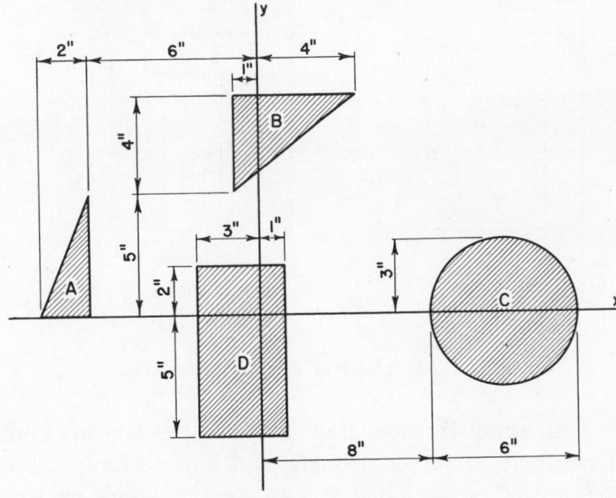

Fig. 16. Areas for Problems 5 to 8 (Art. 3)

5. The triangle A in Fig. 16.
6. The triangle B in Fig. 16.
7. The circle C in Fig. 16.
8. The rectangle D in Fig. 16.

3-4. Moment of a Composite Area.

A *composite area* is an area (usually rather complicated) which can be divided into single parts, such as *rectangles*, *circles*, and *triangles*. We have to study such areas because we will encounter them when we study beams and columns later.

The best method of calculating the moment of a composite area is to divide the area into parts and to calculate the moment of each part separately. The moments of the parts of the area are then added together, to find the moment of the entire area. (This is just another version of the old axiom which states that *the whole is equal to the sum of all its parts.*)

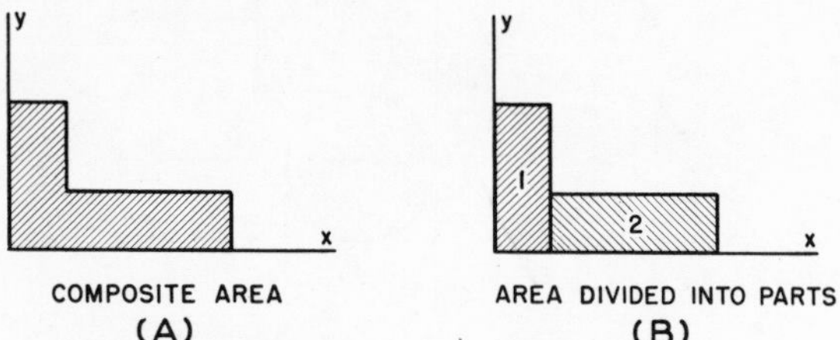

Fig. 17. Division of a Composite Area

This method could be applied to the angle section in Fig. 17*A*. Fig. 17*B* shows the area divided into the rectangles 1 and 2. To calculate the moment of the composite area with respect to the x axis, calculate the moment of each rectangle separately with respect to the x axis. Then add the moments of the rectangles to find the moment of the composite area.

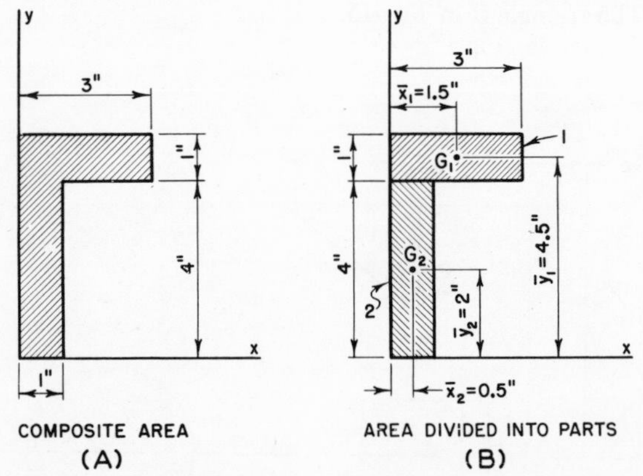

Fig. 18. Moment of a Composite Area

You know by now how to calculate the area of a *rectangle*, *circle*, or *triangle*, and how to find $\bar{x}$ and $\bar{y}$ for each area. Then for an area 1 (such as the rectangle in Fig. 17*B*), the moment with respect to the y axis is

$$A_1\bar{x}_1$$

where the subscripts $_1$ indicate the area 1. The moment of the area 2 with respect to the y axis is

$$A_2\bar{x}_2$$

The moment of the composite area with respect to the y axis is the sum of the moments of 1 and 2, so

$$M_y = A_1\bar{x}_1 + A_2\bar{x}_2$$

The calculation of the x's and y's will be made short, in the following example, since it has been covered previously.

Illustrative Example 1. Calculate the moment of the angle section in Fig. 18*A* with respect to the x axis and with respect to the y axis.

Solution:

Fig. 18*B* shows the area divided into the rectangle 1 and the rectangle 2.

1. For the rectangle 1
   a) $A_1 = 3 \times 1 = 3$ sq. in.
   b) $\bar{x}_1 = \frac{1}{2} \times 3 = 1.5''$
   c) $\bar{y}_1 = 4 + \frac{1}{2} \times 1 = 4.5''$
2. For the rectangle 2
   a) $A_2 = 1 \times 4 = 4$ sq. in.
   b) $\bar{x}_2 = \frac{1}{2} \times 1 = 0.5''$
   c) $\bar{y}_2 = \frac{1}{2} \times 4 = 2''$
3. $M_x = A_1\bar{y}_1 + A_2\bar{y}_2 = 3 \times 4.5 + 4 \times 2 = 13.5 + 8 = 21.5 \text{ in.}^3$
4. $M_y = A_1\bar{x}_1 + A_2\bar{x}_2 = 3 \times 1.5 + 4 \times 0.5 = 4.5 + 2 = 6.5 \text{ in.}^3$

Negative areas are a great help in some problems. Look at Fig. 19, for example. The easiest way to handle this area is to think of it as a rectangle with a circle cut out. This means that the area is divided into a positive rectangle and a negative circle. Calculate the area of a rectangle and the area of a circle. By locating the centroid of a rectangle or a circle, you can calculate the moment of each area. Then the moment of the whole area is equal to the moment of the rectangle minus the moment of the circle. Problems are easily solved in this manner, if precaution is used in working with plus and minus signs.

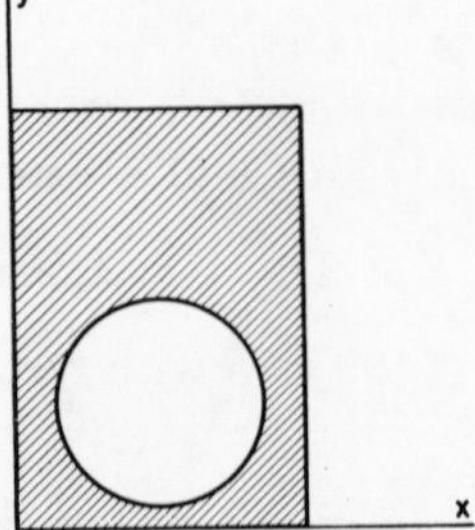

Fig. 19. Composite Area

Illustrative Example 2. Calculate the moment of the area in Fig. 20*A* with respect to the x axis and with respect to the y axis.

Solution:

Fig. 20*B* shows the area divided into the *positive rectangle* 1 (8″ wide and 6″ high) and the *negative triangle* (width = 3″, altitude = 4″).

1. For the rectangle 1
   a) $A_1 = 8 \times 6 = 48$ sq. in.
   b) $\bar{x}_1 = \frac{1}{2} \times 8 = 4''$
   c) $\bar{y}_1 = \frac{1}{2} \times 6 = 3''$
2. For the triangle 2
   a) $A_2 = -\frac{1}{2} \times 3 \times 4 = -6$ sq. in.
   b) $\bar{x}_2 = 8 - \frac{1}{3} \times 3 = 7''$
   c) $\bar{y}_2 = \frac{1}{3} \times 4 = 1.33''$
3. $M_x = A_1\bar{y}_1 + A_2\bar{y}_2 = 48 \times 3 + (-6) \times 1.33 = 144 - 8 = 136$ in.³
4. $M_y = A_1\bar{x}_1 + A_2\bar{x}_2 = 48 \times 4 + (-6) \times 7 = 192 - 42 = 150$ in.³

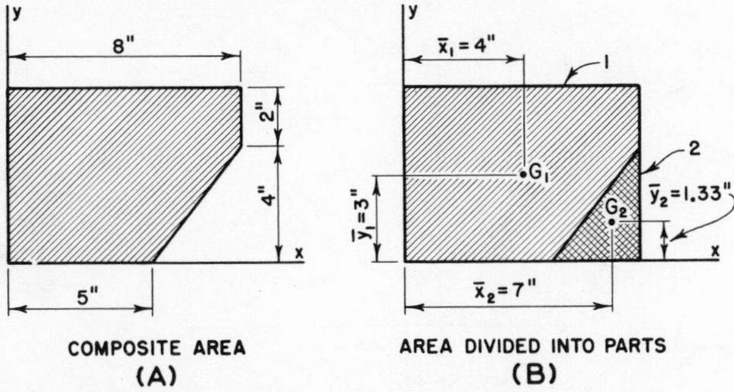

Fig. 20. Moment of a Composite Area

The moment of an area is *zero* with respect to an axis of symmetry. An axis of symmetry is simply this: *if the area is so shaped that, for each part on one side of the axis, there is a matching part on the other side of the axis, the axis is an axis of symmetry.* Fig. 21 shows an area which is symmetrical with respect to the x axis. The rectangle 1, at the top of the area, and the rectangle 1 which matches it, at the bottom of the area, are readily seen. There is a triangle 2 at the top and a matching triangle 2 at the bottom. There is a rectangle 3 above the x axis and a rectangle 3 below the x axis. The x axis is an *axis of symmetry*.

Not only must the matching areas be of the same shape and size, but each area must be at the same distance from the axis. In Fig. 21, for example, the upper rectangle 1 must be at the same distance above the x axis as the lower rectangle 1 is below the x axis, in order for the x axis to be an axis of symmetry.

The moment of an area is *zero* with respect to an axis of symmetry and is easily seen by further illustrations. For instance, in Fig. 21, the two rectangles 1 have the same areas in square inches and the distance from the x axis to each of their centroids is the same. The moment of the upper rectangle 1 is *positive* with respect to the x axis because its $\bar{y}$ is *positive*. But the moment of the lower rectangle 1 is *negative* because its $\bar{y}$ is *negative*. The two moments are of equal amounts, so one cancels the other when the

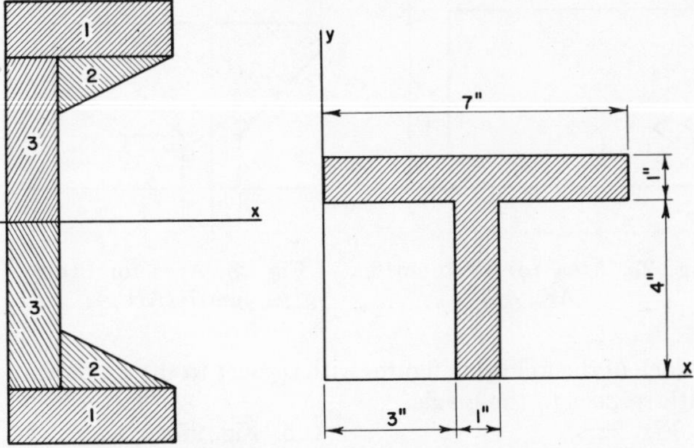

Fig. 21. Symmetrical Area

Fig. 22. Area for Problem 1 (Art. 4)

moments of all the parts are added. In the same way, the moment of the lower triangle 2 cancels the moment of the upper triangle 2. Also, the moment of the lower rectangle 3 cancels the moment of the upper rectangle 3. In this way, it always works out that the moment of an area is *zero* with respect to an axis of symmetry.

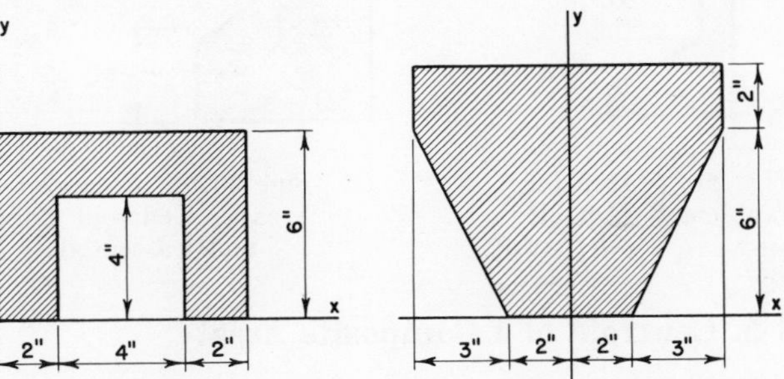

Fig. 23. Area for Problem 2 (Art. 4)

Fig. 24. Area for Problem 3 (Art. 4)

It saves time to recognize an axis of symmetry and to know that the *moment* of the area is *zero*. The same results would be obtained if you calculated the moments completely, but it would be a waste of time.

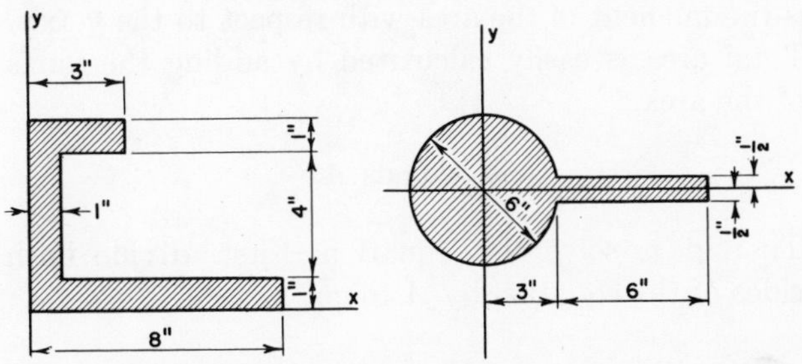

Fig. 25. Area for Problem 4 (Art. 4)

Fig. 26. Area for Problem 5 (Art. 4)

Practice Problems (Art. 3-4). Practice now on *moment of a composite area.* Calculate the moment of the area

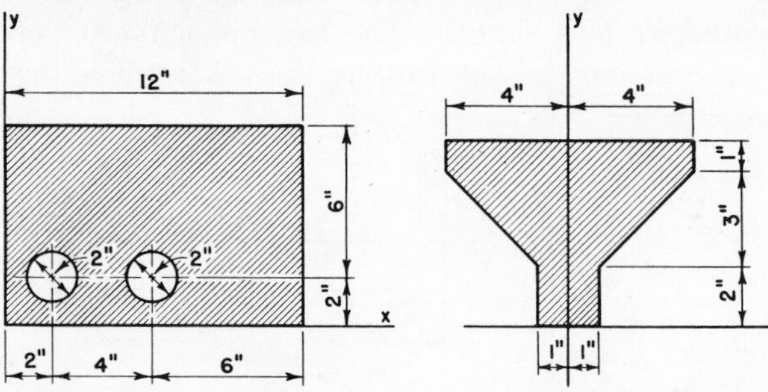

Fig. 27. Area for Problem 6 (Art. 4)

Fig. 28. Area for Problem 7 (Art. 4)

in each of the following figures with respect to the x axis and with respect to the y axis.

1. Fig. 22.
2. Fig. 23.
3. Fig. 24.
4. Fig. 25.
5. Fig. 26.
6. Fig. 27.
7. Fig. 28.
8. Fig. 29.

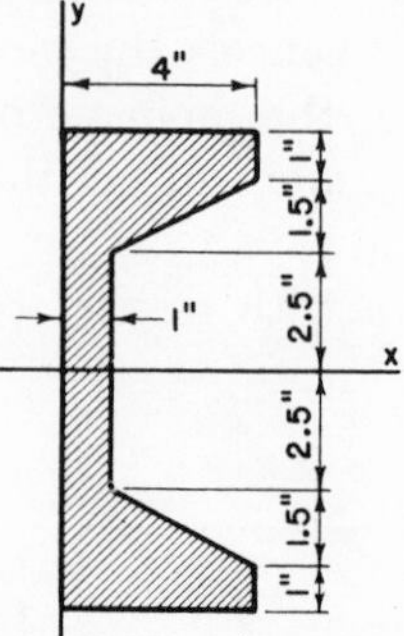

Fig. 29. Area for Problem 8 (Art. 4)

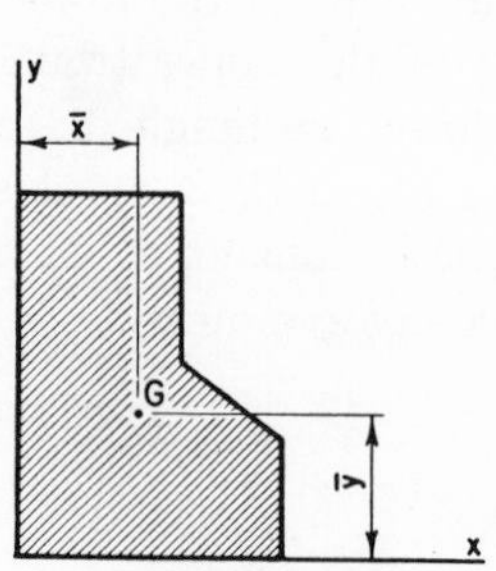

Fig. 30. Composite Area — Centroid Correctly Located

3-5. Centroid of a Composite Area.

The problem of locating the *centroid of a composite area* is the most important part of this chapter. Suppose you want to locate the centroid of the composite area in Fig. 30. The centroid may be designated by G; your problem is to find the location of G. The location of G is given by the distances $\bar{x}$ and $\bar{y}$, so you must find $\bar{x}$ and $\bar{y}$ in order to locate G. You have previously learned to calculate M_y, which is the moment of the area with respect to the y axis. Total area is easily calculated by adding the parts of the area.

$$M_y \text{ equals } A\bar{x}$$

To find $\bar{x}$, solve this equation. First, divide both sides of the equation by A to get

$$\frac{M_y}{A} = \frac{A}{A}\bar{x}$$

Then cancel A on the right side of the equation to get

$$\frac{M_y}{A} = \bar{x} \qquad \text{or} \qquad \bar{x} = \frac{M_y}{A}$$

This is simple, and expressed in words, it is: *the distance from the y axis to the centroid of the area equals the moment of the area with respect to the y axis, divided by the area.*

The formula for $\bar{y}$ is given without proving it. It is

$$\bar{y} = \frac{M_x}{A}$$

That is, the distance from the x axis to the centroid of the area is equal to: *The moment of the area with respect to the x axis, divided by the area.*

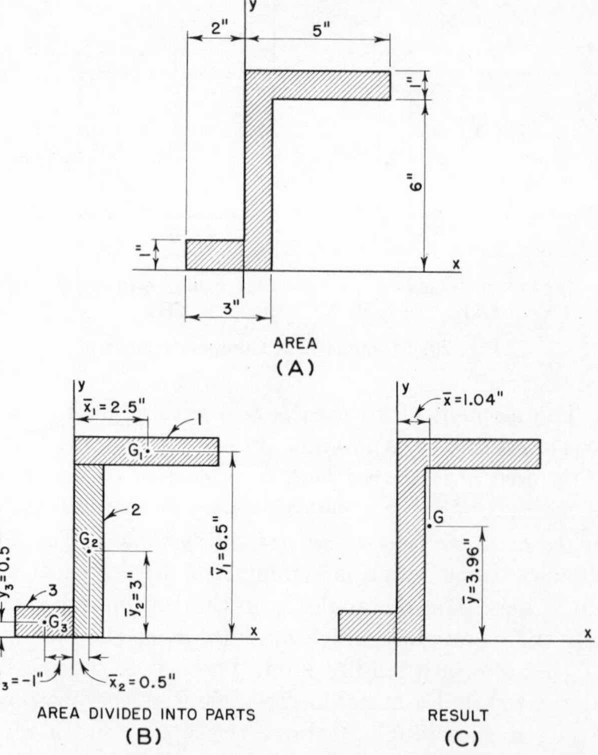

Fig. 31. Centroid of a Composite Area—Three Rectangles

Illustrative Example 1. Locate the centroid of the composite area in Fig. 31*A*.

Solution:

Fig. 31*B* shows the area divided into the rectangles 1, 2, and 3; also, the centroidal distances for the rectangles.

1. For the rectangle 1
   a) $A_1 = 5 \times 1 = 5$ sq. in.
   b) $\bar{x}_1 = \frac{1}{2} \times 5 = 2.5''$
   c) $\bar{y}_1 = 6 + \frac{1}{2} \times 1 = 6.5''$

2. For the rectangle 2
   a) $A_2 = 1 \times 6 = 6$ sq. in.
   b) $\bar{x}_2 = \frac{1}{2} \times 1 = 0.5''$
   c) $\bar{y}_2 = \frac{1}{2} \times 6 = 3''$
3. For the rectangle 3
   a) $A_3 = 2 \times 1 = 2$ sq. in.
   b) $\bar{x}_3 = -\frac{1}{2} \times 2 = -1''$ (Notice the *minus sign.* Why is it *minus?*)
   c) $\bar{y}_3 = \frac{1}{2} \times 1 = 0.5''$
4. The total area is
   $A = A_1 + A_2 + A_3 = 5 + 6 + 2 = 13$ sq. in.
5. $M_y = A_1\bar{x}_1 + A_2\bar{x}_2 + A_3\bar{x}_3 = 5 \times 2.5 + 6 \times 0.5 + 2 \times (-1) = 12.5 + 3 - 2 = 13.5 \text{ in.}^3$
6. $M_x = A_1\bar{y}_1 + A_2\bar{y}_2 + A_3\bar{y}_3 = 5 \times 6.5 + 6 \times 3 + 2 \times 0.5 = 32.5 + 18 + 1 = 51.5 \text{ in.}^3$
7. Then $\bar{x} = \dfrac{M_y}{A} = \dfrac{13.5}{13} = 1.04''$
8. And $\bar{y} = \dfrac{M_x}{A} = \dfrac{51.5}{13} = 3.96''$

Fig. 31*C* shows the centroid *G* in its correct location.

The foregoing example illustrates locating the centroid of a composite area. One more example on negative areas and axes of symmetry will be given.

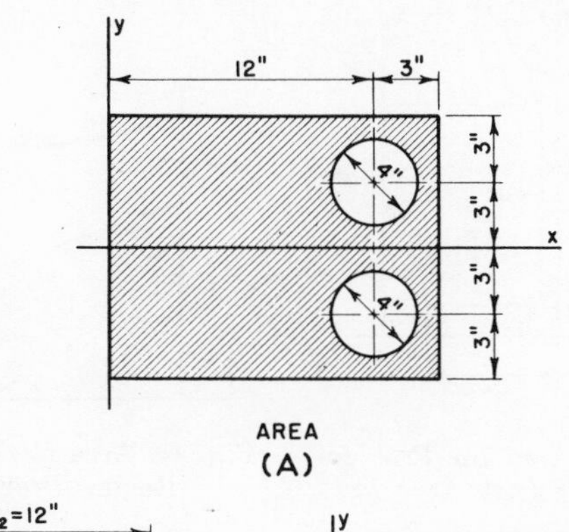

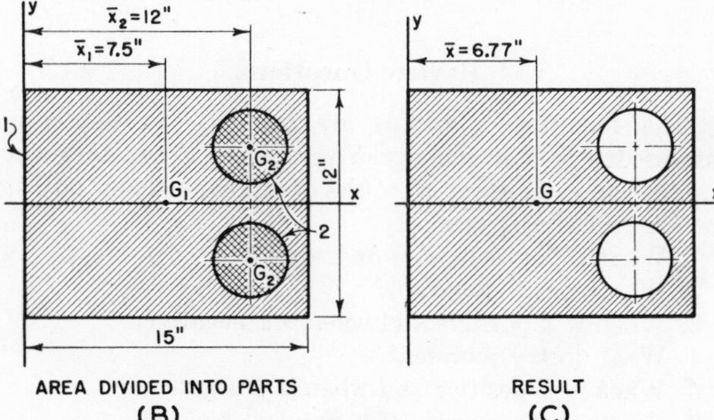

Fig. 32. Centroid of a Composite Area—Positive Rectangle and Two Negative Circles

Illustrative Example 2. Locate the centroid of the area shown in Fig. 32*A*.

Solution:

Fig. 32*B* shows the area divided into the positive rectangle 1 (width = 15″, altitude = 12″) and the two negative circles 2. Notice that the x axis is an axis of symmetry, which means that the moment of the area is *zero* with respect to the x axis. That is, $M_x = 0$.

1. For the rectangle 1
   a) $A_1 = 15 \times 12 = 180$ sq. in.
   b) $\bar{x}_1 = \frac{1}{2} \times 15 = 7.5''$
2. For one of the circles 2
   a) $A_2 = -\dfrac{\pi}{4} d^2 = -\dfrac{\pi}{4} (4)^2 = -12.56$ sq. in.
   b) $\bar{x}_2 = 12''$
3. The entire area A is
   $A = A_1 + 2A_2 = 180 + 2(-12.56) = 180 - 25.1 = 154.9$ sq. in.
4. $M_y = A_1\bar{x}_1 + 2A_2\bar{x}_2 = 180 \times 7.5 + 2(-12.56)12 = 1{,}350 - 302 = 1{,}048 \text{ in.}^3$
5. $M_x = 0$, because of symmetry
6. Then $\bar{x} = \dfrac{M_y}{A} = \dfrac{1{,}048}{154.9} = 6.77''$
7. And $\bar{y} = \dfrac{M_x}{A} = \dfrac{0}{154.9} = 0$

Fig. 32*C* shows the centroid in its correct location.

The foregoing example provides an illustration of an important fact; that is, when there is an axis of symmetry, the centroid lies on this axis. Remember this fact in the next set of practice problems.

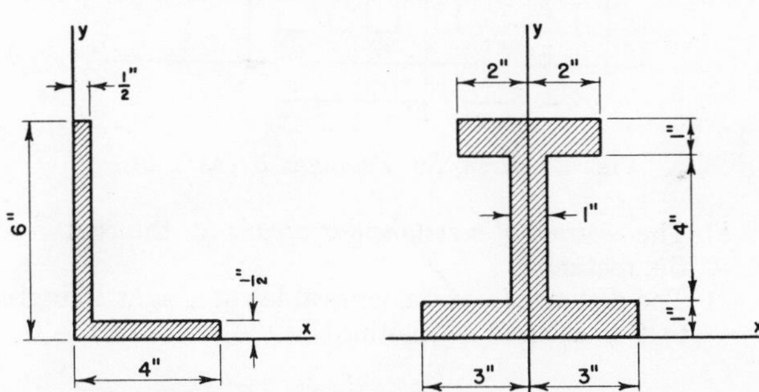

Fig. 33. Area for Problem 1 (Art. 5)

Fig. 34. Area for Problem 2 (Art. 5)

Practice Problems (Art. 3-5). Locate the centroid of the area in each of the following figures. Remember negative areas and axes of symmetry.

1. Fig. 33.
2. Fig. 34.
3. Fig. 35.
4. Fig. 36.
5. Fig. 37.
6. Fig. 38.
7. Fig. 39.
8. Fig. 40.

SUMMARY OF CHAPTER III

The main points of this chapter, on centroid of an area, are covered in this summary.

1. The centroid of an area is a point so located that its distance from any axis is equal to the average distance of the area from that axis.

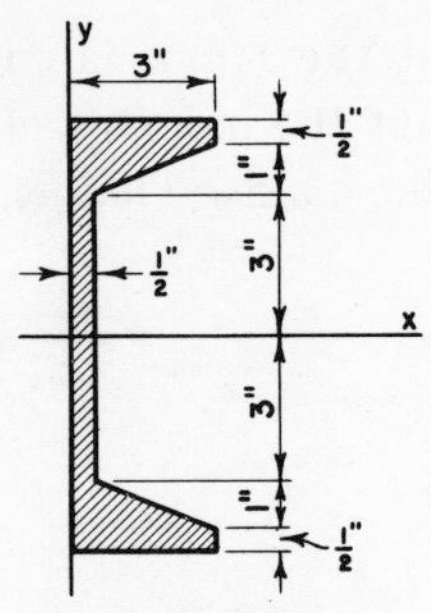

Fig. 35. Area for Problem 3 (Art. 5)

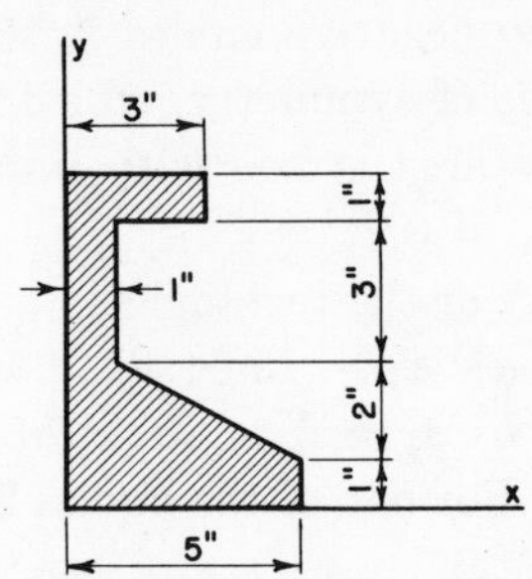

Fig. 36. Area for Problem 4 (Art. 5)

2. The distance from the y axis to the centroid of an area is designated as $\bar{x}$.
   a) $\bar{x}$ is *positive* if measured to the right from the y axis.
   b) $\bar{x}$ is *negative* if measured to the left from the y axis.
3. The distance from the x axis to the centroid of an area is designated as $\bar{y}$.
   a) $\bar{y}$ is *positive* if measured upward from the x axis.
   b) $\bar{y}$ is *negative* if measured downward from the x axis.
4. For the simple areas.
   a) The *centroid of a circular area* is at the center of the circle.

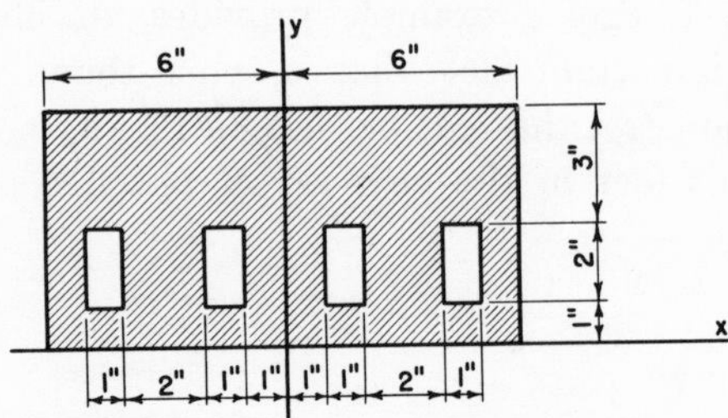

Fig. 37. Area for Problem 5 (Art. 5)

   b) The *centroid of a rectangular area* is at the center of the rectangle.
   c) The distance from the vertical leg of a right triangle to the centroid is one-third of the width of the triangle. The distance from the horizontal leg to the centroid is one-third of the altitude.

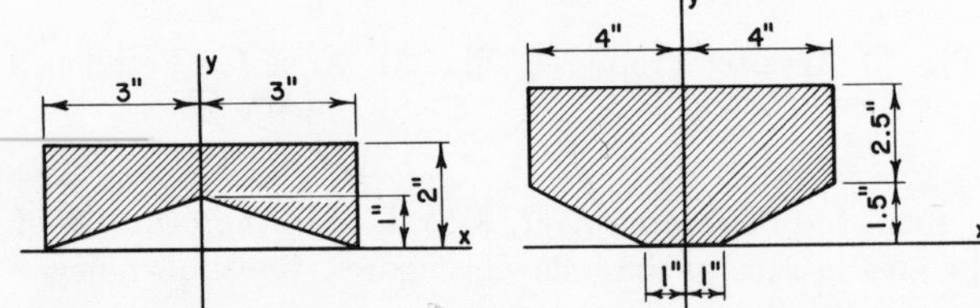

Fig. 38. Area for Problem 6 (Art. 5)

Fig. 39. Area for Problem 7 (Art. 5)

5. The moment of an area with respect to an axis equals the *product of the area* and the *distance from the axis to the centroid of the area.*
   a) The moment of an area with respect to the x axis is

$$M_x = A\bar{y}$$

   b) The moment of an area with respect to the y axis is

$$M_y = A\bar{x}$$

6. A *composite area* is an area which can be divided into simple parts, such as *rectangles, triangles,* and *circles.*
7. The *moment of a composite area* with respect to an axis is equal to the *sum of the moments of the parts of the area with respect to the axis.*
8. The distance from an axis to the centroid of an area equals *the moment of the area with respect to the axis, divided by the area.*
   a) The distance from the y axis to the centroid of an area is

$$\bar{x} = \frac{M_y}{A}$$

   b) The distance from the x axis to the centroid of an area is

$$\bar{y} = \frac{M_x}{A}$$

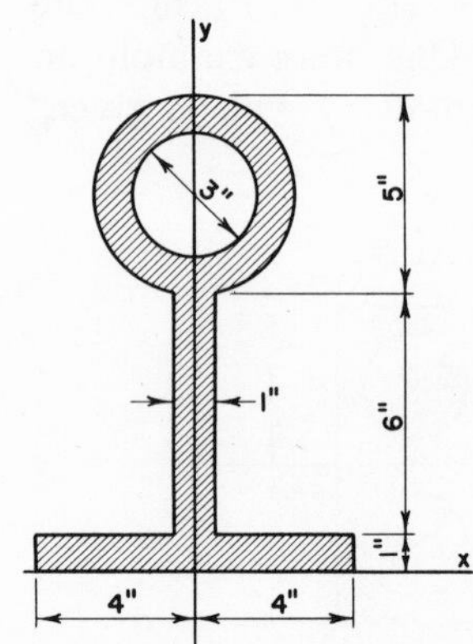

Fig. 40. Area for Problem 8 (Art. 5)

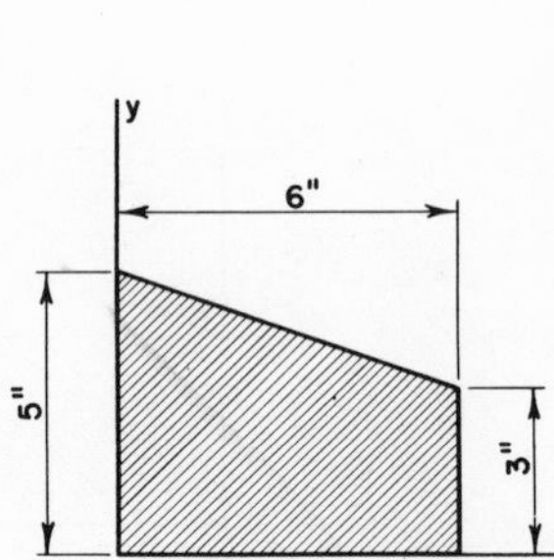

Fig. 41. Area for Problem 1 (Review Problems)

Review Questions

The following questions are provided to test your knowledge of this chapter. You are not ready to go on unless you can answer all of the questions without looking at the preceding pages.

1. What is the *centroid of an area?*
2. What does $\bar{x}$ stand for?
3. When is $\bar{x}$ positive and when is $\bar{x}$ negative?
4. What does $\bar{y}$ represent?
5. When is $\bar{y}$ positive and when is $\bar{y}$ negative?
6. Where is the *centroid of a circular area?*
7. Where is the *centroid of a rectangular area?*
8. Where is the *centroid of the area of a right triangle?*
9. What is the *area of a circle?*
10. What is the *area of a right triangle?*
11. What is the *moment of an area with respect to an axis?*
12. In what units is the moment of an area expressed?
13. What is a *composite area?*
14. How do you find the amount of a composite area?

15. How do you calculate the moment of a composite area with respect to an axis?
16. How do you find $\bar{x}$ for a composite area?
17. How do you find $\bar{y}$ for a composite area?

Review Problems

The following problems are a final check. You should know how to locate the centroid of an area after finding $\bar{x}$ and $\bar{y}$ for the area in each of the following figures.

1. Fig. 41.
2. Fig. 42.
3. Fig. 43.
4. Fig. 44.
5. Fig. 45.

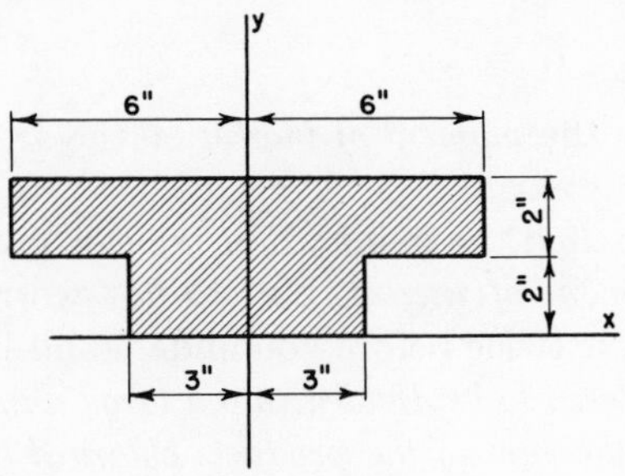

Fig. 42. Area for Problem 2 (Review Problems)

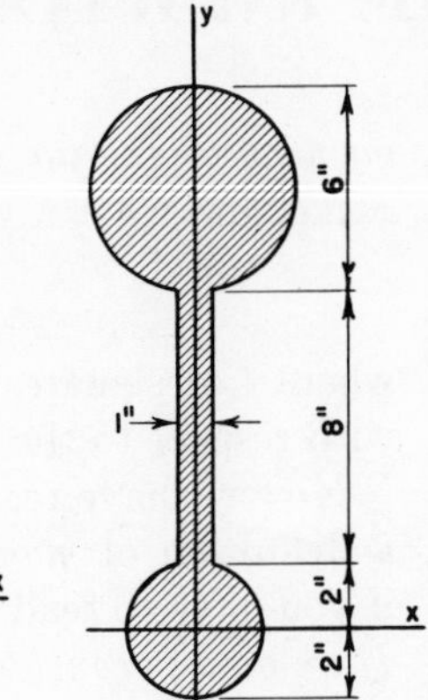

Fig. 43. Area for Problem 3 (Review Problems)

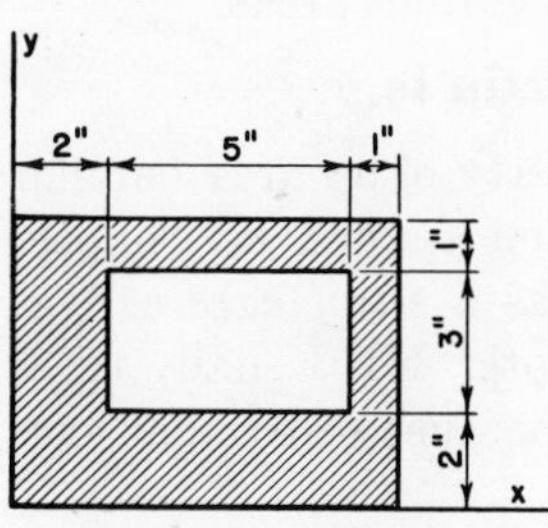

Fig. 44. Area for Problem 4 (Review Problems)

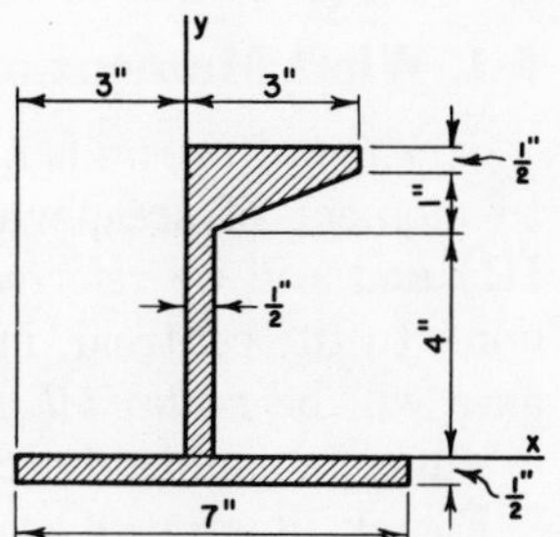

Fig. 45. Area for Problem 5 (Review Problems)

CHAPTER IV

MOMENT OF INERTIA

PURPOSE OF THIS CHAPTER. In this chapter you will learn the definition, as well as the methods of calculating *moment of inertia* for various areas.

4-1. What Moment of Inertia Is.

Moment of inertia is a property of an area (similar to moment of area, which you studied in Chapter III) and will be referred to as a *set of axes* as was done to the centroid, in Chapter III. Usually these axes will be *centroidal axes*, because centroidal axes are used in engineering work.

Fig. 1 illustrates a *rectangular area* with the x axis passing through the center. Imagine that the area of the rectangle is divided into small parts, each of area a, the distance of the center of one small part from the x axis is y. The area a could be multiplied by the square of the distance y to get y^2a.

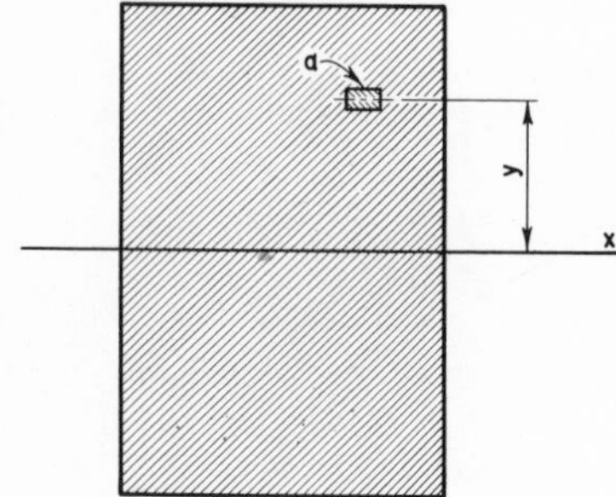

Fig. 1. Rectangular Area Made Up of Many Small Parts

Think of the rectangle as being divided into many small parts (1,000 or more). The area of each small part is a and the distance from the x axis to any small part is y. Now y is not the same for all of the small parts of the rectangle. For instance, the distance y is relatively small for a small part which is close to the x axis, and y is much larger for a small part which is at some distance from the x axis. You can see then that the product y^2a is going to be larger for a small area a which is far away from the axis than for a small area a which is close to the axis.

Multiply each small area a by the square of its distance y and then add the products. The result can be written as

$$\Sigma y^2a$$

where Σ (Greek letter *sigma*) stands for *summation* or *sum*, just as in Chapter II, when working with equilibrium problems. This final sum, y^2a, is the *moment of inertia* of the area with respect to the x axis and we can write

$$I_x = \Sigma y^2a$$

where I_x designates the *moment of inertia* of the area with respect to the x axis.

Now we have reached the point where we can give a definition of *moment of inertia*, but do not worry if you have to read it twice before you understand it. *If an area is considered to be divided into a large number of small parts, the sum of the products obtained by multiplying the area of each small part by the square of its distance from an axis is equal to the moment of inertia of the area with respect to the axis.*

You will be interested in the units in which we express moment of inertia. Look again at the quantity y^2a. Each small area (in square inches) is multiplied by y^2 and y is in inches. Then y^2 is in the units in.^{2} (inches to the second power), because we are multiplying

$$\text{in.} \times \text{in.} = \text{in.}^2$$

just as you learned in algebra,

$$x \times x = x^2$$

Each of the small areas a is in square inches; that is, in.^{2} Then we are multiplying y^2 (in in.^{2}) by a (in in.^{2}); and if we write the multiplication in terms of units, we have

$$\text{in.}^2 \times \text{in.}^2 = \text{in.}^4$$

You performed the same type of multiplication in algebra when you wrote

$$x^2 \times x^2 = x^4$$

In algebra, the 2 in x^2 and the 4 in x^4 are called *exponents* (remember?). The rule for multiplying exponents is to add the exponents of the multiplicand and the multiplier to get the exponent of the answer. So, whether you multiply

$$\text{in.}^2 \times \text{in.}^2 \quad \text{or} \quad x^2 \times x^2$$

you add the exponents $(2 + 2 = 4)$ to get

$$\text{in.}^2 \times \text{in.}^2 = \text{in.}^4 \quad \text{or } x^2 \times x^2 = x^4$$

Then the results for *moment of inertia* of area are

going to be expressed in in.[4] (inches to the fourth power). In.[4] cannot be visualized. It has to be accepted as a true statment.

4-2. Moment of Inertia of Simple Areas.

The moments of a few simple areas will be calculated, such as the *rectangle*, *circle*, and *triangle*. The proving of the formulas for finding the moments of inertia requires calculus but since the formulas alone can be used just as well without the proof, no proof will be given.

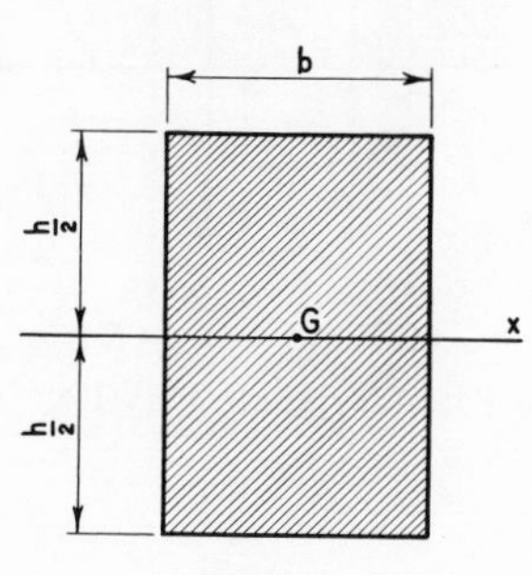

Fig. 2. Rectangular Area with Centroid Shown at G

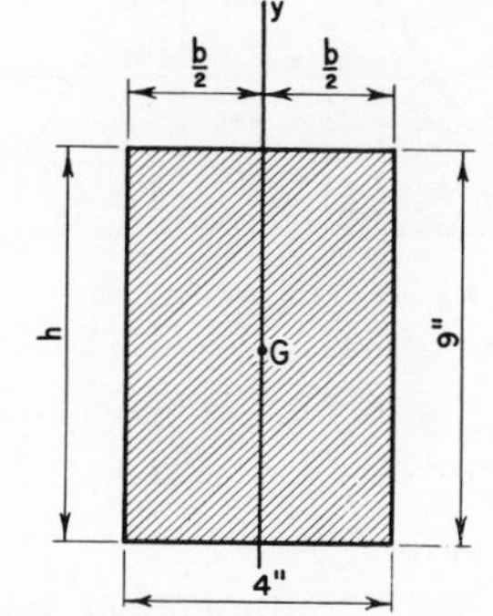

Fig. 3. Rectangular Area with Y a Centroidal Axis

The rectangle will be considered first. Fig. 2 shows a rectangular area of width b and altitude h. The x axis passes through G, the centroid of the area; the centroid is at a distance of $\frac{h}{2}$ above the base of the rectangle. Now the moment of inertia of the area with respect to the x axis is

$$I_x = \frac{1}{12} bh^3$$

This formula is easy to use and should not cause you any trouble. Just remember that the *moment of inertia* of a *rectangular area* with respect to an axis which passes through the centroid and is parallel to the base is *one-twelfth times* the *width* times the *cube* of the depth. The *width* is the dimension parallel to the x axis and the *altitude* is the dimension perpendicular to the x axis. So, then, the *moment of inertia* is equal to one-twelfth of the dimension parallel to the axis, times the cube of the dimension perpendicular to the axis.

The x axis was placed at the centroid of the rectangle, and the moment of inertia with respect to the centroidal axis was given because the centroidal axis is the important axis in the applications which will be studied later.

Illustrative Example 1. The width of the rectangle in Fig. 2 is 6″ and the depth is 8″. Calculate the moment of inertia with respect to the x axis.

Solution:

1. The dimension *parallel to the axis* is $b = 6''$
2. The dimension *perpendicular to the axis* is $h = 8''$
3. Then, $I_x = \frac{1}{12} bh^3 = \frac{1}{12} \times 6 \times (8)^3 = \frac{1}{12} \times 6 \times 8 \times 8 \times 8 = 256$ in.[4]

Sometimes the moment of inertia with respect to the x axis is used and sometimes the moment of inertia with respect to the y axis is used. You should learn to calculate the *moment of inertia of a rectangle* with respect to the y axis. This is not hard if you remember that the *moment of inertia of a rectangular area, with respect to an axis through the centroid and parallel to one side, is equal to one-twelfth of the dimension parallel to the axis, times the cube of the dimension perpendicular to the axis.* In Fig. 3, the y axis passes through G, the centroid of the rectangle; the dimension parallel to the axis is h and the dimension perpendicular to the axis is b. So

$$I_y = \frac{1}{12} hb^3$$

Illustrative Example 2. In Fig. 3, the horizontal dimension of the rectangle is 4″ and the vertical dimension is 9″. Calculate the moment of inertia with respect to the y axis.

Solution:

1. The dimension parallel to the axis is $h = 9''$
2. The dimension perpendicular to the axis is $b = 4''$
3. Then,

$$I_y = \frac{1}{12} hb^3 = \frac{1}{12} \times 9 \times (4)^3 = 48 \text{ in.}^4$$

The circular area in Fig. 4 will be solved next. The diameter is d, and the x and y axes pass through the

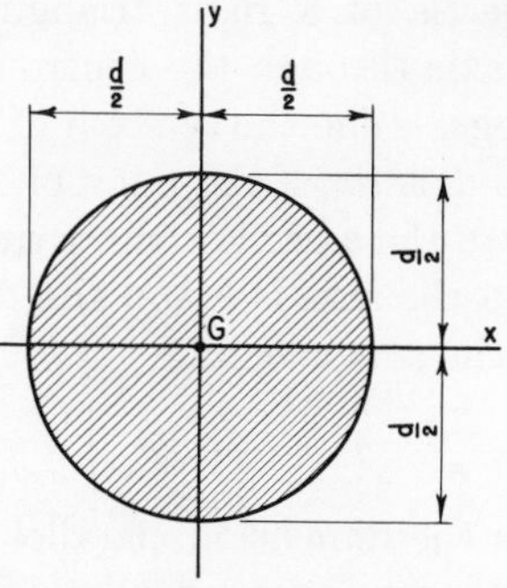

Fig. 4. Circular Area Showing X and Y Axes Passing through Centroid G

center of the circle. Here the moment of inertia with respect to the x axis is equal to the moment of inertia with respect to the y axis; each is $\frac{\pi}{64} d^4$. (It takes calculus to prove this.) So

$$I_x = \frac{\pi}{64} d^4, \quad \text{and} \quad I_y = \frac{\pi}{64} d^4$$

(You recall π equals 3.14.)

Illustrative Example 3. Calculate the moment of inertia of a circular area, 2″ in diameter, with respect to an axis through the center.

Solution:

1. The diameter d is 2″
2. Then,

$$I = \frac{\pi}{64} d^4 = \frac{\pi}{64} (2)^4 = \frac{3.14}{64} \times 2 \times 2 \times 2 \times 2$$
$$= 0.785 \text{ in.}^4$$

Calculating the moment of inertia of a triangular area will be next. Fig. 5 shows the area; the width is b and the altitude is h. The centroid of the area is at G (as you may remember) and both the x and y axis pass through G. The general formula for the

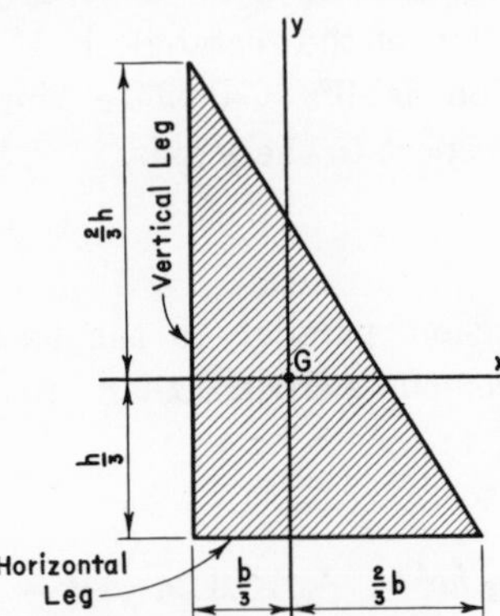

Fig. 5. Triangular Area with X and Y Axes Passing through Centroid G

moment of inertia of a right triangular area with respect to an axis through the centroid and parallel to one of the legs, is one thirty-sixth of the dimension parallel to the axis *times* the cube of the dimension perpendicular to the axis. For the x axis, the dimension parallel to the axis is b and the dimension perpendicular to the axis is h, so

$$I_x = \tfrac{1}{36} bh^3$$

For the y axis the dimension parallel to the axis is h and the dimension perpendicular to the axis is b. Then,

$$I_y = \tfrac{1}{36} hb^3$$

Illustrative Example 4. In Fig. 5 the dimension b is 3″, and the dimension h is 6″. Calculate I_x and I_y.

Solution:

1. For I_x,
   a) The dimension parallel to the axis is b = 3″
   b) The dimension perpendicular to the axis is h = 6″
   c) Then,

$$I_x = \tfrac{1}{36} bh^3 = \tfrac{1}{36} \times 3 \times (6)^3 = 18 \text{ in.}^4$$

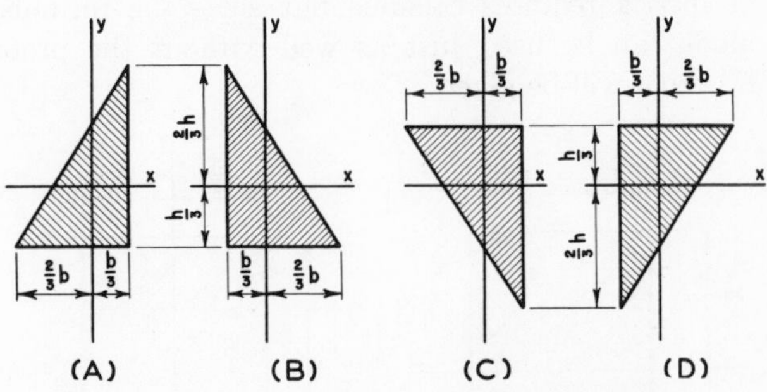

Fig. 6. Four Different Ways a Right Triangle May Be Turned

2. For I_y,
   a) The dimension parallel to the axis is h = 6″
   b) The dimension perpendicular to the axis is b = 3″
   c) Then,

$$I_y = \tfrac{1}{36} hb^3 = \tfrac{1}{36} \times 6 \times (3)^3 = 4.5 \text{ in.}^4$$

In a triangular area, the moment of inertia of the area is the same, no matter whether the triangle is turned as in Fig. 6A, 6B, 6C, or 6D. For each case,

$$I_x = \tfrac{1}{36} bh^3, \quad \text{and} \quad I_y = \tfrac{1}{36} hb^3$$

Study the triangles carefully with the foregoing statement in mind.

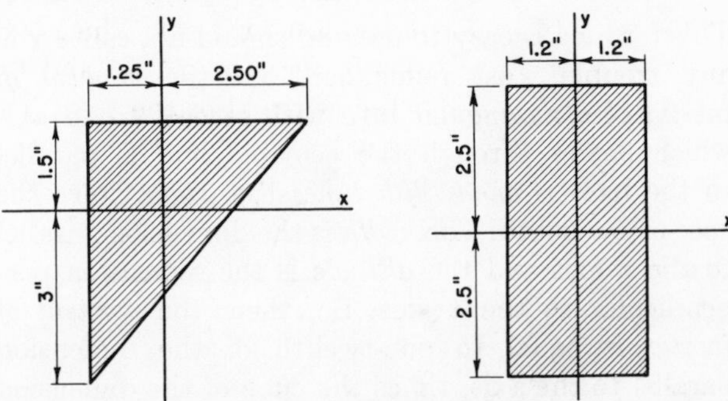

Fig. 7. Triangular Area for Problem 5 (Art. 2)

Fig. 8. Rectangular Area for Problem 6 (Art. 2)

Practice Problems (Art. 4-2). The following problems should be done without looking up the formulas.

1. Calculate the *moment of inertia of a circular area*, 6″ in diameter, with respect to an axis through the center.
2. A rectangular area is 8″ wide and 10″ high. Calculate (a) the moment of inertia with respect to a horizontal axis through the centroid, and (b) with respect to a vertical axis through the centroid.

3. Calculate (*a*) the moment of inertia of a rectangular area, 12″ wide and 2″ high, with respect to a horizontal axis through the centroid, and (*b*) with respect to a vertical axis through the centroid.
4. The width of a certain right triangle is 5″ and the altitude is 4″. Calculate (*a*) the moment of inertia with respect to a horizontal axis through the centroid, and (*b*) with respect to a vertical axis through the centroid.

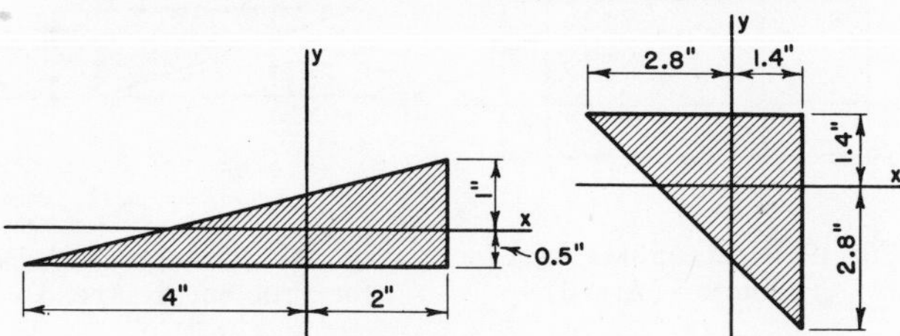

Fig. 9. Triangular Area for Problem 7 (Art. 2)

Fig. 10. Triangular Area for Problem 8 (Art. 2)

Calculate I_x and I_y for the area in each of the following figures.

5. Fig. 7.
6. Fig. 8.
7. Fig. 9.
8. Fig. 10.

4-3. The Parallel-Axis Theorem.

You have probably noticed that all of the formulas, used for moment of inertia, are with respect to centroidal axes. However, at times there is a need for the moment of inertia of an area with respect to an axis which is not through the centroid of the area. The *parallel-axis theorem* is used in such cases. With it, the moment of inertia with respect to any axis may be calculated.

The *parallel-axis theorem states that the moment of inertia of an area, with respect to any axis, is equal to the moment of inertia with respect to a parallel axis, through the centroid of the area, plus the area times the square of the distance between the two axes.* Here is how it works for the circular area in Fig. 11. The x axis is parallel to the x_g axis (g for centroid G) and the x_g axis passes through the centroid of the area. The

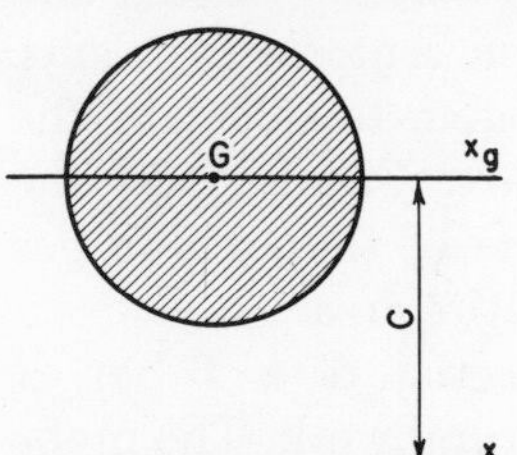

Fig. 11. Circular Area with X_g Axis Passing through Centroid

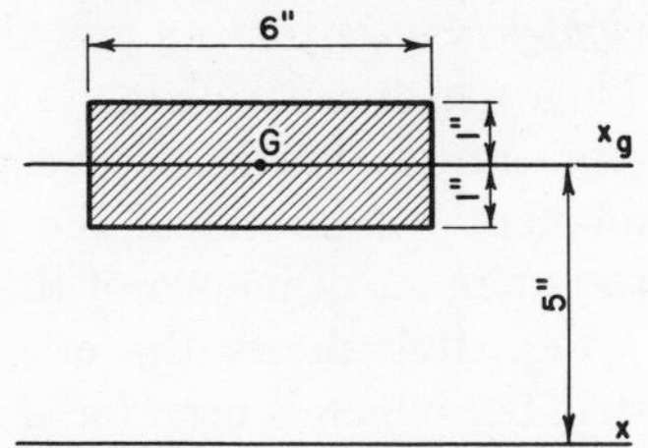

Fig. 12. Finding Moment of Inertia of a Rectangular Area

distance between the two axes is c. When we write the parallel-axis theorem as a formula, it is

$$I_x = I_{xg} + Ac^2$$

Here I_x is the moment of inertia with respect to the x axis, I_{x_g} is the moment of inertia with respect to the parallel axis x_g, A is the area in square inches, and c is the distance between the two axes. Now check this formula with the statement of the theorem. The moment of inertia of an area with respect to any axis (the x axis) is equal to the moment of inertia with respect to a parallel axis through the centroid (the x_g axis) plus the area (A) times the square of the distance (c) between the two axes. (This theorem is given without proof, because calculus would have to be used to prove it.) Remember the previous formulas for moment of inertia.

Illustrative Example 1. Calculate the moment of inertia of the rectangular area in Fig. 12 with respect to the x axis.

Solution:

1. The dimension parallel to the x_g axis is 6″
2. The dimension perpendicular to the x_g axis is 2″
3. Then,
$$I_{xg} = \tfrac{1}{12}\, bh^3 = \tfrac{1}{12} \times 6 \times (2)^3 = 4 \text{ in.}^4$$
4. The area of the rectangle is $A = bh = 6 \times 2 = 12$ sq. in.
5. The distance between the two axes is $c = 5''$
6. Then,
$$I_x = I_{xg} + Ac^2 = 4 + 12 \times (5)^2 = 4 + 300 = 304 \text{ in.}^4$$

You must remember, when you use the parallel-axis theorem, that the two axes must be parallel and one of them must pass through the centroid of the area. Remember this is an important fact.

It makes no difference whether the x axis is above or below the x_g axis. The theorem is the same, and the formula is

$$I_x = I_{xg} + Ac^2$$

Illustrative Example 2. Calculate the moment of inertia of the triangular area in Fig. 13 with respect to the x axis.

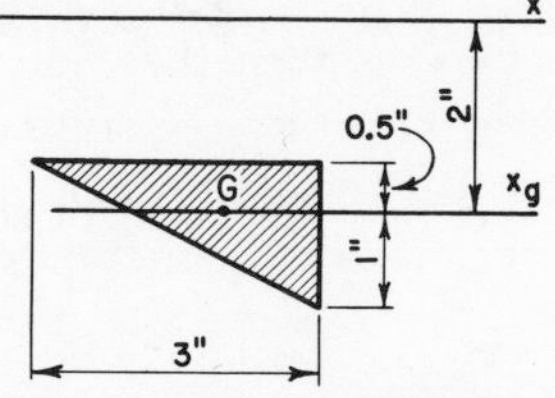

Fig. 13. Finding Moment of Inertia of a Triangular Area

Solution:

1. The dimension parallel to the x_g axis is 3″
2. The dimension perpendicular to the x_g axis is 1.5″
3. So
$$I_{xg} = \tfrac{1}{36}\, bh^3 = \tfrac{1}{36} \times 3 \times (1.5)^3 = 0.281 \text{ in.}^4$$
4. The area of the triangle is
$$A = \tfrac{1}{2}\, bh = \tfrac{1}{2} \times 3 \times 1.5 = 2.25 \text{ sq. in.}$$

5. The distance between the two axes is $c = 2''$
6. Then,

$$I_x = I_{xg} + Ac^2 = 0.28 + 2.25 \times (2)^2$$
$$= 0.28 + 9 = 9.28 \text{ in.}^4$$

The parallel-axis theorem works for vertical axes, too, although then we designate the axes as y and y_g. We write the formula as,

$$I_y = I_{yg} + Ac^2$$

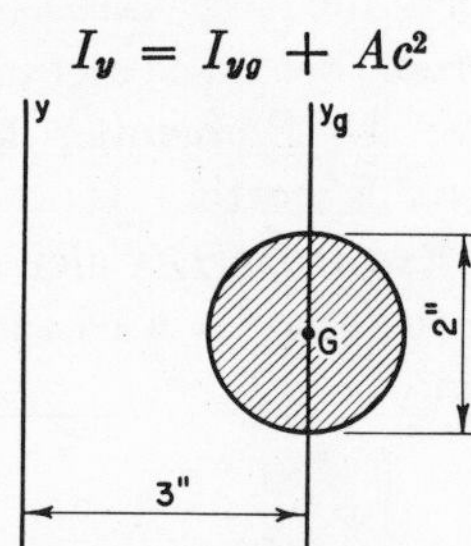

Fig. 14. Finding Moment of Inertia of a Circular Area

Illustrative Example 3. Calculate the moment of inertia of the circular area in Fig. 14 with respect to the y axis.

Solution:

1. The diameter of the circle is $d = 2''$

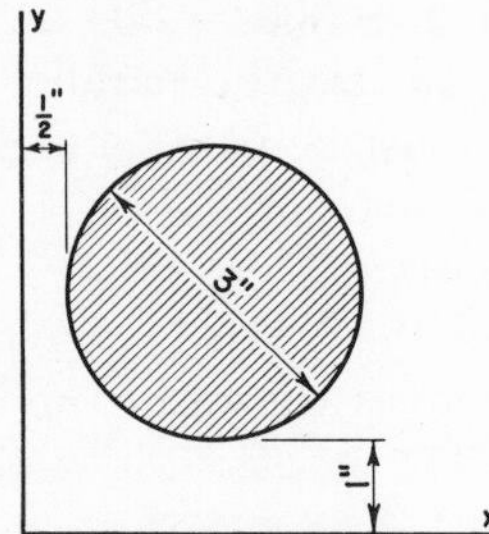

Fig. 15. Circular Area for Problem 1 (Art. 3)

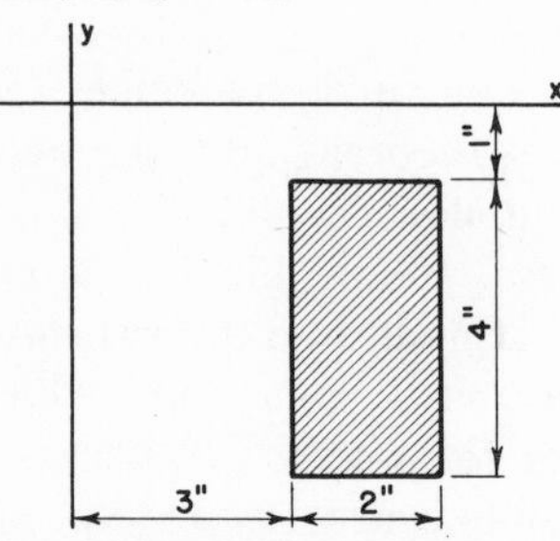

Fig. 16. Rectangular Area for Problem 2 (Art. 3)

2. Then,

$$I_{yg} = \frac{\pi}{64} d^4 = \frac{\pi}{64} (2)^4 = 0.785 \text{ in.}^4$$

3. The area of the circle is

$$A = \frac{\pi}{4} d^2 = \frac{\pi}{4} (2)^2 = 3.14 \text{ sq. in.}$$

Fig. 17. Triangular Area for Problem 3 (Art. 3)

Fig. 18. Circular Area for Problem 4 (Art. 3)

4. The distance between the two axes is $c = 3''$
5. Then,

$$I_y = I_{yg} + Ac^2 = 0.79 + 3.14 (3)^2$$
$$= 0.79 + 28.3 = 29.1 \text{ in.}^4$$

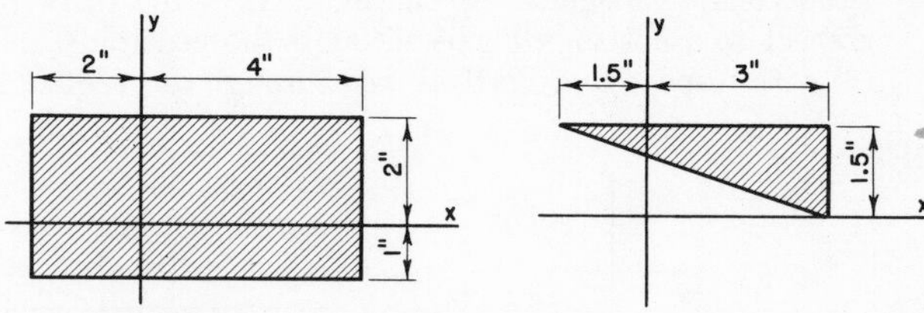

Fig. 19. Rectangular Area for Problem 5 (Art. 3)

Fig. 20. Triangular Area for Problem 6 (Art. 3)

Practice Problems (Art. 4-3). Calculate I_x and I_y for the area in each of the following figures to become more proficient in the use of the parallel-axis theorem.

1. Fig. 15.
2. Fig. 16.
3. Fig. 17.
4. Fig. 18.
5. Fig. 19.
6. Fig. 20.

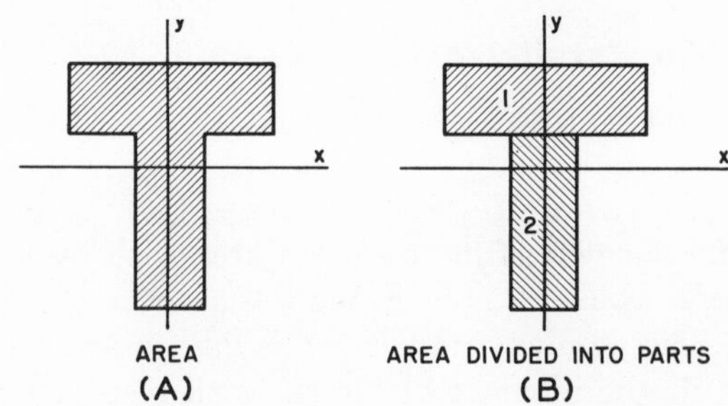

Fig. 21. Cross Section of Steel T Bar

4-4. Moment of Inertia of Composite Areas.

You previously learned to locate the centroid of a composite area. Now you will have to learn to calculate the moment of inertia, because it is used when you study beams and columns. Divide the area into simple parts, such as *rectangles*, *circles*, and *right triangles* just as you did in centroid problems. Then use the parallel-axis theorem to calculate the moment of inertia of each part. Finally, add the moments of inertia of the parts of the area to get the moment of inertia of the entire area.

Fig. 21*A* shows the cross section of a **T** bar, a steel bar which is used for structural work. The problem is to calculate the moment of inertia of this area with respect to the x axis and the y axis. The easiest way to do this is to divide the area into the rectangles 1 and 2 as in Fig. 21*B*. Then, you can calculate the moments of inertia of the two rectangles separately and add them. You can represent the moment of inertia of the rectangle 1 with respect to the x axis by I_{1x}, and the moment of inertia of the rectangle 2 by I_{2x}. Then the moment of inertia of the entire area is I_x and it is equal to the sum of I_{1x} and I_{2x} as illustrated by the following example:

$$I_x = I_{1x} + I_{2x}$$

The solution is not difficult, since you already know how to calculate I_{1x} and I_{2x}.

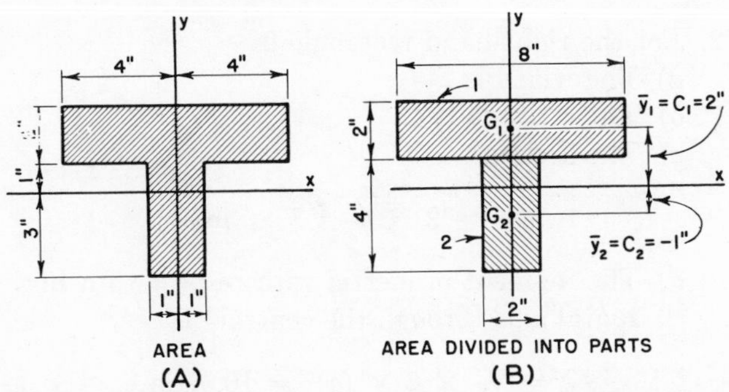

Fig. 22. Finding Moment of Intertia of Composite Area

Illustrative Example 1. Calculate the moment of inertia of the area in Fig. 22*A* with respect to the *x* axis.

Solution:

Fig. 22*B* shows the area divided into the rectangle 1 and the rectangle 2. Previously explained parts of the problem will be discussed briefly.

1. For the rectangle 1,
   a) The width is 8″
   b) The altitude is 2″
   c) The moment of inertia with respect to a horizontal axis through the centroid is
   $$I_{xg} = \tfrac{1}{12}bh^3 = \tfrac{1}{12} \times 8 \times (2)^3 = 5.33 \text{ in.}^4$$
   d) The distance from the *x* axis to the centroid of the rectangle 1 is
   $$y_1 = c_1 = 1 + \tfrac{1}{2} \times 2 = 1 + 1 = 2''$$
   e) The area of 1 is
   $$A_1 = bh = 8 \times 2 = 16 \text{ sq. in.}$$
   f) Then the moment of inertia of the rectangle 1 with respect to the *x* axis is (parallel-axis theorem)
   $$I_{1x} = I_{xg} + A_1c_1^2 = 5.33 + 16 \times (2)^2 = 5.33 + 64 = 69.33 \text{ in.}^4$$
2. For the rectangle 2,
   a) The width is 2″
   b) The altitude is 4″
   c) The moment of inertia with respect to a horizontal axis through the centroid is
   $$I_{xg} = \tfrac{1}{12}bh^3 = \tfrac{1}{21} \times 2 \times (4)^3 = 10.67 \text{ in.}^4$$
   d) The distance from the *x* axis to the centroid of 2 is
   $$\bar{y}_2 = c_2 = 1 - \tfrac{1}{2} \times 4 = 1 - 2 = -1''$$
   e) The area of 2 is
   $$A_2 = bh = 2 \times 4 = 8 \text{ sq. in.}$$
   f) The moment of inertia of the rectangle 2 with respect to the *x* axis is
   $$I_{2x} = I_{xg} + A_2c_2^2 = 10.67 + 8 \times (-1)^2 = 10.67 + 8 = 18.67 \text{ in.}^4$$
3. For the entire area, the moment of inertia is equal to the sum of the moments of inertia of the parts of the area, so
   $$I_x = I_{1x} + I_{2x} = 69.33 + 18.67 = 88 \text{ in.}^4$$

The same method of solution that was used in solving problems on centroids with negative areas will be applied to calculating moment of inertia. Fig. 23, for example, has a square with a circle cut out. In order to calculate the moment of inertia of the area with respect to the *x* axis you can think of the circular area as a *negative area*, or one which is cut away from the square. Then subtract the moment of inertia of the circular area from the moment of inertia of the square area to get the moment of inertia of the hollow area.

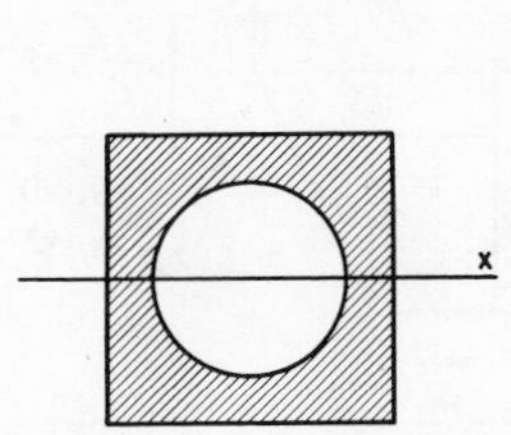

Fig. 23. Square with Hollow Circular Area

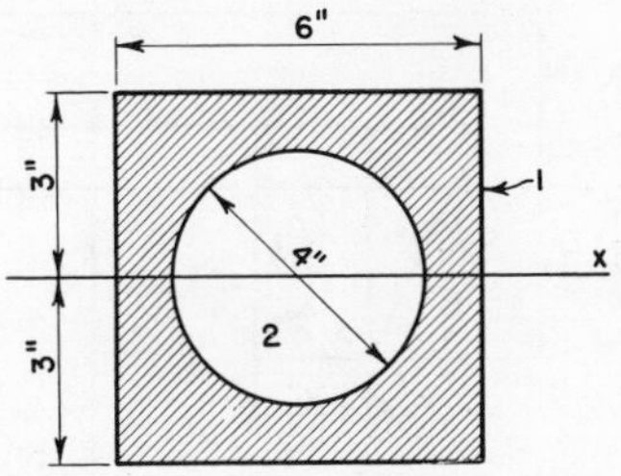

Fig. 24. Area for Example 2 (Art. 4)

Illustrative Example 2. Fig. 24 shows a square area with a circle cut out; the center of the circle is on the *x* axis. Calculate the moment of inertia of the hollow area with respect to the *x* axis.

Solution:

Divide the area into the *positive square* 1 and the *negative circle* 2. This will be easy because the centroid of each area is on the *x* axis, and the parallel-axis theorem will not have to be used.

1. For the square 1,
   a) The width is 6″
   b) The altitude is 6″
   c) So, the moment of inertia of the square area is
   $$I_{1x} = \tfrac{1}{12}bh^3 = \tfrac{1}{12} \times 6 \times (6)^3 = 108 \text{ in.}^4$$
2. For the circle 2,
   a) The diameter is 4″
   b) The moment of inertia of the circular area is
   $$I_{2x} = \frac{\pi}{64}d^4 = \frac{3.14}{64}(4)^4 = 12.6 \text{ in.}^4$$
3. For the hollow area,
   $$I_x = I_{1x} - I_{2x} = 108 - 12.6 = 95.4 \text{ in.}^4$$

So far only the moment of inertia of a *composite area* with respect to the *x* axis has been considered. The calculation of moment of inertia with respect to the y axis will be studied at this point. Notice the steps in the following problem carefully.

Illustrative Example 3. Calculate the moment of inertia of the area in Fig. 25A with respect to the x axis, and with respect to the y axis.

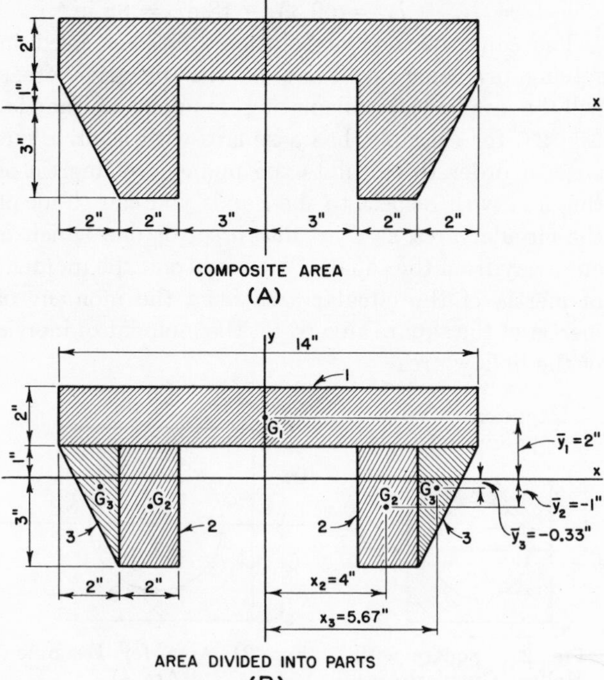

Fig. 25. Composite Area for Example 3 (Art. 4)

Solution:

Fig. 25B shows the area divided into the rectangle 1, the two rectangles 2 and the two triangles 3.

1. For the rectangle 1,
   a) The width is 14″
   b) The altitude is 2″
   c) The area is
   $$A_1 = 14 \times 2 = 28 \text{ sq. in.}$$
   d) The moment of inertia with respect to a horizontal axis through the centroid is
   $$I_{xg} = \tfrac{1}{12}\, bh^3 = \tfrac{1}{12} \times 14 \times (2)^3 = 9.33 \text{ in.}^4$$
   e) The distance from the x axis to the centroid of 1 is
   $$\bar{y}_1 = 1 + \tfrac{1}{2} \times 2 = 1 + 1 = 2''$$
   ($\frac{1}{2}$ × the width, since G is always at the center of a rectangle)
   f) The moment of inertia of the rectangle 1 with respect to the x axis is
   $$I_{1x} = I_{xg} + A_1\bar{y}_1^2 = 9.33 + 28(2)^2$$
   $$= 9.33 + 112 = 121.33 \text{ in.}^4,$$
   or rounded to the whole number, 121 in.^{4}
   g) Notice that the centroid of the rectangle 1 is on the y axis, so that the moment of inertia with respect to the y axis is the moment of inertia with respect to a vertical axis through the centroid. This is
   $$I_{1y} = \tfrac{1}{12}\, hb^3 = \tfrac{1}{12} \times 2 \times (14)^3 = 458 \text{ in.}^4$$
2. For the right-hand rectangle 2,
   a) The width is 2″
   b) The altitude is 4″
   c) The area is
   $$A_2 = 2 \times 4 = 8 \text{ sq. in.}$$
   d) The moment of inertia with respect to a horizontal axis through the centroid is
   $$I_{xg} = \tfrac{1}{12} \times 2 \times (4)^3 = 10.67 \text{ in.}^4$$
   e) The distance from the x axis to the centroid of 2 is
   $$\bar{y}_2 = 1 - \tfrac{1}{2} \times 4 = 1 - 2 = -1''$$
   ($\frac{1}{2}$ × the length)
   f) The moment of inertia of 2 with respect to the x axis is
   $$I_{2x} = I_{xg} + A_2\bar{y}_2^2 = 10.67 + 8(-1)^2$$
   $$= 10.67 + 8 = 18.67 \text{ in.}^4$$
   g) The moment of inertia with respect to a vertical axis through the centroid is
   $$I_{yg} = \tfrac{1}{12}\, hb^3 = \tfrac{1}{12} \times 4 \times (2)^3 = 2.67 \text{ in.}^4$$
   h) The distance from the y axis to the centroid of the rectangle 2 is
   $$\bar{x}_2 = 3 + \tfrac{1}{2} \times 2 = 3 + 1 = 4''$$
   i) The moment of inertia of 2 with respect to the y axis is
   $$I_{2y} = I_{yg} + A_2\bar{x}_2^2 = 2.67 + 8\,(4)^2$$
   $$= 2.67 + 128 = 130.67 \text{ in.}^4, \text{ or } 31 \text{ in.}^4$$
3. For the triangle 3 on the right side of the x axis,
   a) The width is 2″
   b) The altitude is 4″
   c) The area is
   $$A_3 = \tfrac{1}{2}\, bh = \tfrac{1}{2} \times 2 \times 4 = 4 \text{ sq. in.}$$
   d) The moment of inertia of the triangle 3 with respect to a horizontal axis through the centroid is
   $$I_{xg} = \tfrac{1}{36}\, bh^3 = \tfrac{1}{36} \times 2 \times (4)^3 = 3.55 \text{ in.}^4$$

e) The distance from the x axis to the centroid of 3 is

$$\bar{y}_3 = 1 - \tfrac{1}{3} \times 4 = 1 - 1.33 = -0.33''$$

f) The moment of inertia of 3 with respect to the x axis is

$$I_{3x} = I_{xg} + A_3\bar{y}_3^2 = 3.55 + 4\,(-0.33)^2$$
$$= 3.55 + 0.44 = 4 \text{ in.}^4$$

g) The moment of inertia with respect to a vertical axis through the centroid is

$$I_{gy} = \tfrac{1}{36}\,hb^3 = \tfrac{1}{36} \times 4 \times (2)^3 = 0.89 \text{ in.}^4$$

h) The distance from the y axis to the centroid of 3 is

$$\bar{x}_3 = 5 + \tfrac{1}{3} \times 2 = 5 + 0.67 = 5.67''$$

i) The moment of inertia of 3 with respect to the y axis is

$$I_{3y} = I_{gy} + A_3\bar{x}_3^2 = 0.89 + 4\,(5.67)^2$$
$$= 0.89 + 129 = 130 \text{ in.}^4$$

4. For the entire area, remember there are two rectangles 2 and two rectangles 3
   a) The moment of inertia with respect to the x axis is equal to the sum of the moments of inertia of the parts of the area with respect to the x axis.

$$I_x = I_{1x} + 2\,I_{2x} + 2\,I_{3x} = 121 + 2 \times 18.67$$
$$+ 2 \times 4 = 121 + 37.33 + 8 = 166.33 \text{ in.}^4\text{, or}$$
$$166 \text{ in.}^4$$

   b) The moment of inertia of the entire area with respect to the y axis is

$$I_y = I_{1y} + 2\,I_{2y} + 2\,I_{3y} = 458 + 2 \times 131$$
$$+ 2 \times 130 = 458 + 262 + 260 = 980 \text{ in.}^4$$

Practice Problems (Art. 4-4). Calculate I_x and I_y for the area in each of the following figures.

1. Fig. 26.
2. Fig. 27.
3. Fig. 28.
4. Fig. 29.
5. Fig. 30.
6. Fig. 31.

SUMMARY OF CHAPTER IV

Study the summary of the main points in this chapter.

1. Moment of inertia of an area is defined in this way. If the area is considered to be divided into small parts, the moment of inertia with respect to an axis is equal to the sum of the quantities obtained by multiplying the area of each part by the square of its distance from the axis. (You should not only memorize, but, also, know how to apply, this formula. Be sure that it means something to you.)
   a) Moment of inertia of an area is expressed in in.^{4} (inches to the fourth power)
2. For the simple areas,
   a) The moment of inertia of a rectangular area, with respect to an axis through the centroid and parallel to one side, is equal to one-twelfth of the dimension parallel to the axis times the cube of the dimension perpendicular to the axis. For example, $\frac{1}{12}\,bh^3$.

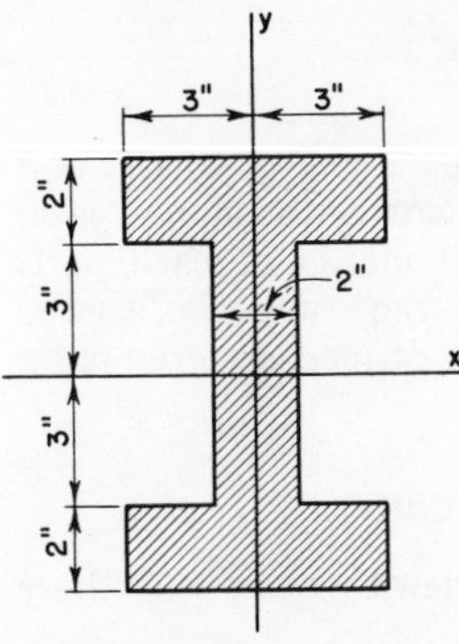

Fig. 26. Composite Area for Problem 1 (Art. 4)

Fig. 27. Hollow Rectangular Area for Problem 2 (Art. 4)

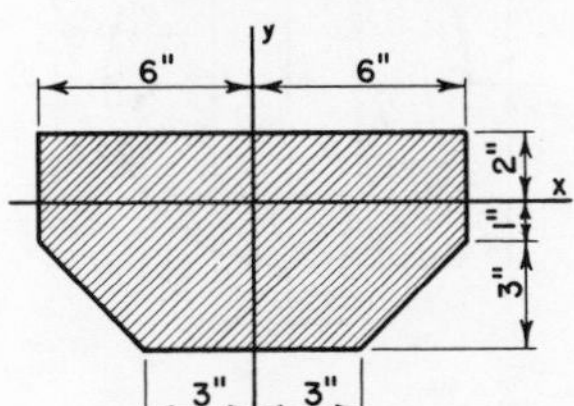

Fig. 28. Composite Area for Problem 3 (Art. 4)

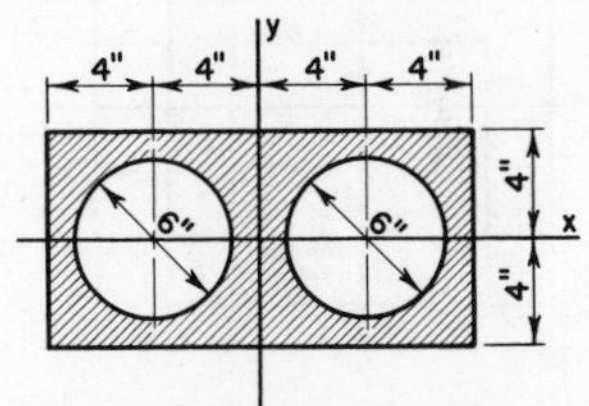

Fig. 29. Rectangular Area with Two Hollow Circles for Problem 4 (Art. 4)

   b) The moment of inertia of a circular area, with respect to an axis through the center, is equal to

$$\frac{\pi}{64}\,d^4$$

   where d is the diameter of the circle.
   c) The moment of inertia of the area of a right triangle, with respect to an axis through the centroid and parallel to a leg, is equal to one thirty-sixth of the leg parallel to the axis *times* the cube of the leg perpendicular to the axis. For example, $\frac{1}{36}\,bh^3$.

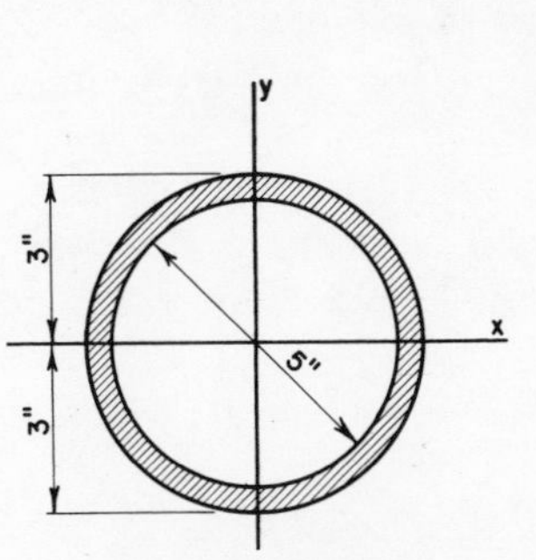

Fig. 30. Hollow Circular Area for Problem 5 (Art. 4)

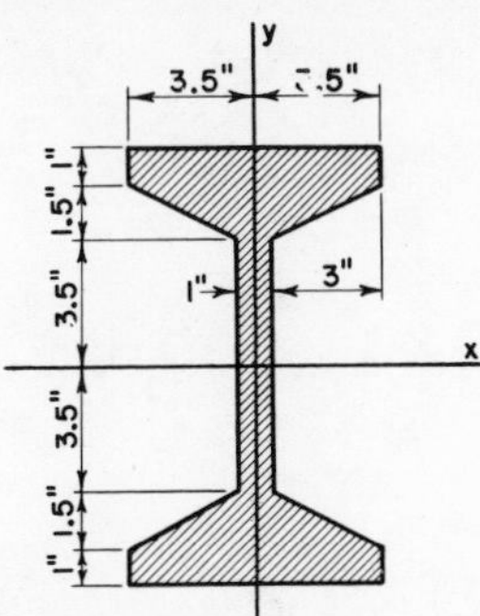

Fig. 31. Composite Area for Problem 6 (Art. 4)

3. The parallel-axis theorem is: *The moment of inertia with respect to any axis is equal to the moment of inertia with respect to a parallel axis through the centroid of the area, plus the area times the square of the distance between the two axes.* As a formula,

$$I_x = I_{xg} + Ac^2$$

4. The proper way to calculate the *moment of inertia of a composite area* is to divide the area into simple parts and to calculate the moment of inertia of each part. Then the moment of inertia of the composite area is equal to the sum of the moments of inertia of the parts of the area.

Review Questions

You can give yourself a quick review by answering these questions.

1. What is *moment of inertia?*
2. What is the *moment of inertia of a rectangular area* with respect to an axis through the centroid and parallel to one side?
3. What is the *moment of inertia of a circular area* with respect to an axis through the center?
4. What is the *moment of inertia of the area of a right triangle* with respect to an axis through the centroid and parallel to a leg?
5. State the parallel-axis theorem.
6. In what units is moment of inertia expressed?
7. How do you calculate the moment of inertia of a composite area?
8. What is a *negative area?*

Review Problems

Calculate I_x and I_y for the area in each of the following figures.

1. Fig. 32.
2. Fig. 33.
3. Fig. 34.
4. Fig. 35.

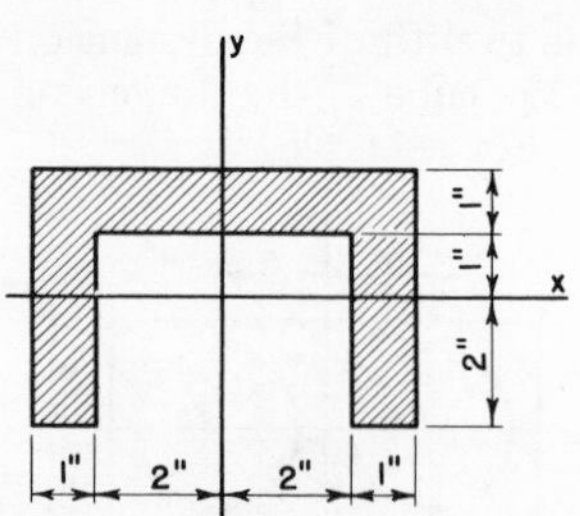

Fig. 32. Composite Area for Problem 1 (Review Problems)

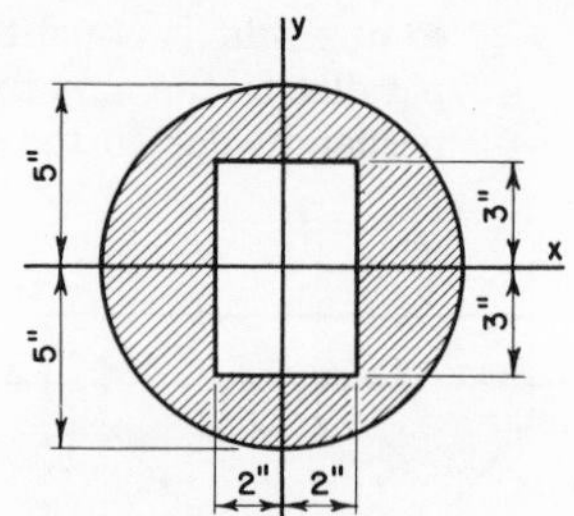

Fig. 33. Composite Area for Problem 2 (Review Problems)

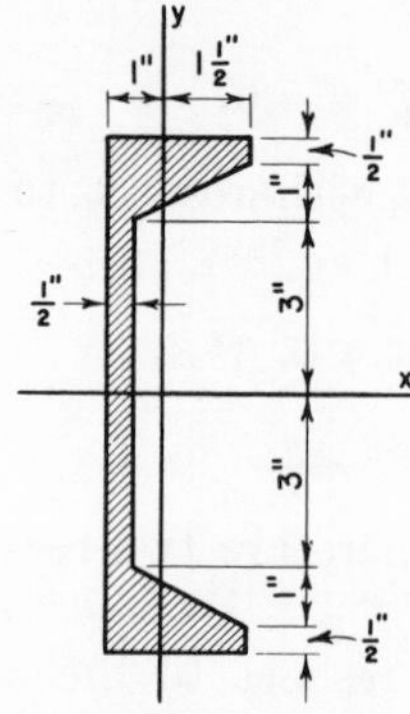

Fig. 34. Composite Area for Problem 3 (Review Problems)

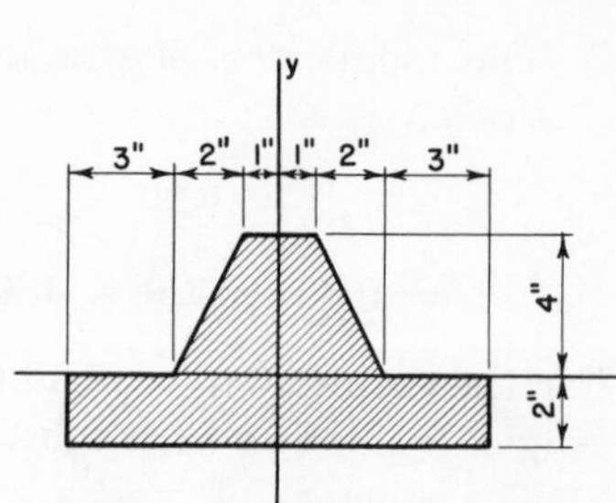

Fig. 35. Composite Area for Problem 4 (Review Problems)

Chapter V

SIMPLE STRESS AND STRAIN

Purpose of This Chapter. In this chapter you will learn how structural materials behave when force is applied to them. You remember *force* was studied in Chapter I and *equilibrium of forces* in Chapter II. The next step is to see what happens to the common materials such as steel, concrete, and wood when they are subjected to force. You will calculate the strength of steel (or any other material) and, to do that, you must know how to express the strength. You will have to learn many new words, but they will be introduced one at a time.

5-1. Compression and Compressive Stress.

The first new word for you to learn now is *compression*. Begin with Fig. 1*A* which shows a post supporting the first floor of a building. The post rests upon the basement floor and, in turn, the beam which supports the first floor rests upon the post.

Fig. 1*B* shows the free-body diagram of the post. (You remember from Chapter II that a free-body diagram is a picture of the object which shows all of the forces acting on the object.) Here you see the force P (pushing down) which the beam exerts on the post, and another force P (pushing up) which the basement floor exerts on the post. The upward force must equal the downward force in order for the post to be in equilibrium; the post would move if it were not in equilibrium.

Notice that the forces tend to squeeze the post or shorten it. This is what we call *compression*. Material is in compression whenever the forces acting on it tend to squeeze it together.

The next word for you to learn is *stress*, which is equal to *force divided by area* or force per unit area. Look again at Fig. 1 and notice Fig. 1*C* which shows the cross section of the post. Representing the area in square inches by A, then, the stress is

$$S = \frac{P}{A}$$

where S is the *stress*, P is the *force in pounds* and A is the *area in square inches*. The stress is *compressive stress* when the post (or whatever it may be) is in compression.

To study stress a little more, the forces P in Fig. 1*B* are shown as concentrated at single points. Then Fig. 1*D* shows the free-body diagram of the upper part of the post. The lower part of the post exerts a force P on the upper part; it must do this in order for the upper part to be in equilibrium; so that the equilibrium equation, $\Sigma F_y = 0$, is satisfied. In this case the equation is

$$\Sigma F_y = 0$$

$$P - P = 0$$

The force P exerted by the lower part of the post upon the upper part is distributed over the cross section of the post. This distributed force is *stress* and is expressed in pounds per square inch.

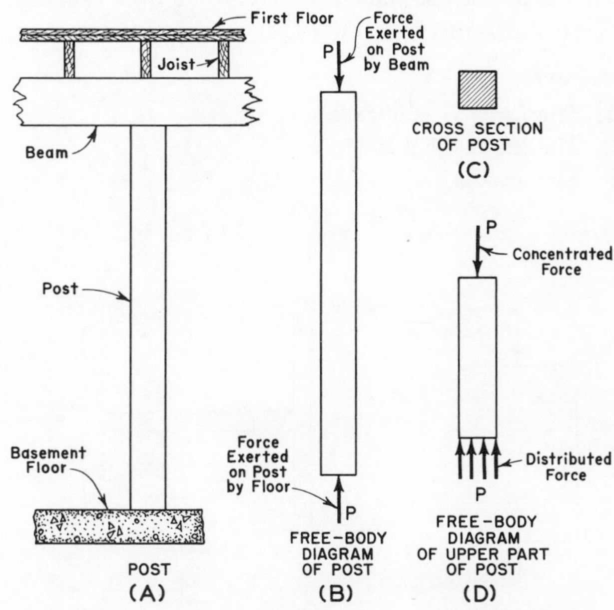

Fig. 1. A Post in Compression

All you have to do to calculate the stress is to divide the force by the area. This gives force in pounds divided by area in square inches. Like this,

$$\frac{\textit{pounds}}{\textit{square inches}}$$

which is often abbreviated as lbs. per sq. in. or #/in.²

This formula applies only when the force passes through the centroid of the cross section. Fig. 2 shows a block in compression on which the stress on section AA is to be calculated. Here the force passes through the centroid of the cross section so the formula,

$$S = \frac{P}{A}$$

can be used. But remember not to use this formula if the force is off center. Chapter X will be devoted to problems of this type.

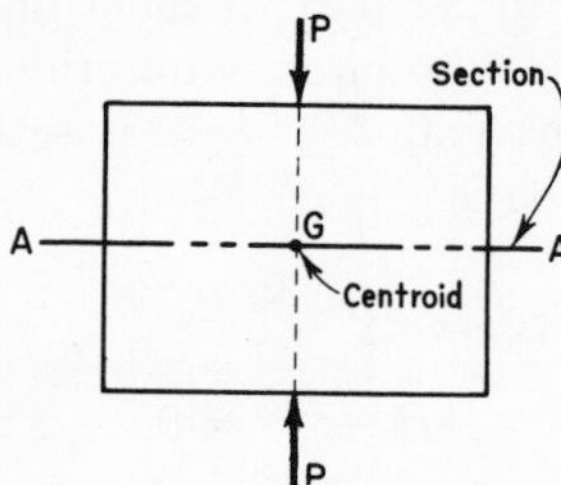

Fig. 2. A Block in Compression

Illustrative Example 1. Fig. 3 shows a *circular bar* which is subjected to a force of 90,000 lbs. The force is applied so that it passes through the centroid of each cross section. Find the compressive stress.

Solution:

1. The force P is 90,000 #
2. The diameter d is 3″
3. The area is

$$A = \pi \frac{d^2}{4} = \pi \frac{(3)^2}{4} = 7.07 \text{ sq. in.}$$

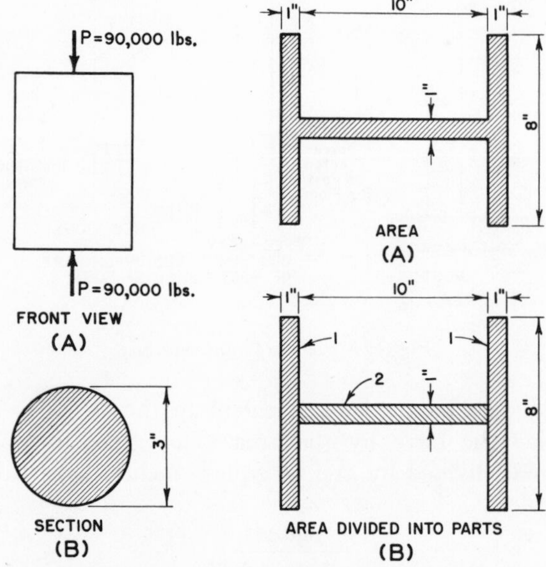

Fig. 3. A Bar in Compression

Fig. 4. Section of a Compression Member

4. The stress is

$$S = \frac{P}{A} = \frac{90{,}000}{7.07} = 12{,}800 \,\#/\text{in.}^2$$

Stress is important because expressing force in pounds is not significant enough.

A large block of steel might withstand a force of one million pounds, whereas a slender wire might collapse under a force of one pound. When we divide the force by the area and get the stress we have a figure which tells how severely the block is loaded and which means the same, regardless of the size of the block.

When you know the dimensions of the bar and the stress, and you want to calculate the force P, you turn the formula around, and start with

$$S = \frac{P}{A}$$

Multiply both sides of the equation by A to get

$$AS = \frac{P}{A} A$$

Next you cancel A on the right side of the equation to get

$$AS = P, \text{ or } P = AS$$

Then you use this formula.

Illustrative Example 2. Fig. 4*A* shows the cross section of a compression member which is subjected to a stress of 9,000 lbs. per sq. in. What is the total force?

Solution:

1. Fig. 4*B* shows the area divided into the two rectangles 1 and 2
   a) The area of one rectangle 1 is

   $$A_1 = 1 \times 8 = 8 \text{ sq. in.}$$

   b) The area of the rectangle 2 is

   $$A_2 = 10 \times 1 = 10 \text{ sq. in.}$$

   c) The total area is equal to the sum of the areas of the parts. (Remember that there are two rectangles 1.) So

$$A = 2A_1 + A_2 = 2 \times 8 + 10 = 16 + 10 = 26 \text{ sq. in.}$$

2. The stress S is 9,000 #/in.²
3. Then,

$$P = AS = 26 \times 9{,}000 = 234{,}000 \text{ lbs.}$$

Practice Problems (Art. 5-1). Practice what you have just learned, on these problems and remember that practice makes perfect.

1. A square wood post, 5.5″ on a side, carries a compressive force of 42,000 lbs. What is the stress?
2. What stress will be caused by a vertical compressive force of 260,000 lbs. on the steel tube of Fig. 5?
3. The steel angle bar of Fig. 6 is to be subjected to a horizontal compressive force of 51,000 lbs. which passes through the centroid of each cross section. Find the stress.

4. A circular steel bar, 2″ in diameter, is subjected to a compressive stress of 8,000 lbs. per sq. in. What is the total force on the bar?

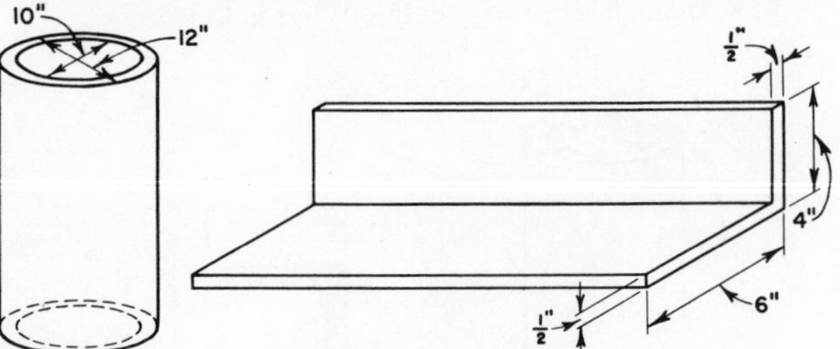

Fig. 5. Steel Tube for Problem 2 (Art. 5–1)

Fig. 6. An Angle Bar for Problem 3 (Art. 5–1)

5. The concrete block in Fig. 7 can withstand a compressive stress of 1,000 lbs. per sq. in. What vertical compressive force can be applied?
6. What horizontal compressive force will cause a stress of 800 lbs. per sq. in. on section AA of the concrete block of Fig. 7.

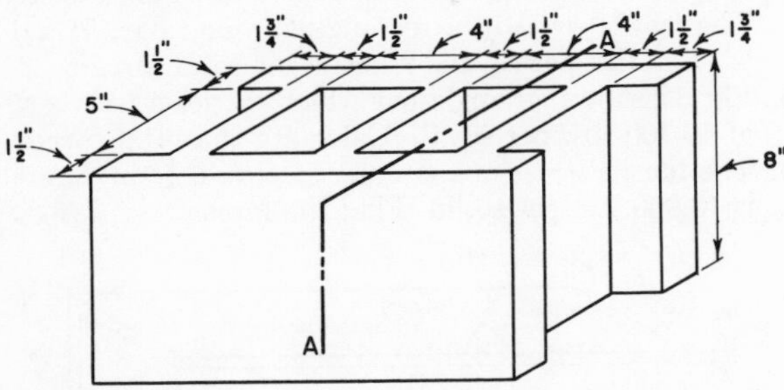

Fig. 7. Concrete Block for Problem 5 (Art. 5–1)

5-2. Tension and Tension Stress.

Tension is the opposite of compression. Material is in *tension* when the forces acting on it tend to stretch it. Look at Fig. 8 for an example. Fig. 8A shows a rack used for storing pipe in a shop. The floor of the rack is bolted to support rods and the rods are bolted to joists overhead. Then Fig. 8B shows the free-body diagram of the support rod AB. Here you see the force P (downward) at the bottom of the rod and this force is exerted by the bolt at the lower end. Also, you see the force P (upward) at the top of the rod and this force is exerted by the bolt at the upper end. The rod is in tension because the forces tend to stretch it.

Now look at Fig. 8C which shows the free-body diagram of the upper part of the rod. Here you see the concentrated force P at the top and, at the bottom, the distributed force P which is exerted on the upper part of the rod by the lower part. The force directed downward must equal the force directed upward in order for this part of the rod to be in equilibrium. We can write the equilibrium equation, $\Sigma F_y = 0$. Thus,

$$\Sigma F_y = 0$$

$$P - P = 0$$

The stress is calculated in the same way, whether the bar is in tension or compression. It is just,

$$S = \frac{P}{A}$$

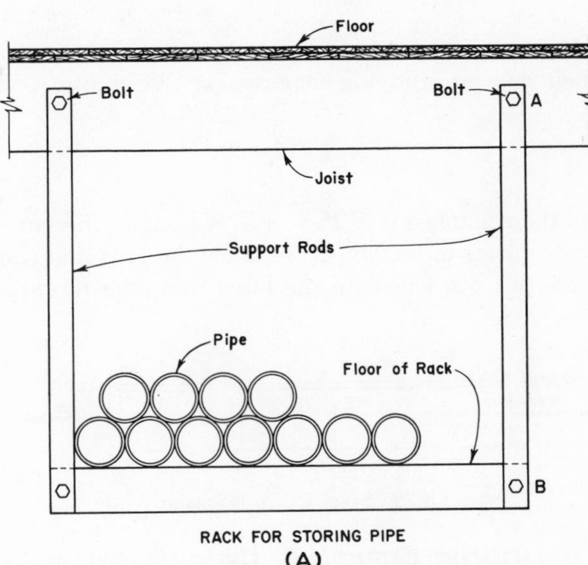

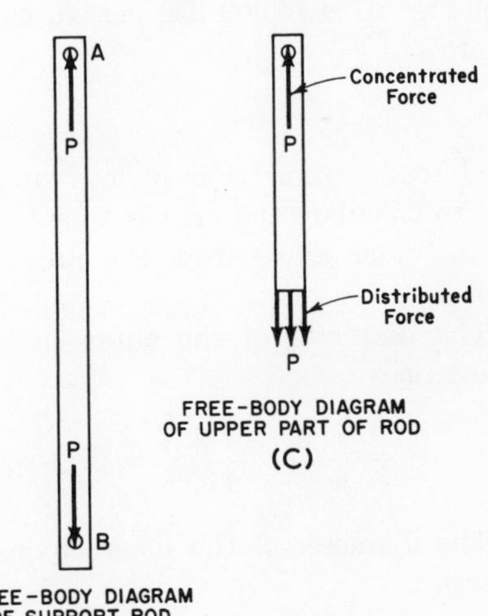

Fig. 8. A Rack for Storing Pipe, and Rods in Tension

where S is *stress* in pounds per square inch, P is *force* in pounds and A is the *area* of cross section of the bar in square inches. The stress is called *tensile stress* when the bar is in tension. Remember that the force must pass through the centroid of the cross section for the formula to be correct.

Illustrative Example 1. Calculate the stress in the steel bar in Fig. 9.

Solution:

1. The bar is rectangular in section and the area is

$$A = \tfrac{3}{8} \times 2 = 0.75 \text{ sq. in.}$$

2. The *force* is $P = 12{,}800$ lbs.
3. The *stress* is

$$S = \frac{P}{A} = \frac{12{,}800}{0.75} = 17{,}000 \,\#/\text{in.}^2$$

Remember how we turned this formula around when we were studying compression. We wrote it as

$$S = \frac{P}{A}$$

and then changed it to $P = AS$. We can do the same for problems in *tension*. If we know the area and the stress, we can calculate the force from the formula $P = AS$.

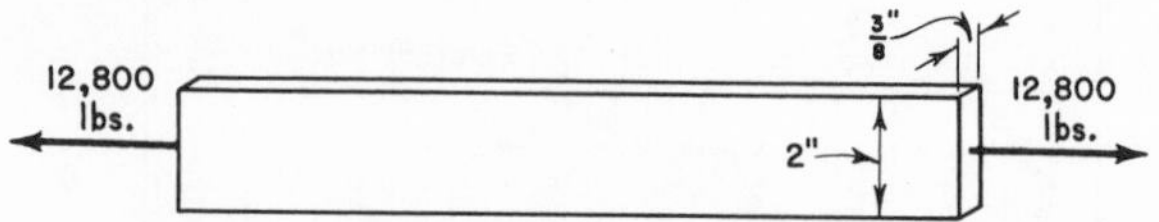

Fig. 9. Steel Bar in Tension

Illustrative Example 2. The *tensile stress* in the tube of Fig. 10 is 16,000 lbs. per sq. in. What is the total force?

Solution:

1. The cross section is a hollow circle. The best way to calculate the area is to subtract the area of the inner circle from the area of the outer circle.
   a) The diameter of the outer circle is 2″. The area is

$$A_1 = \frac{\pi}{4} d^2 = \frac{\pi}{4} (2)^2 = 3.14 \text{ sq. in.}$$

   b) The diameter of the inner circle is 1.5″. The area is

$$A_2 = \frac{\pi}{4} d^2 = \frac{\pi}{4} (1.5)^2 = 1.77 \text{ sq. in.}$$

   c) The area of the cross section is

$$A = A_1 - A_2 = 3.14 - 1.77 = 1.37 \text{ sq. in.}$$

2. The stress S is 16,000 lbs. per sq. in.
3. The total force is

$$P = AS = 1.37 \times 16{,}000 = 21{,}900 \text{ lbs.}$$

Practice Problems (Art. 5-2).

1. A tensile force of 18,000 lbs. is applied to a circular bar, 1.25″ in diameter. Calculate the *tensile stress.*
2. A rectangular steel bar, 6″ x $\tfrac{3}{4}$″ in section, is subjected to a *tensile force* of 68,000 lbs. What is the stress?

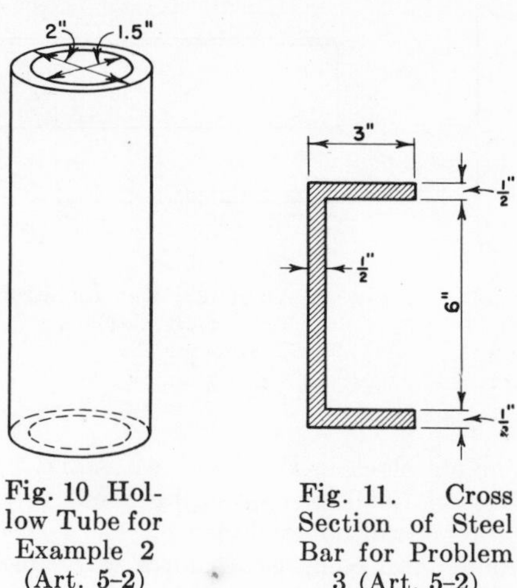

Fig. 10 Hollow Tube for Example 2 (Art. 5-2)

Fig. 11. Cross Section of Steel Bar for Problem 3 (Art. 5-2)

3. Fig. 11 shows the cross section of a steel bar which is subjected to a *tensile force* of 74,300 lbs. Find the stress.
4. The *tensile stress* in a rectangular wood bar, $5\tfrac{1}{2}$ x $1\tfrac{3}{8}$″, is 1,200 lbs. per sq. in. What is the total force?
5. Fig. 12 shows an angle bar which carries a *tensile stress* of 15,700 lbs. per sq. in. Calculate the total force.
6. The tensile stress in a circular steel rod, $\tfrac{3}{4}$″ in diameter, is 13,900 lbs. per sq. in. Find the force.

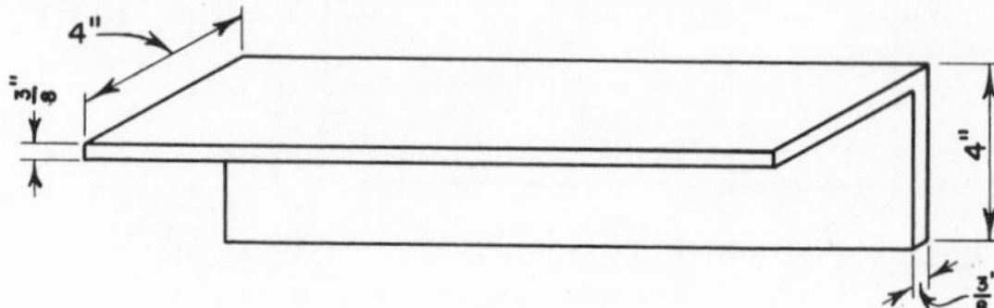

Fig. 12. Steel Angle Bar for Problem 5 (Art. 5-2)

5-3. Shear and Shearing Stress.

Fig. 13*A* shows a column with a beam resting on a projection of the column. Fig. 13*B* shows the projection alone with the force *P* exerted on the projection by the beam. You can see that the force tends to push the projection down and make it slide along the face of the column. This is called *shear*, which is sliding or a tendency to slide. A large enough force would make the projection slide along the plane *ABCD*.

The column exerts an upward force on the projection to keep the projection from sliding down, and this upward force is distributed over the area *ABCD*. You can see this distributed force in Fig. 13*C*. The distributed force is *shearing stress.*

The amount of the shearing stress is

$$S = \frac{P}{A}$$

just as before. Here, S is the *stress* in pounds per

square inch, P is the *force in pounds*, and A is the *area in shear*.

Another example of shear, in Fig. 14A, shows three steel plates which are fastened together by a bolt. A force P is applied to the center plate and this is balanced by the two forces $\frac{P}{2}$ on the outer plates. The force P tends to slide the center plate out from between the outer plates, which is prevented by the bolt.

Fig. 13. Column and Beam in Shear

The center plate tends to move the bolt to the right and the outer plates tend to move the bolt to the left. Fig. 14B shows the free-body diagram of the bolt. It is easy to see here that the force P tends to slide the center part of the bolt to the right past the outer parts. The sliding would occur on the cross sections AA and BB, which are the planes of contact between the center plate and the outer plates. Sliding is *shear* so the bolt is *in shear*. There is shearing stress on the cross sections AA and BB.

Fig. 14C shows a partly sheared bolt; this is what actually happens when the forces are large enough.

Fig. 14D shows the free-body diagram of the center part of the bolt. The force P is directed to the right and is balanced by shearing stress on the cross sections AA and BB. The shearing stress is equal to

$$S = \frac{P}{A}$$

Here A is the total area in shear; that is, two times the area of one cross section of the bolt.

Illustrative Example 1. In Fig. 14C, the force P is 9,450 lbs. and the bolt is $\frac{3}{4}''$ in diameter. Find the shearing stress.

Solution:

1. The area of one cross section of the bolt is $\pi d^2/4$, where d is the diameter of the bolt. However, there are two cross sections in shear, so

$$A = 2\frac{\pi}{4}d^2 = 2\frac{\pi}{4}(\tfrac{3}{4})^2 = 0.884 \text{ sq. in.}$$

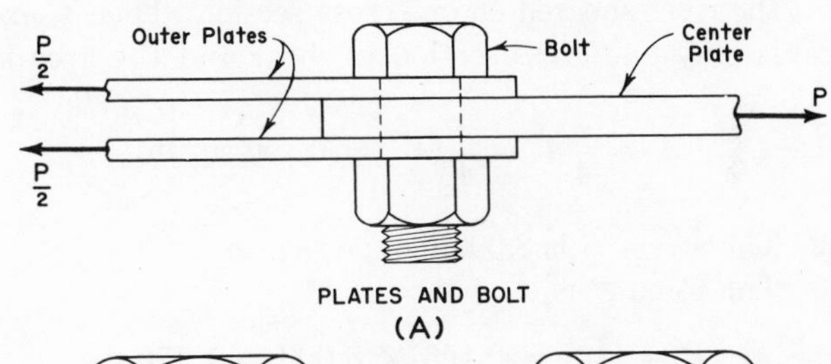

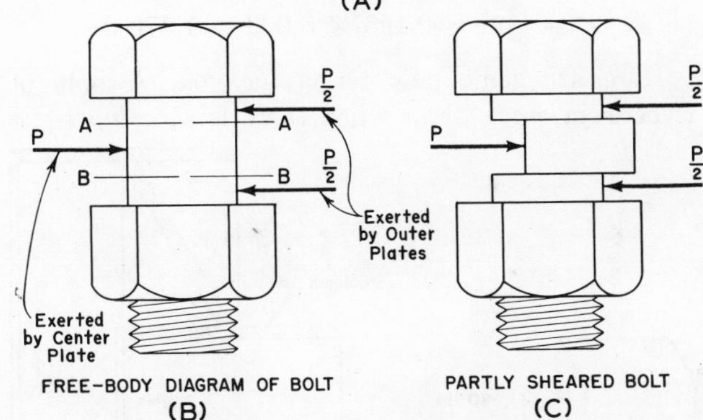

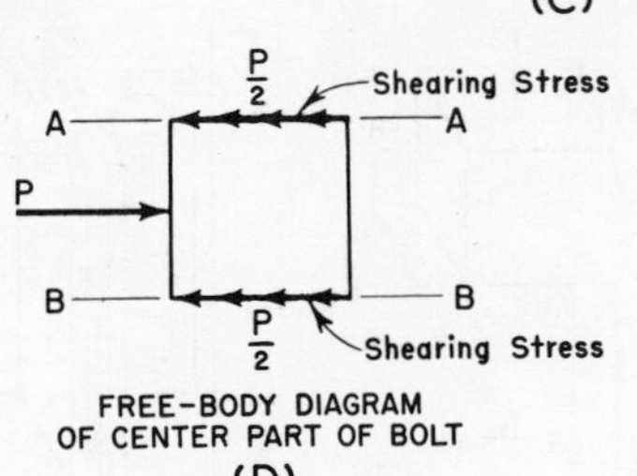

Fig. 14. Shear in Bolt

2. The force P is 9,450 lbs.
3. The shearing stress is

$$S = \frac{P}{A} = \frac{9{,}450}{0.884} = 10{,}700 \,\#/\text{in.}^2$$

We can write the formula as

$$S = \frac{P}{A}$$

when we want to calculate the stress; and we can write it as $P = AS$ if we know the stress and want to calculate the force.

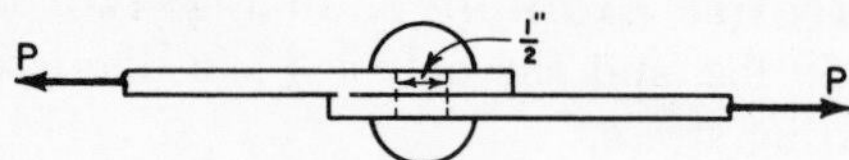

Fig. 15. A Riveted Joint

Illustrative Example 2. Fig. 15 shows two plates which are fastened together by a rivet $\frac{1}{2}''$ in diameter. The shearing stress in the rivet is 8,000 lbs. per sq. in. Find the force P.

Solution:

1. Notice here that the plates would slide apart if the rivet sheared on one cross section. Then there is only one cross section in shear and the area is

$$A = \frac{\pi}{4} d^2 = \frac{\pi}{4} (\tfrac{1}{2})^2 = 0.196 \text{ sq. in.}$$

2. The stress S is 8,000 lbs. per sq. in.
3. The force P is

$$P = AS = 0.196 \times 8{,}000 = 1{,}570 \text{ lbs.}$$

Here are some new terms for you. A bolt or rivet is in *single shear* when there is *shearing stress* on only one cross section, as in Fig. 15; it is in *double shear* when there is *shearing stress* on two cross sections as in Fig. 14.

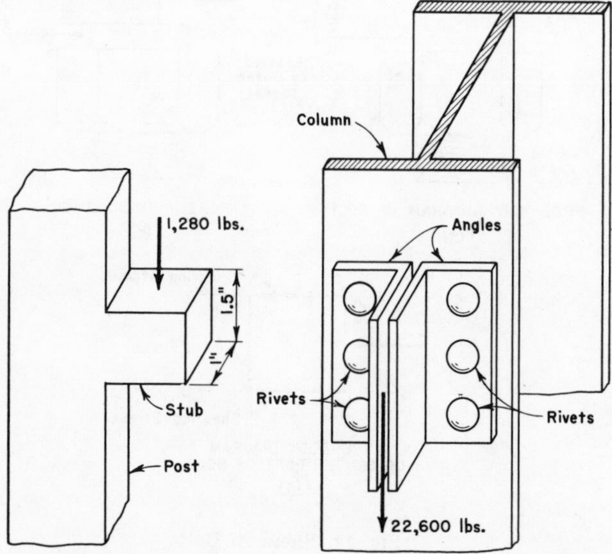

Fig. 16. Post and Stub for Problem 1 (Art. 5-3)

Fig. 17. Steel Angle Bars Riveted to Column for Problem 2 (Art. 5-3)

Practice Problems (Art. 5-3). Work the following problems on *shear*.

1. Fig. 16 shows a small post with a stub projection. Find the shearing stress between the post and stub.
2. Fig. 17 shows a common type of structural connection in which two short lengths of steel angle are riveted to a short column. The force of 22,600 lbs. is applied to the angles; the rivets are $\frac{7}{8}''$ in diameter. Find the shearing stress in the rivets.
3. A bolt in single shear is subjected to a force of 8,800 lbs. The bolt is 1″ in diameter. What is the shearing stress?

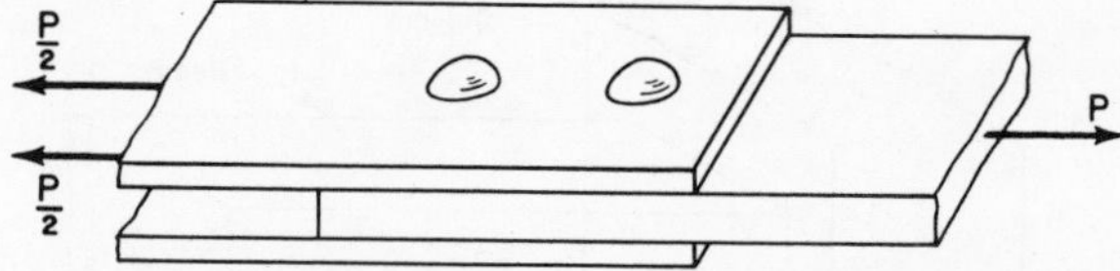

Fig. 18. Riveted Joint for Problem 4 (Art. 5-3)

4. The steel plates in Fig. 18 are fastened together by two rivets, each $\frac{5}{8}''$ in diameter. The shearing stress in the rivets is 9,600 lbs. per sq. in. Find the force P.
5. Fig. 19 shows the end portion of a plate with a hole. The force P is applied at the edge of the hole and tends to push the shaded part away from the rest of the plate. The plate is $\frac{1}{2}''$ thick and the shearing stress on sections AA and BB is 12,000 lbs. per sq. in. Find the force P.

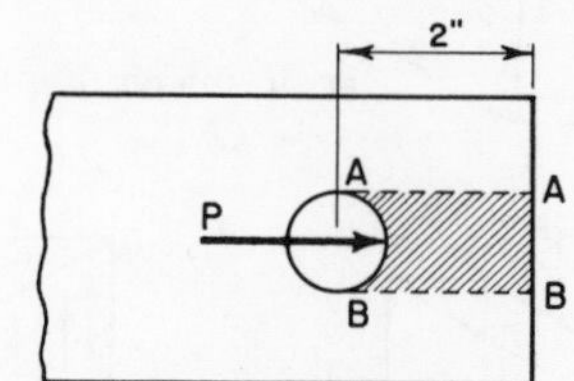

Fig. 19. Portion of Plate for Problem 5 (Art. 5-3)

6. A rivet, $\frac{3}{8}''$ in diameter, is in double shear and is subjected to a shearing stress of 10,300 lbs. per sq. in. What is the force applied to the rivet? (Note: This is the same as the force P in Fig. 14.)

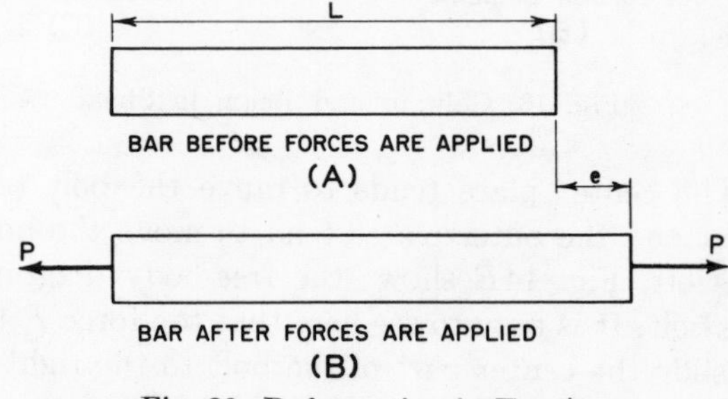

Fig. 20. Deformation in Tension

5-4. Deformation and Strain in Tension.

A good structural engineer should know how a body deforms when a force is applied. Fig. 20 shows the deformation of a bar in tension; Fig. 20A shows the bar before the forces are applied and Fig. 20B shows the bar after the forces are applied. Notice that the original length of the bar is L and that the bar stretches by the amount e when the forces are applied. The length e is the *deformation* and it is usually measured in inches.

Next, we will consider *strain* which is *unit deformation;* that is, it is the deformation e divided by the length L. We usually designate strain by ϵ (Greek letter epsilon), so the formula is

$$\epsilon = \frac{e}{L}$$

We divide inches by inches when we calculate strain, so the result is a pure number; it has no dimension. Be sure to take both e and L in inches when you calculate *strain.*

Illustrative Example 1. A steel bar, 10 ft. long, is stretched by an amount of 0.219″. Calculate the strain.

Solution:

1. The deformation e is 0.219″
2. The length L is 10′ or 120″
3. The strain is

$$\epsilon = \frac{e}{L} = \frac{0.219}{120} = 0.001825$$

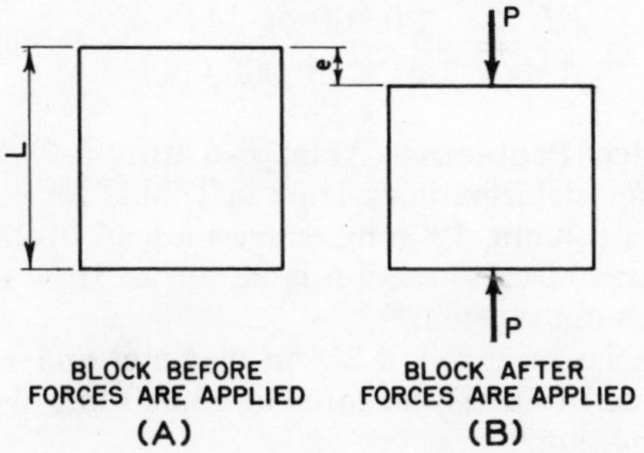

Fig. 21. Deformation of Block in Compression

5-5. Deformation and Strain in Compression.

Compression is just as easy as *tension.* Look at Fig. 21 to see the picture. Fig. 21A shows a block before the forces are applied and Fig. 21B shows the block after compressive forces have been applied. Here, also, the original length of the block is L and the deformation is e. However, the block in *compression shortens* whereas a bar in *tension stretches.*

The strain in compression is found in the same way as strain in tension. It is represented by the same symbol and is

$$\epsilon = \frac{e}{L}$$

Illustrative Example 1. A block of wood, which is originally 16″ long, is compressed by an amount of 0.034″. Find the *strain.*

Solution:

1. The deformation e is 0.034″
2. The length L is 16″
3. The strain is

$$\epsilon = \frac{e}{L} = \frac{0.034}{16} = 0.00213$$

Practice Problems (Arts. 5-4 and 5-5). Solve the following problems on *strain.*

1. A steel bar, 27″ long, is stretched 0.041″. Calculate the strain.
2. What is the strain in a rod which is 6′6″ long originally and which is stretched 0.099″?
3. Find the stretch of a bar which had an original length of 20′ and a strain of 0.000872.
4. A steel column is compressed 0.052″. The original length of the column is 9′. Find the strain.
5. Calculate the strain in a concrete post which is compressed 0.112″ from an original length of 12′.

5-6. Relation between Stress and Strain—Modulus of Elasticity.

The relation between stress and strain will be discussed next. This is simple, because *stress* is proportional to *strain,* as long as the stress is not too great. The equation which expresses the proportionality of stress to strain is

$$S = E\epsilon$$

Here E is a constant which gives the relation between stress and strain; E is called the modulus of elasticity of a material. The *modulus of elasticity* is expressed in pounds per square inch, the same units as stress.

We can rewrite the equation $S = E\epsilon$. First, divide both sides of the equation by ϵ. This gives

$$\frac{S}{\epsilon} = E\frac{\epsilon}{\epsilon}$$

Then cancel ϵ on the right side of the equation. This leaves

$$\frac{S}{\epsilon} = E \quad \text{or} \quad E = \frac{S}{\epsilon}$$

The last equation leads to a simple way of realizing the meaning of E; E is just *stress divided by strain,* or the ratio of stress to strain.

Table I gives the value of the *modulus of elasticity* of some of the common structural materials.

TABLE I. VALUES OF MODULUS OF ELASTICITY

Material	E in Pounds per Square Inch
Structural steel	30,000,000
Douglas fir	1,600,000
Southern pine	1,600,000
Concrete	2,000,000 to 5,000,000

You do not need to memorize the numbers in Table I, but remember what *modulus of elasticity* is, and where the table is found.

It may surprise you that the modulus of elasticity of concrete varies so widely, but this variation can be explained easily. Concrete is a mixture of cement (usually Portland cement), sand, gravel, and water. These ingredients are put in the drum of a concrete mixer and mixed for a minute or more. Then the wet concrete is placed in forms which hold it in place until it dries.

There are many factors which affect the strength and modulus of elasticity of concrete. For one thing, using more cement makes E greater. Also, using less water makes E greater. Besides this, the longer the time of mixing, the greater E is. Moreover, keeping the concrete wet for several days after mixing makes E greater. With all of these things to consider, it isn't surprising that the *modulus of elasticity* is not always the same.

You may wonder what value of E to use for concrete. The value of E will be given in each of the problems where it is needed. In practical engineering work, you will probably know enough about the proportions of cement and water, the time of mixing, and other needed information, to know what E is.

5-7. How to Find the Deformation When You Know the Load.

You will learn next how to find the *deformation* of a bar in tension or compression when you know the force and the dimensions of the member. You can do so by putting together some formulas that you already know. Start with $P = AS$. Then use $S = E$ to replace S by E. This gives

$$P = AS = AE$$

Now you know that

$$\epsilon = \frac{e}{L}$$

so

$$P = AE\epsilon = AE\frac{e}{L}$$

$$P = AE\frac{e}{L}$$

We want to solve the last equation for e. To do so, divide each side of the equation by AE and multiply by L. Then we have

$$\frac{PL}{AE} = AE\frac{e}{L}\frac{L}{AE}$$

Cancel A, E, and L on the right side of the equation to get

$$\frac{PL}{AE} = e \quad \text{or} \quad e = \frac{PL}{AE}$$

There it is. You can calculate the deformation e if you know P, L, A, and E. Be sure to take the length L in inches.

Illustrative Example 1. A rectangular steel bar, 2″ by $\frac{3}{4}$″ in section and 12′ long, is subjected to a tensile force of 20,700 lbs. How much does it stretch?

Solution:

1. The force P is 20,700 lbs.
2. The length L is 12′ or 144″
3. The area of the cross section of the bar is

$$A = 2 \times \tfrac{3}{4} = 1.5 \text{ sq. in.}$$

4. The modulus of elasticity of steel is (see Table I)

$$E = 30{,}000{,}000 \text{ lbs. per sq. in.}$$

5. Then,

$$e = \frac{PL}{AE} = \frac{20{,}700 \times 144}{1.5 \times 30{,}000{,}000} = 0.0663''$$

Practice Problems (Arts. 5-6 and 5-7). Now calculate a few deformations. Look in Table I for values of E.

1. A steel column, 12′ long, carries a load of 276,000 lbs. The area of cross section is 22 sq. in. How much does the column shorten?
2. A circular steel rod, 1.25″ in diameter and 18′ long, is subjected to a tensile force of 13,600 lbs. What is the deformation?
3. A compressive force of 47,300 lbs. is applied to a Douglas-fir post which is 8″ square and 8′ long. Calculate the deformation.

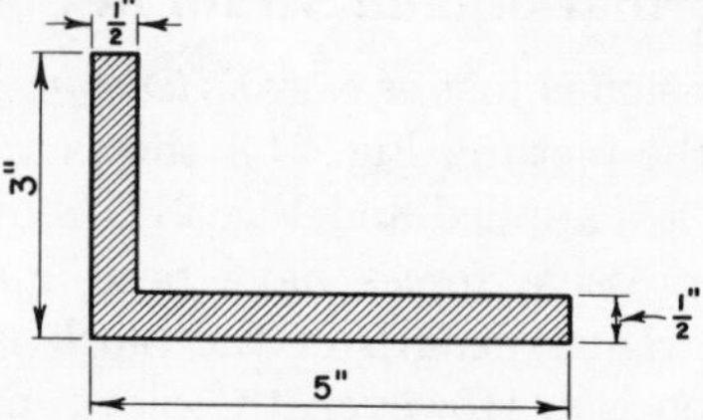

Fig. 22. Cross Section of Steel Angle for Problem 4 (Art. 5–7)

4. Fig. 22 shows the cross section of a steel angle which is 12′6″ long. A tensile force of 73,400 lbs. is applied to the angle. How much does it stretch?
5. A circular concrete column, 24″ in diameter and 14′ long, is subjected to a compressive force of 386,000 lbs. Find the deformation of the column. (Note: Use E = 3,000,000 lbs. per sq. in.)

5-8. Stress-Strain Diagrams—Yield Point—Ultimate Strength.

The usual way of finding the strength of a piece of steel is to put it into a testing machine and pull it in two; the testing machine is provided with a means of measuring the force on the piece of steel; this gives the force P. Also, an instrument called an extensiometer (it measures extension) is fastened to the piece of steel and the stretch is measured; the stretch is e. The force P is increased slowly and each time the force is measured, the stretch e is measured. So, a value of e is obtained for each value of P.

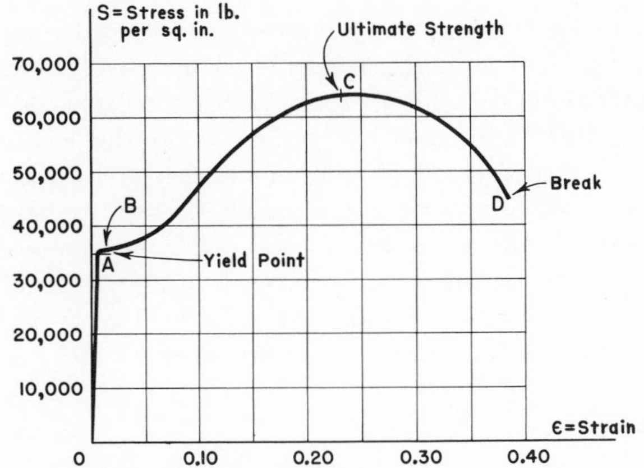

Fig. 23. Stress-Strain Diagram for Structural Steel in Tension

The steel specimen is measured carefully before the test is performed. Thus, the length L is known and the area A can be calculated. The stress is

$$S = \frac{P}{A}$$

and the strain is

$$\epsilon = \frac{e}{L}$$

Values of the *load* and *stretch* are measured during the test and then the values of *stress and strain* are calculated. For each value of stress there is a corresponding value of strain. Then the values of stress and strain are plotted in a stress-strain diagram. Fig. 23 shows a stress-strain diagram for structural steel and will give you an idea of how stress-strain diagrams look. Here is how such a diagram is obtained. Values of stress and strain are obtained from the test of the steel specimen, and there is a value of strain ϵ corresponding to each value of stress S. Each value of stress is plotted vertically in Fig. 23 and the corresponding value of strain is plotted horizontally (just as you plotted y and x in plotting curves in algebra). This gives one point in the diagram for each value of stress, and when all points are plotted, the curve is drawn through the points.

Look carefully at Fig. 23 and get ready to learn some new words. Notice that the diagram is a straight line from the starting point to point A. Point A is called the *proportional limit*, because stress is not proportional to strain beyond this point. Then notice the flat part B of the curve just above A. This is called the *yield point* (about 36,000 lbs. per sq. in. for structural steel). You can see that there is an increase in strain at the yield point without any increase in stress. As the stress increases beyond B, there is a considerably greater strain and the maximum stress is reached at C. The stress at C is called the *ultimate strength* (about 60,000 lbs. per sq. in. for structural steel). The *ultimate strength* is the maximum stress which can be applied to the material and is enough to break the specimen. The *ultimate strength* is a measure of the strength of a material. It is the figure which you would give if you wanted to tell someone how strong a material is.

Notice the values of ϵ in Fig. 23. The piece of steel breaks at point D and the value of ϵ at D is about 0.35. This means that there is about a 35 per cent increase in length of the specimen when it breaks. We say that a material is *ductile* if it stretches considerably before breaking. Steel is certainly a ductile material. A material which breaks without much deformation is *brittle*.

Concrete is not nearly as strong as steel. Besides, concrete is brittle; that is, it doesn't deform much

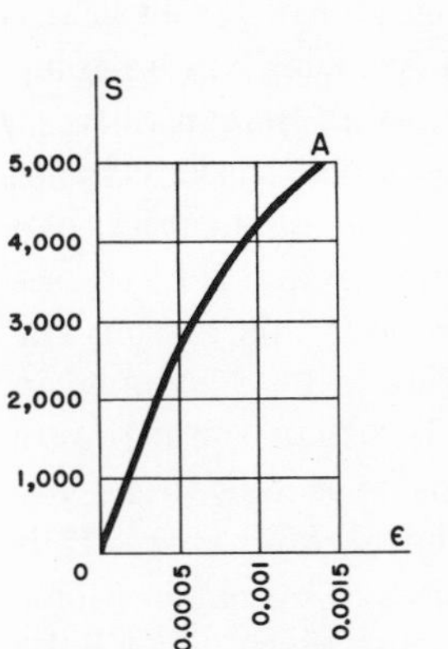

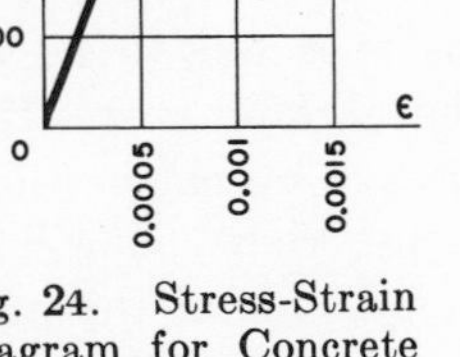

Fig. 24. Stress-Strain Diagram for Concrete in Compression

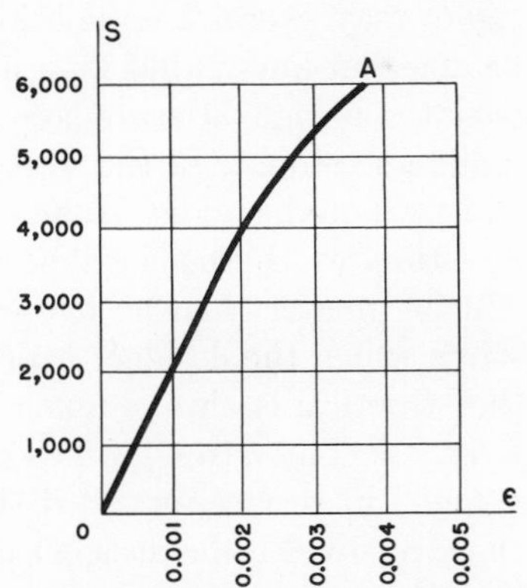

Fig. 25. Stress-Strain Diagram for Douglas Fir in Compression Parallel to Grain

before breaking. Fig. 24 shows a stress-strain diagram for concrete in compression. Concrete is used mostly in compression because its strength in tension is usually considered to be relatively low.

Fig. 25 shows a stress-strain diagram for Douglas fir in compression parallel to the grain. Wood is ordinarily used either, in compression parallel to the grain, or in beams. (Beams will be studied in the next chapter.)

Notice there is no yield point in Figs. 24 and 25. As a matter of fact, structural steel is about the only important material that does have a yield point. Points A in Figs. 24 and 25 represent the ultimate strength.

You are not expected to memorize these stress-strain diagrams, but you should study them enough to know what they are and what they show.

5-9. Working Stress and Factor of Safety.

It is not hard to see that you would not design a bridge or building in such a way that the material is stressed up to the ultimate strength. For one thing, the bridge or building would be at the point of breaking. (How would you like to drive over a bridge that was just ready to break, or live in a building that was on the point of falling down?) Besides steel stretches about 30 per cent before it breaks in tension, which is too much deformation. If you designed a building so that the stresses were anywhere near the ultimate strength, there would be so much sag in the floors you would have to go up and down hill to walk across a room.

An engineer always *tries* to design a structure so the stresses will be well below the ultimate strengths of the materials used. But he can never know for sure just what stresses will actually occur. Possibly, the greatest uncertainty is in figuring the loads, or forces, that will be applied to the structure. A designer may expect a large bridge to last for 40 years; he does not know what kind of vehicles will be going over the bridge 20 years later, so all he can do is to make an estimate of the forces which these vehicles will exert on the bridge. If the vehicles are heavier than he estimates, the loads will be greater and the stresses will be greater than he figures. For this reason, the stress which the designer expects to be developed in the structure is always much less than the ultimate strength. This stress, which is expected to be developed in service, is called the *working stress*. It is the stress which the designer uses in his calculations, and if everything works out just right, it will be the actual stress. *Working stress* is one of the most important terms used in *Elementary Structural Design*.

Another term which is used by structural engineers is *factor of safety*. The *factor of safety* is usually taken as equal to the *ultimate strength divided by the working stress*. We can write it this way:

$$\textit{factor of safety} = \frac{\textit{ultimate strength}}{\textit{working stress}}$$

Illustrative Example 1. The ultimate strength of structural steel in tension is 60,000 lbs. per sq. in. The working stress, for one particular use, is 18,000 lbs. per sq. in. What is the *factor of safety?*

Solution:

1. The ultimate strength is 60,000 lbs. per sq. in.
2. The working stress is 18,000 lbs. per sq. in.
3. The factor of safety is

$$\textit{factor of safety} = \frac{\textit{ultimate strength}}{\textit{working stress}} = \frac{60{,}000}{18{,}000} = 3.33$$

You will probably be interested in knowing some values for working stress. Working stresses vary somewhat, depending upon the particular type of structure, and, also, depending upon the location of the structure. Most cities of any size have building codes which specify the working stresses for structures. Working stresses for all conditions, cannot be given, but enough can be given to give you an idea of what is reasonable and safe. Table II gives working stresses for some of the common structural materials.

TABLE II. TYPICAL VALUES OF WORKING STRESS IN POUNDS PER SQUARE INCH

Material	Tension	Compression (Short Lengths)		Shear	Bending
Structural steel...	16,000–20,000	16,000–20,000		10,000–15,000	16,000–20,000
Concrete.........	——	600–1,200		50–100	1,000–2,000
Common brick, with Portland cement mortar.	——	175–200		——	——
		Compression		Shear	
		Parallel to Grain	Perpendicular to Grain	Parallel to Grain	
Douglas fir.....	——	1,000–1,300	300–400	80–120	1,400–1,800
Southern pine....	——	1,200–1,500	380	100	1,600–2,000

You can see there are some blank spaces in the table. This is due to the fact that some materials are only used in special ways and the working stresses are only established for those special uses. For instance, common brick is only used in compression, so we can only give you a working stress in compression for brick.

You are not supposed to memorize Table II, but you can profit from studying it carefully.

5-10. How to Use a Working Stress.

You should know working stresses, and how to use them. The following formula will illustrate how stresses are used. Remember the formula,

$$S = \frac{P}{A}$$

where S is *stress*, P is *force*, and A is *area*. We also used it as $P = AS$. Now it is written in a third way, as (check for yourself to see whether it is correct)

$$A = \frac{P}{S}$$

This is the form in which the equation is used for design. Here P is the *force* which is applied to a post or bar, S is the *working stress*, and A is the *area* needed for the cross section of the post or bar. Usually, the shape of the cross section is decided upon beforehand, so the dimensions can be calculated when the area is known.

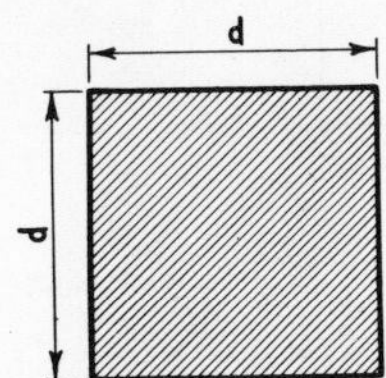

Fig. 26. Cross Section of Post for Example 1 (Art. 5–10)

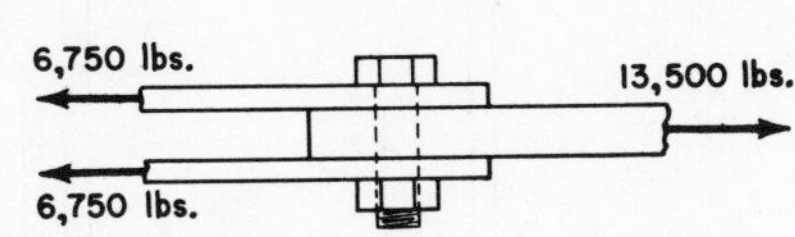

Fig. 27. Bolt in Shear for Example 2 (Art. 5–10)

Illustrative Example 1. A square wood post is to carry a compressive load of 92,000 lbs., with a working stress of 1,200 lbs. per sq. in. What size of post is required?

Solution:

Fig. 26 shows the cross section of the square post; the length of one side of the square is d.

1. The load P is 92,000 lbs.
2. The working stress is 1,200 lbs. per sq. in.
3. The required area of the cross section is

$$A = \frac{P}{S} = \frac{92{,}000}{1{,}200} = 76.7 \text{ sq. in.}$$

4. The area of the square is $A = d^2$. So

$$d^2 = A = 76.7$$

$$d = \sqrt{76.7} = 8.77''$$

Now try an example with shearing stress. The formula is the same.

Illustrative Example 2. Fig. 27 shows three plates which are held together by a bolt. The working stress for the bolt in shear is 10,000 lbs. per sq. in. What diameter of bolt is required?

Solution:

1. The force P is 13,500 lbs.
2. The working stress S is 10,000 lbs. per sq. in.
3. The area required for the bolt in shear is

$$A = \frac{P}{S} = \frac{13{,}500}{10{,}000} = 1.35 \text{ sq. in.}$$

4. This bolt is in double shear (remember double shear from Article 5-3, Example 2) so there are two cross sections of the bolt in shear. The area of one cross section is $\pi d^2/4$, where d is the diameter. Then

$$\frac{1.35}{2} = 0.675 \text{ (2, since two cross sections are in shear)}$$

$$\frac{3.14}{4} = 0.785$$

$$\frac{0.675}{0.785} = 0.86 \quad \text{or} \quad d^2 = 0.86$$

$$d = \sqrt{0.86} = 0.927''$$

Practice Problems (Art. 5-10). Work the practice problems so you will remember how to design simple structural members.

1. A circular concrete column is to carry a compressive load of 360,000 lbs. and the working stress is 1,000 lbs. per sq. in. What diameter is required for the column?
2. A rectangular steel bar, $\frac{1}{2}''$ thick, is to be subjected to a tensile force of 62,000 lbs. The working stress is 18,000 lbs. per sq. in. Calculate the width needed for the bar.
3. A rivet is used to connect two steel plates as in Fig. 28. The working stress for the rivet in shear is 12,000 lbs. per sq. in. Find the required diameter for the rivet.

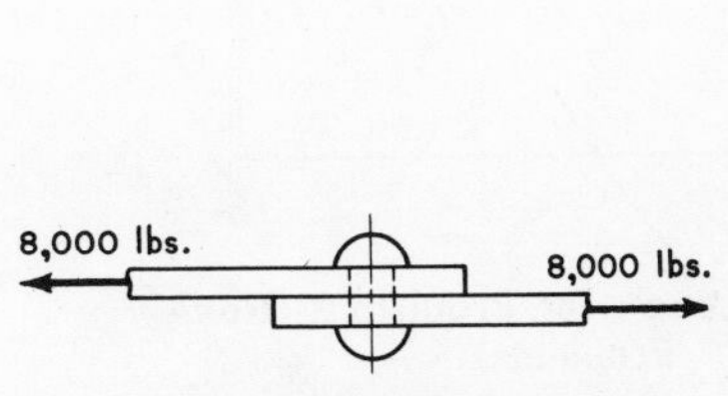

Fig. 28. Rivet in Shear for Problem 3 (Art. 5–10)

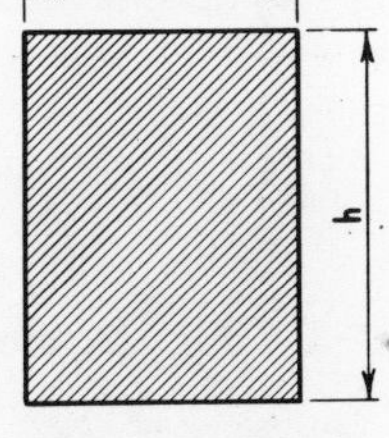

Fig. 29. Cross Section of Wood Block for Problem 5 (Art. 5–10)

4. A circular steel bar is to carry a tensile force of 23,600 lbs. with a working stress of 20,000 lbs. per sq. in. What diameter is required for the bar?
5. A wood block with the cross section shown in Fig. 29 is to carry a compressive force of 212,000 lbs. with a working stress of 1,200 lbs. per sq. in. Find the dimension h.
6. A square, concrete column is to be designed for a compressive force of 93,000 lbs. The working stress is 1,200 lbs. per sq. in. Find the size required for the column.

SUMMARY OF CHAPTER V

1. You already know what *force* is, and *stress* is force per unit area

$$\text{or } S = \frac{P}{A}$$

   a) Material *shortens* under *compressive stress.*
   b) Material *stretches* under *tensile stress.*
   c) Material *slides* under *shearing stress.*
2. *Strain* is unit deformation, $\epsilon = \frac{e}{L}$
3. The modulus of elasticity, E, of a material is equal to the stress divided by the strain. Table I gives values of E.
4. The deformation of a bar is

$$e = \frac{PL}{AE}$$

5. A stress-strain diagram shows stress plotted against strain
   a) The *proportional limit* is the greatest stress for which stress is proportional to strain.
   b) The *yield point* is the point where the strain increases without any increase in stress.
   c) The ultimate strength of a material is the greatest stress which can be applied to it. A stress equal to the ultimate strength causes failure.
6. The working stress is the stress which is expected to be developed in service. Table II gives some values for working stress.
   a) The factor of safety is equal to the ultimate strength divided by the working stress.
7. For design purposes use the formula, $A = P/S$, where A is the area required, P is the load and S is the working stress.

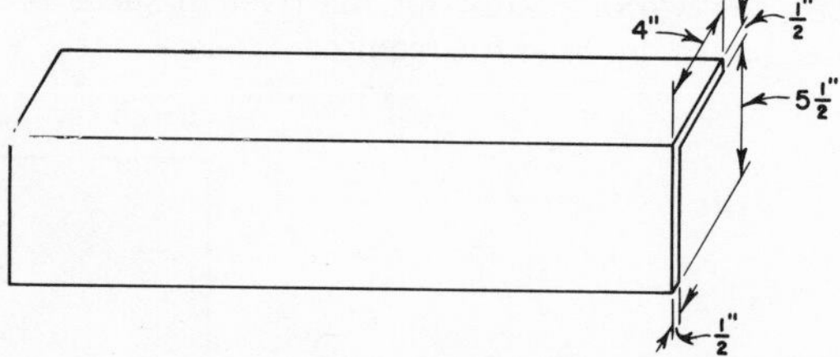

Fig. 30. Steel Angle for Problem 2 (Review Problems)

Review Questions

Be sure you know the answers to these questions, before you go on with the study of the next chapter.

1. What is *compression?*
2. What is *tension?*
3. What is *shear?*
4. Define *stress.*
5. How do you calculate the stress in a bar which is in tension or compression?
6. What is *strain?*
7. How do you calculate strain in tension or compression?
8. What is the difference between deformation and strain?
9. How is stress related to strain for low values of stress?
10. What is the *modulus of elasticity* of a material?
11. Tell what the formula

$$e = \frac{PL}{AE}$$

can be used for, and explain what each letter represents.

12. Define *proportional limit.*
13. What is *yield point?*
14. What is meant by the *ultimate strength* of a material?
15. What is a *working stress?*
16. What is a *factor of safety?*
17. Why use a factor of safety?
18. How would you calculate the size of cross section for a post in compression or a bar in tension?

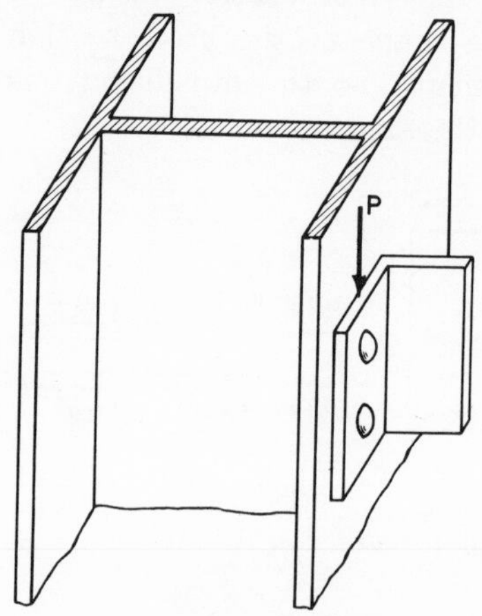

Fig. 31. Steel Angle Riveted to Columns for Problem 6 (Review Problems)

Review Problems

Remember that *shear* and *strain* are important, because they will be used later.

1. A rectangular bar, 6"x$\frac{3}{4}$" in cross section, carries a tensile force of 92,000 lbs. Calculate the stress.
2. A compressive force of 56,000 lbs. is applied to the steel angle of Fig. 30. What is the stress?
3. A circular steel rod, $\frac{1}{2}$" in diameter and 11' long, carries a tensile force of 3,800 lbs. How much does it stretch?

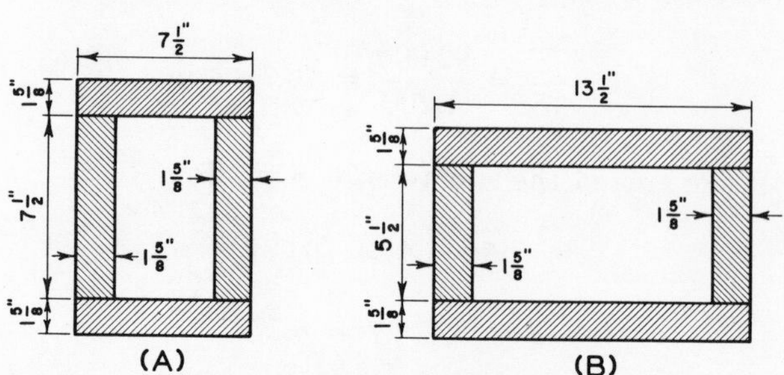

Fig. 32. Cross Section of Built-Up Wood Posts for Problem 7 (Review Problems)

4. A compressive force of 149,000 lbs. is applied to a rectangular post, 11.5"x13.5", of Douglas fir, which is 10' long. Calculate the deformation of the post.
5. The compressive stress in a square, concrete column,

14″x14″, is 600 lbs. per sq. in. Find the force.

6. The angle in Fig. 31 is fastened to the column by means of two rivets which are $\frac{7}{8}$″ in diameter and which are in single shear. The shearing stress in the rivets is 12,000 lbs. per sq. in. Find the force *P*.

7. A built-up wood post must have one of the cross sections shown in Fig. 32. The compressive force is 60,000 lbs. and the working stress is 1,000 lbs. per sq. in. Would you use (*a*) or (*b*)?

8. How many rivets, 1″ in diameter, in double shear are needed to carry a force of 44,600 lbs. with a working stress of 12,000 lbs. per sq. in?

Chapter VI

BEAMS

Purpose of This Chapter. The purpose of this chapter is the study of *beams*—to show you how to find the stress in a beam, and how to design a beam for the loads it must carry.

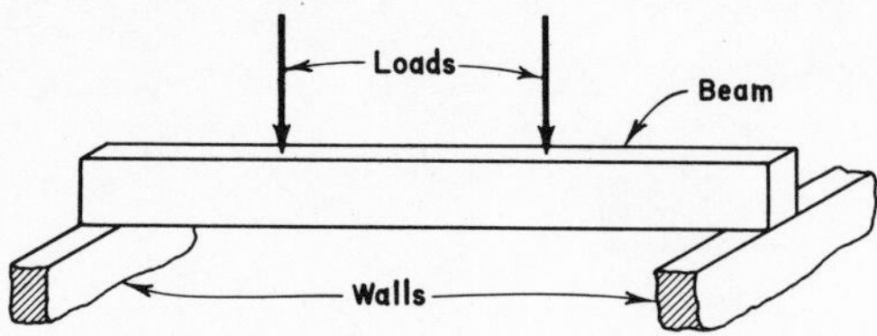

Fig. 1. Beam with Two Loads

A *beam* is a slender structural member which is subjected to loads perpendicular to its length. Fig. 1 shows a type of beam used in a building. The beam has a rectangular cross section and is supported by walls at the ends; the loads are exerted by other objects which the beam supports. Notice that the beam is a *slender member;* that is, the length is several times the width or depth. Also, notice that the loads are perpendicular to the beam; the loads are vertical and the beam is horizontal.

Not all beams are horizontal. A beam may be in any direction but the loads must be perpendicular to the beam.

Beams are probably the most common type of structural member. The roof and floors of a building of any size, as well as floors of bridges, are usually supported by beams. A structural designer must know many facts about beams.

You will learn how to calculate the stress in a beam and how to design a beam. To *design a beam* means to determine the size and shape of the beam so it will be strong enough to carry the loads.

Sometimes the problem is to calculate the stresses in a beam, but more often the problem is to design the beam. The structural designer must consider every beam in the building and make calculations to find what size of beam is necessary.

You cannot study beams unless you know how to find the reactions on a beam, how to locate the centroid of an area and how to calculate the moment of inertia of an area. These subjects were covered in the first part of this book. However, if you have forgotten some of the material, the following review will be helpful.

6-1. Review of Beam Reactions.

The reactions on a beam are the forces which the supports exert to hold up the beams. You should remember that the first step in finding the reactions is to draw the free-body diagram of the beam. (A free-body diagram is a picture of the object showing all of the forces exerted on the object.) The procedure in drawing the free-body diagram is to draw a line to represent the beam, then to draw the loads and finally to draw the reactions. Draw the free-body diagram for the beam in Fig. 2*A*. This is a steel beam which is supported by walls at A and B. At points C and D, the beam supports other steel beams which exert loads. Fig. 2*B* shows the free-body diagram. First, draw the heavy line $ACDB$ to represent the beam. Then draw the loads at C and D and, finally, the reactions at A and B. Designate the reactions as R_1 and R_2.

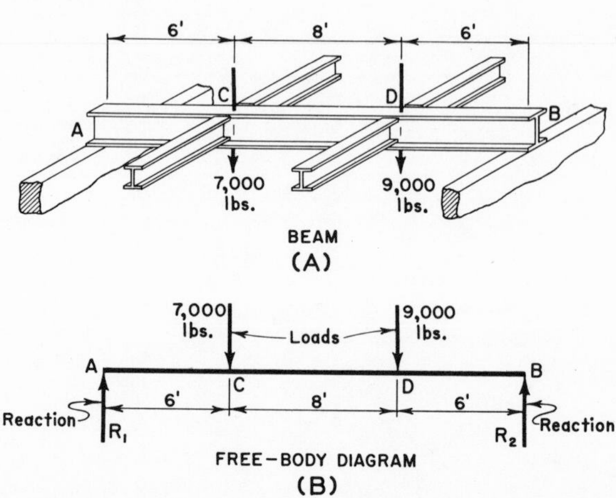

Fig. 2. Steel Beam with Loads and Reactions

The problem now is to calculate the reactions R_1 and R_2. Look at Fig. 2*B* while we review. You should remember that we find reactions on beams by writing moment equations. (The moment of a force with respect to a point is equal to the product of the force and the perpendicular distance of the force from the point. A *counterclockwise* moment is *negative* and a *clockwise* moment is *positive*.) We can write a moment equation with respect to point A to find the reaction R_2. The moment equation is

$$M_a = 0$$

This equation is to include the moment of each force with respect to point A and then we can solve the equation for R_2.

We can write a moment equation with respect to point B to find R_1. Thus,

$$M_b = 0$$

Then we can check the reactions by writing the equation

$$F_y = 0$$

This equation states that the sum of the vertical forces is *zero*.

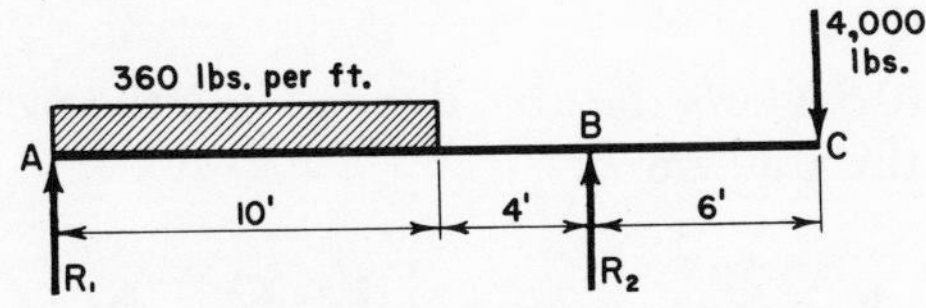

Fig. 3. Free-Body Diagram of a Beam

Illustrative Example 1. Fig. 3 shows the free-body diagram of a beam which is supported at A and B and which carries a concentrated load at C. A uniformly distributed load of 360 lbs. per ft. is applied over a ten-foot length. Calculate the reactions R_1 and R_2.

Solution:

1. We find the reaction R_2 by writing a moment equation with center at A. Thus,

$$M_a = 0$$

The moment of the uniformly distributed load is

$$360 \times 10 \times 5$$

This is equal to the number of lbs. per ft., times the length of the distributed load, times the distance from A to the center of the load. It is *positive* because the moment is clockwise. Then,

$$M_a = 360 \times 10 \times 5 - 14R_2 + 4{,}000 \times 20 = 0$$

We transpose the term containing R_2 to get

$$14R_2 = 360 \times 10 \times 5 + 4{,}000 \times 20$$

$$= 18{,}000 + 80{,}000 = 98{,}000$$

$$R_2 = 7{,}000 \text{ lbs.}$$

2. We find the reaction R_1 by writing a moment equation with center at B. Thus,

$$M_b = 14R_1 - 360 \times 10 \times 9 + 4{,}000 \times 6 = 0$$

We transpose the second and third terms to get

$$14R_1 = 360 \times 10 \times 9 - 4{,}000 \times 6$$

$$= 32{,}400 - 24{,}000 = 8{,}400$$

$$R_1 = 600 \text{ lbs.}$$

3. We check the reactions by writing the equation for the sum of the vertical forces, so

$$F_y = 0$$

$$600 - 360 \times 10 + 7{,}000 - 4{,}000 = 0$$

$$7{,}600 - 7{,}600 = 0$$

$$0 = 0$$

With this check we can be reasonably sure that the reactions are correct.

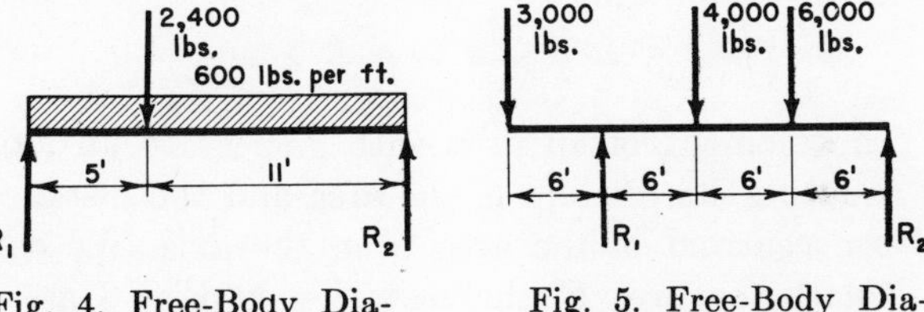

Fig. 4. Free-Body Diagram for Problem 1 (Art. 6-1)

Fig. 5. Free-Body Diagram for Problem 2 (Art. 6-1)

Practice Problems (Art. 6-1). Calculate the reactions on the beam for which the free-body diagram is given.

1. Fig. 4.
2. Fig. 5.
3. Fig. 6.
4. Fig. 7.

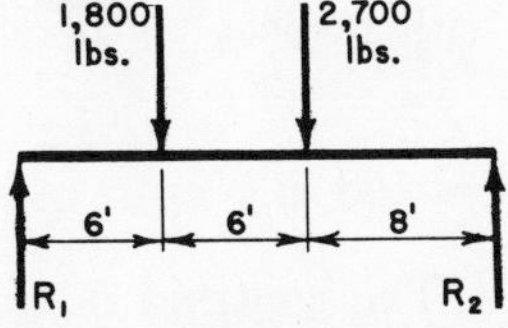

Fig. 6. Free-Body Diagram for Problem 3 (Art. 6-1)

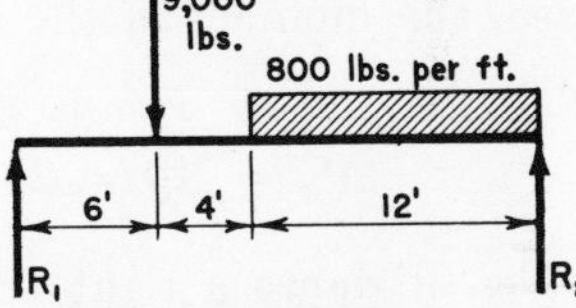

Fig. 7. Free-Body Diagram for Problem 4 (Art. 6-1)

6-2. Review of Centroid of an Area.

Start this review of centroids by going over a few terms which you are supposed to know but which you may have forgotten. First, the *centroid of an area* is a point whose distance from any axis is equal to the average distance of the area from that axis. Look now at the rectangular area in Fig. 8. The centroid of this rectangle is at the center of the rectangle and we designate this point by G. The distance from the y axis to the centroid is $\bar{x}$; $\bar{x}$ is equal to the 3″ distance from the y axis to the left side of the rectangle, plus half of the 6″ width of the rectangle, so

$$\bar{x} = 3 + \tfrac{1}{2} \times 6 = 3 + 3 = 6''$$

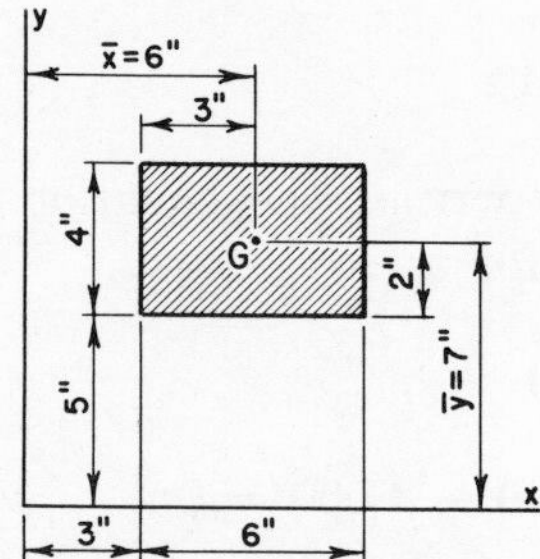

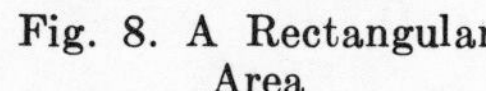

Fig. 8. A Rectangular Area

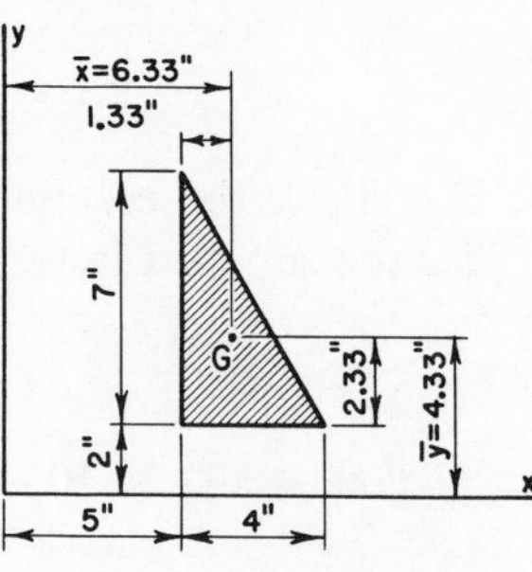

Fig. 9. A Triangular Area

The distance from the x axis to the centroid of the rectangle is $\bar{y}$; $\bar{y}$ is equal to the 5″ distance from the x axis to the lower side of the rectangle, plus half of the 4″ altitude of the rectangle. Thus,

$$\bar{y} = 5 + \tfrac{1}{2} \times 4 = 5 + 2 = 7''$$

The moment of an area with respect to an axis is equal to the product of the area and the distance of the centroid of the area from the axis. We can calculate the area of the rectangle in Fig. 8 as

$$A = bh = 6 \times 4 = 24 \text{ sq. in.}$$

Then the moment of the area with respect to the y axis is

$$M_y = A\bar{x} = 24 \times 6 = 144 \text{ in.}^3$$

Also, the moment of the area with respect to the x axis is

$$M_x = A\bar{y} = 24 \times 7 = 168 \text{ in.}^3$$

Fig. 9 shows a right triangle. The centroid is to the right of the vertical leg of the triangle by a distance of one-third of the width, so

$$\bar{x} = 5 + \tfrac{1}{3} \times 4 = 5 + 1.33 = 6.33''$$

Also, the centroid is above the horizontal leg of the triangle by a distance of one-third of the altitude. Thus,

$$\bar{y} = 2 + \tfrac{1}{3} \times 7 = 2 + 2.33 = 4.33''$$

A composite area is one which can be divided into simple parts. You should remember that this type of area was divided into simple parts such as rectangles and triangles. The area of each part was then calculated and the parts added, to get the total area A. Also, the moment of each part was calculated with respect to the y axis and added to get the moment of the entire area with respect to the y axis, and was designated at M_y; $\bar{x}$ for the entire area was found by dividing M_y by A, giving

$$\bar{x} = \frac{M_y}{A}$$

Then $\bar{y}$ for the entire area was found by dividing M_x by A. Thus,

$$\bar{y} = \frac{M_x}{A}$$

Illustrative Example 1. Locate the centroid of the area in Fig. 10*A*.

Solution:

Fig. 10*B* shows the area divided into the rectangle *A* and the triangle *B*.

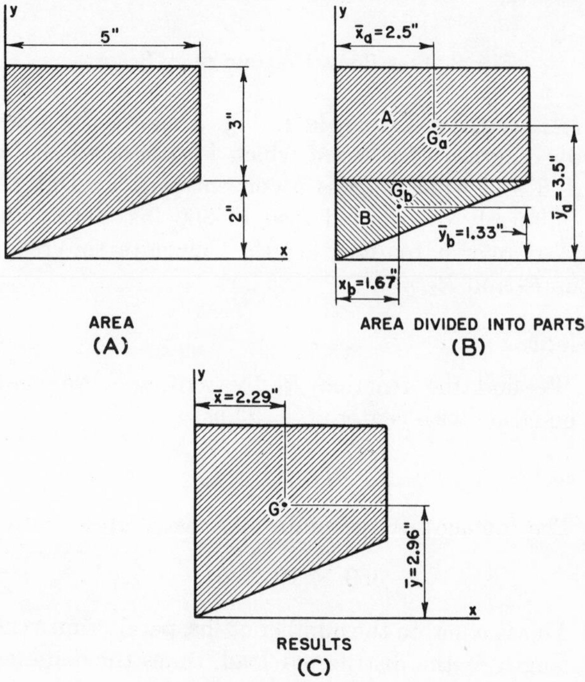

Fig. 10. A Composite Area

1. For the rectangle A,
   a) The area is
   $$A_a = bh = 5 \times 3 = 15 \text{ sq. in.}$$
   b) $\bar{x}_a = \tfrac{1}{2} \times 5 = 2.5''$
   c) $\bar{y}_a = 2 + \tfrac{1}{2} \times 3 = 2 + 1.5 = 3.5''$
2. For the triangle B,
   a) $A_b = \tfrac{1}{2}\, bh = \tfrac{1}{2} \times 5 \times 2 = 5$ sq. in.
   b) $\bar{x}_b = \tfrac{1}{3} \times 5 = 1.67''$
   c) $\bar{y}_b = 2 - \tfrac{1}{3} \times 2 = 2 - 0.67 = 1.33''$
3. For the entire area,
   a) The total area is
   $$A = A_a + A_b = 15 + 5 = 20 \text{ sq. in.}$$

b) The moment with respect to the y axis is

$$M_y = A_a\bar{x}_a + A_b\bar{x}_b = 15 \times 2.5 + 5 \times 1.67 = 37.5 + 8.35 = 45.85 \text{ in.}^3$$

c) The moment with respect to the x axis is

$$M_x = A_a\bar{y}_a + A_b\bar{y}_b = 15 \times 3.5 + 5 \times 1.33 = 52.5 + 6.65 = 59.15 \text{ in.}^3$$

d) $\bar{x} = \dfrac{M_y}{A} = \dfrac{45.85}{20} = 2.29''$

e) $\bar{y} = \dfrac{M_x}{A} = \dfrac{59.15}{20} = 2.96''$

Fig. 10C shows the location of the centroid of the composite area.

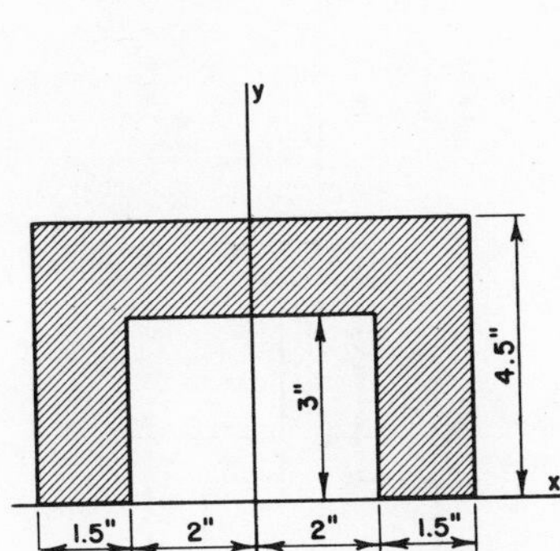

Fig. 11. Area for Problem 1 (Art. 6-2)

Fig. 12. Area for Problem 2 (Art. 6-2)

Practice Problems (Art. 6-2). Locate the centroid of the area in each of the following figures.
1. Fig. 11.
2. Fig. 12.
3. Fig. 13.
4. Fig. 14.

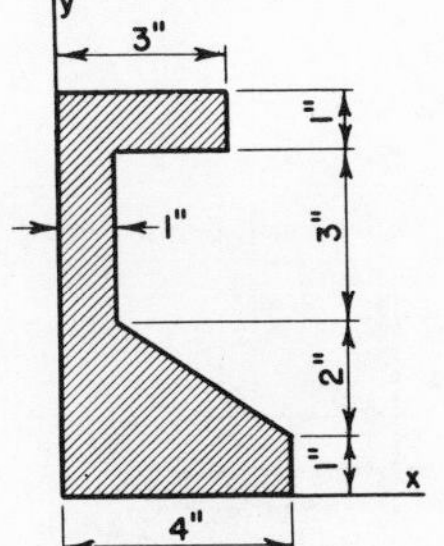

Fig. 13. Area for Problem 3 (Art. 6-3)

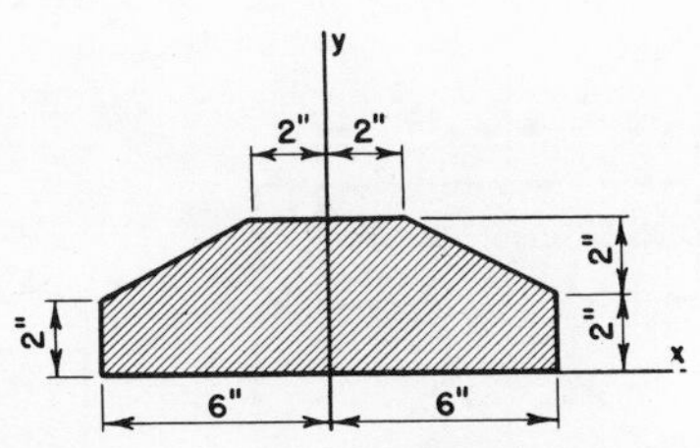

Fig. 14. Area for Problem 4 (Art. 6-2)

6-3. Review of Moment of Inertia of Area.

We will review moment of inertia briefly, because you will soon be using it. You should remember that the moment of inertia of a rectangular area with respect to an axis which is through the centroid and parallel to one side is equal to one-twelfth of the dimension parallel to the axis times the cube of the dimension perpendicular to the axis. Fig. 15 shows a rectangle of width b and altitude h. You should remember that

$$I_x = \tfrac{1}{12}bh^3$$

and

$$I_y = \tfrac{1}{12}hb^3$$

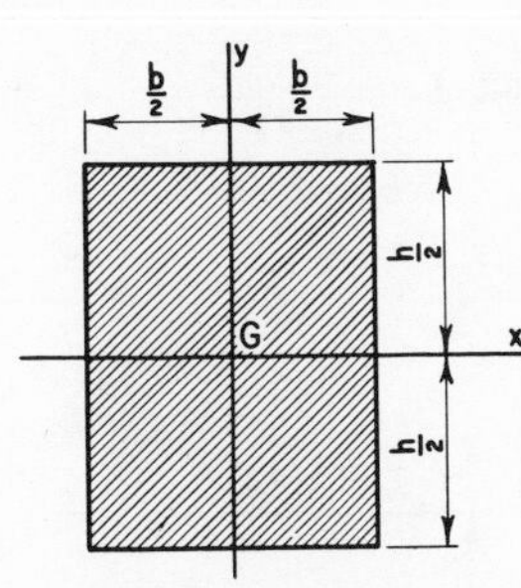

Fig. 15. Rectangular Area Showing Location of Centroid

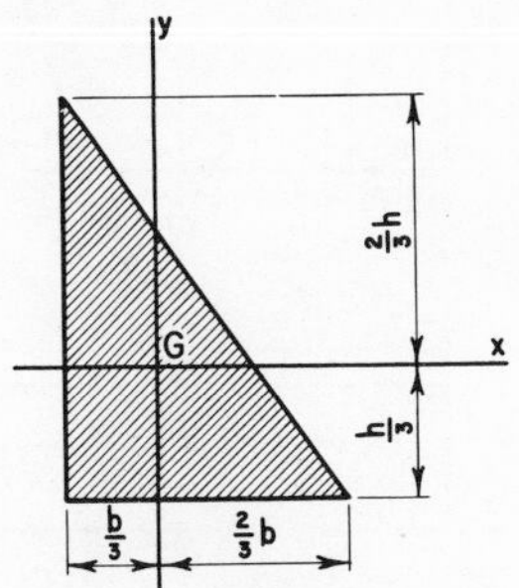

Fig. 16. Right Triangular Area Showing Location of Centroid

Fig. 16 shows a right triangle of width b and altitude h. Notice that both the x and y axes pass through the centroid of the area. Now, as you may remember from Chapter IV, the moment of inertia of the area of a right triangle, with respect to an axis which is through the centroid and parallel to a leg of the triangle, is equal to $\frac{1}{36}$ times the dimension parallel to the axis times the cube of the dimension perpendicular to the axis. So, for the triangle in Fig. 16

$$I_x = \tfrac{1}{36}bh^3$$

and

$$I_y = \tfrac{1}{36}hb^3.$$

Apply the parallel-axis theorem for the circular area in Fig. 17. Here, the diameter of the circle is d, and the x_g axis is through the centroid. The x axis is parallel to the x_g axis and the distance between the axes is c. The parallel-axis theorem is

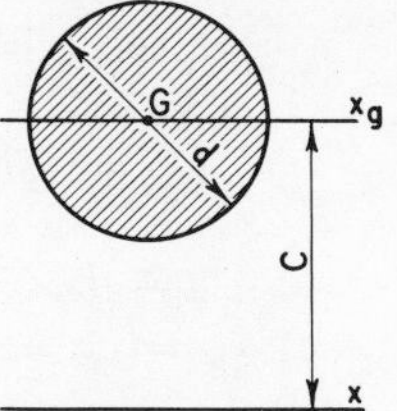

Fig. 17. Circular Area Showing Location of Centroid

$$I_x = I_{xg} + Ac^2$$

We can use this formula to calculate I_x when we know I_{xg}. In case you have forgotten,

$$I_{xg} = \frac{\pi}{64} d^4$$

We calculated the moment of inertia of composite areas in Chapter IV by dividing a composite area

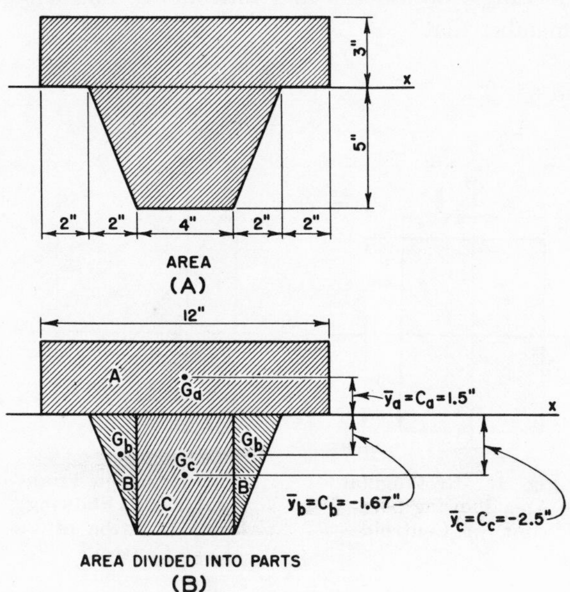

Fig. 18. Composite Area Divided into Parts

into simple parts (such as *rectangles* and *triangles*), and calculating the moment of inertia of each part by using the parallel-axis theorem. Then we added the moments of inertia of the parts of the area to get the moment of inertia of the whole area. An example will help you to remember.

Illustrative Example 1. Calculate I_x for the area in Fig. 18*A*.

Solution:

Fig. 18*B* shows the area divided into the rectangle *A*, the two triangles *B*, and the rectangle *C*.

1. For the rectangle *A*,
   a) The moment of inertia with respect to a horizontal axis through the centroid is

$$I_{ag} = \tfrac{1}{12}bh^3 = \tfrac{1}{12} \times 12\,(3)^3 = 27 \text{ in.}^4$$

   b) $A_a = bh = 12 \times 3 = 36$ sq. in.
   c) $\bar{y}_a = c_a = \frac{1}{2} \times 3 = 1.5''$
   d) $I_{ax} = I_{ag} + A_a c_a^2 = 27 + 36\,(1.5)^2 = 27 + 81 = 108 \text{ in.}^4$
2. For one of the triangles *B*,
   a) The moment of inertia with respect to a horizontal axis through the centroid is

$$I_{bg} = \tfrac{1}{36}bh^3 = \tfrac{1}{36} \times 2(5)^3 = 6.95 \text{ in.}^4$$

   b) $A_b = \frac{1}{2}bh = \frac{1}{2} \times 2 \times 5 = 5$ sq. in.
   c) $\bar{y}_b = c_b = -\frac{1}{3} \times 5 = -1.67''$
   d) $I_{bx} = I_{bg} + A_b c_b^2 = 6.95 + 5\,(-1.67)^2 = 6.95 + 13.90 = 20.85 \text{ in.}^4$
3. For the rectangle *C*,
   a) The moment of inertia with respect to a horizontal axis through the centroid is

$$Ic_g = \tfrac{1}{12}bh^3 = \tfrac{1}{12} \times 4\,(5)^3 = 41.7 \text{ in.}^4$$

   b) $A_c = bh = 4 \times 5 = 20$ sq. in.
   c) $\bar{y}_c = c_c = -\frac{1}{2} \times 5 = -2.5''$
   d) $I_{cx} = I_{cg} + A_c c_c^2 = 41.7 + 20\,(-2.5)^2 = 41.7 + 125 = 166.7 \text{ in.}^4$
4. For the entire area (remember that there are two triangles *B*),

$$I_x = I_{ax} + 2I_{bx} + I_{cx} = 108 + 2 \times 20.85 + 166.7 = 108 + 41.7 + 166.7 = 316.4 \text{ in.}^4$$

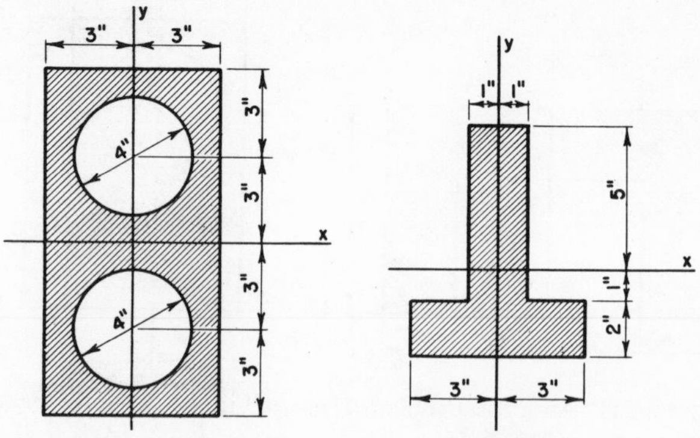

Fig. 19. Area for Problem 1 (Art. 6-3)

Fig. 20. Area for Problem 2 (Art. 6-3)

Practice Problems (Art. 6-3). You can carry on your own review by calculating I_x and I_y for the area in each of the following figures.

1. Fig. 19.
2. Fig. 20.
3. Fig. 21.
4. Fig. 22.

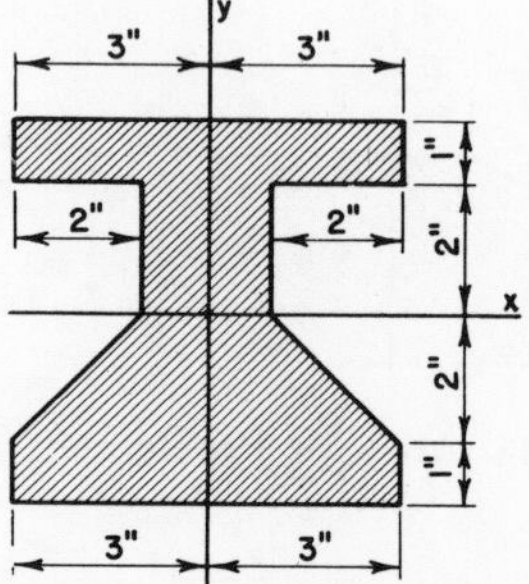

Fig. 21. Area for Problem 3 (Art. 6-3)

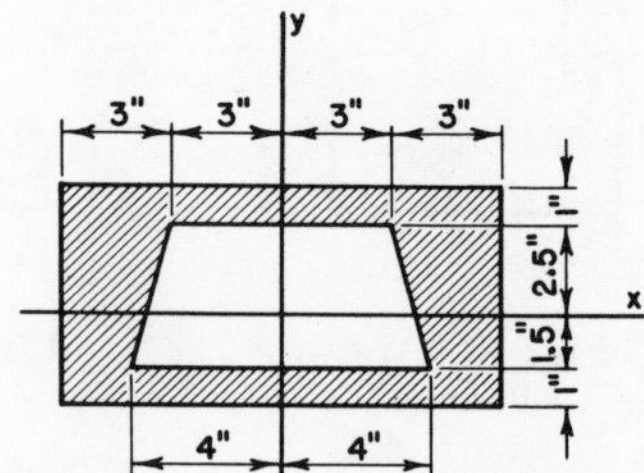

Fig. 22. Area for Problem 4 (Art. 6-3)

6-4. Shear in Beams.

First, you should learn what the shearing force in a beam is, and how to calculate it. Then, later, you will learn how to calculate the stress due to this force.

Fig. 23*A* shows a beam with a load of 2,800 lbs. and the reactions R_1 and R_2. The beam is in equilibrium; the reactions balance the load and hold the beam in place. Now imagine that the beam was cut on section *AA*. Fig. 23*B* shows the part of the beam to the right of section *AA*. Here the force *V* is a shearing force and is exerted by the left part of the beam. (There must be a force there to hold up the right-hand part of the beam.) Fig. 23*C* shows what might happen to the beam if it is not strong enough to withstand the shearing force.

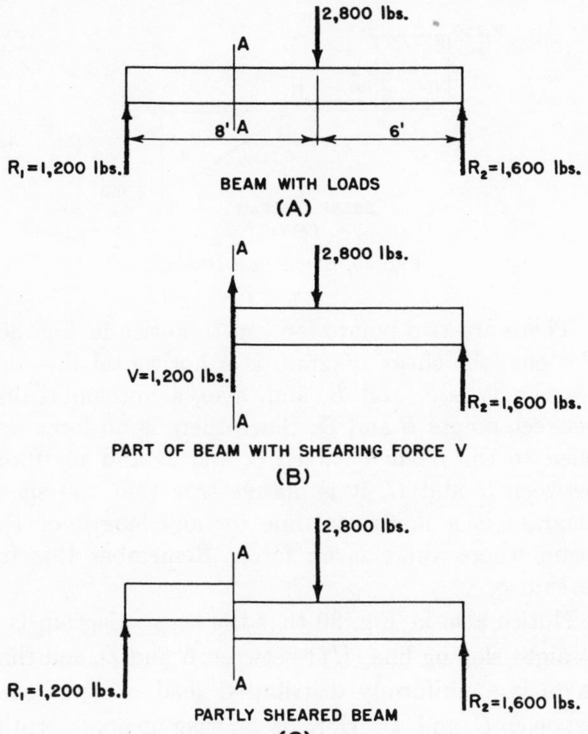

Fig. 23. Shearing Force in a Beam

You may have noticed in Fig. 23 that the force *V* is equal to the force R_1; also, that the force *V* is equal to the sum of all of the forces to the left of section *AA*. Now it isn't always true that the shearing force is equal to the reaction, but *it is always true that the shearing force at any cross section is equal to the sum of the forces to the left of the cross section.* All you have to do, to calculate the shearing force at a point in a beam, is to take the sum of the forces to the left of the point. Take *upward forces as positive* and *downward forces as negative.* A positive result for the shearing force *V* indicates that the shearing force is upward. A negative result indicates that the shearing force is downward.

Illustrative Example 1. Fig. 24 shows the free-body diagram of a beam with two concentrated loads. Calculate the shearing forces at points *A*, *B*, and C.

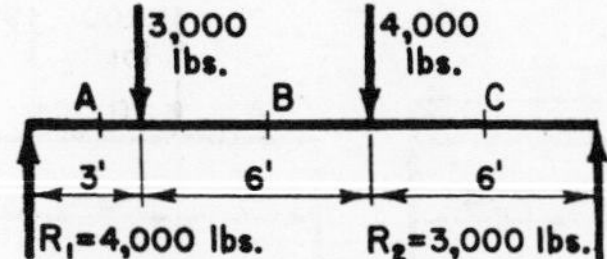

Fig. 24. Free-Body Diagram for Example 1 (Art. 6-4)

Solution:

Remember that the shearing force is equal to the sum of the forces to the left of the point.

1. At point *A*, there is only the reaction R_1 to the left, so

$$V_a = 4{,}000 \text{ lbs.}$$

2. At point *B*, there are two forces to the left,

$$V_b = 4{,}000 - 3{,}000 = 1{,}000 \text{ lbs.}$$

3. There are three forces to the left of point *C*,

$$V_c = 4{,}000 - 3{,}000 - 4{,}000 = -3{,}000 \text{ lbs.}$$

When you calculate the shear at a point on a beam with a uniformly distributed load, you take the part of the distributed load to the left of the point.

Illustrative Example 2. Fig. 25 shows the free-body diagram of a beam with a uniformly distributed load and a concentrated load. Find the shearing forces at points *A*, *B*, and *C*.

Solution:

1. The only force to the left of point *A* is a two-foot length of the distributed load which is downward and so it is *negative.*

$$V_a = -400 \times 2 = -800 \text{ lbs.}$$

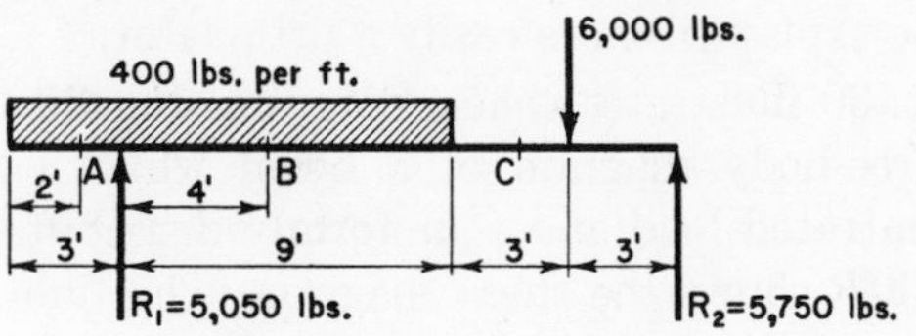

Fig. 25. Free-Body Diagram for Example 2 (Art. 6-4)

2. There are seven feet of the distributed load to the left of point *B*, and also, the reaction R_1. Then,

$$V_b = -400 \times 7 + 5{,}050$$
$$= -2{,}800 + 5{,}050 = 2{,}250 \text{ lbs.}$$

3. All of the distributed load is to the left of point C.

$$V_c = -400 \times 12 + 5{,}050$$
$$= -4{,}800 + 5{,}050 = 250 \text{ lbs.}$$

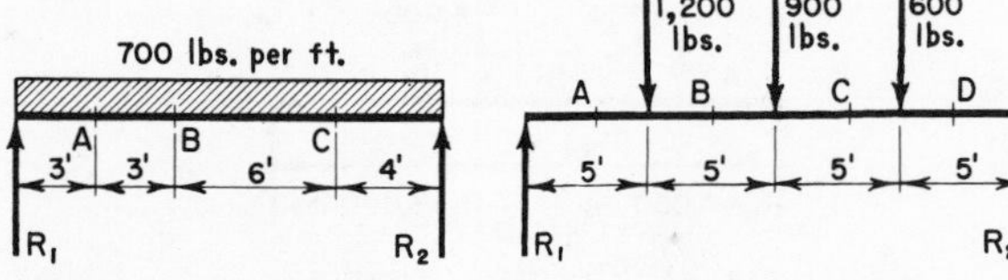

Fig. 26. Free-Body Diagram for Problem 1 (Art. 6-4)

Fig. 27. Free-Body Diagram for Problem 2 (Art. 6-4)

Practice Problems (Art. 6-4). Calculate the shearing force in the beams of the following problems. The reactions will have to be calculated first. The free-body diagrams will be given for each problem.

1. Calculate the shearing forces at points A, B, and C in Fig. 26.
2. Find the shearing forces at points A, B, C, and D in Fig. 27.
3. What are the shearing forces at points A, B, and C in Fig. 28?
4. Determine the shearing forces at points A, B, and C in Fig. 29.

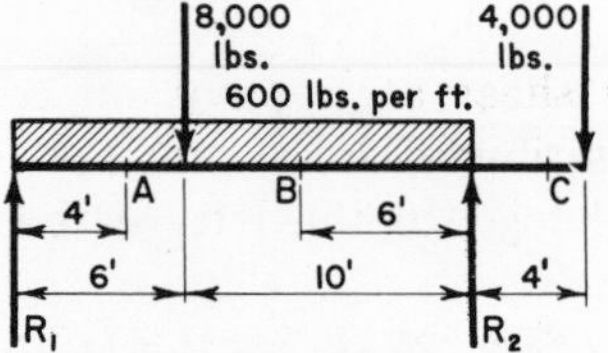

Fig. 28. Free-Body Diagram for Problem 3 (Art. 6-4)

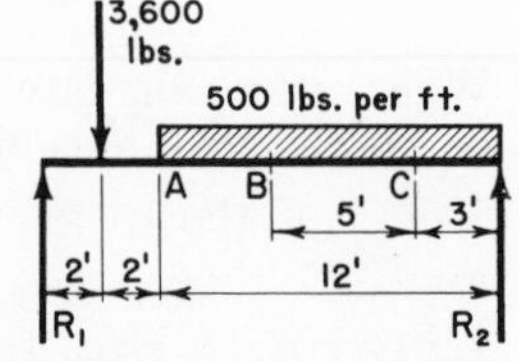

Fig. 29. Free-Body Diagram for Problem 4 (Art. 6-4)

6-5. Shear Diagrams.

A *shear diagram* is a diagram which shows the value of the shearing force at each point along a beam. A shear diagram is useful because you can look at it and see how the shear varies and where the shear is maximum. There are other uses, too, but they can be explained more easily a little later.

Fig. 30 illustrates a shear diagram. Fig. 30*A* shows the free-body diagram of a beam which carries a concentrated load and a uniformly distributed load. Fig. 30*B* shows the shear diagram. The line *ABCD* in Fig. 30*B* is a base line and values of the shearing force are measured from this line (*positive* upward and *negative* downward), using any convenient scale. It is a good idea to draw the shear diagram directly below the free-body diagram, so you can see which point in the shear diagram corresponds to a particular point in the free-body diagram.

You can see in Fig. 30*B* that the shearing force for any point between A and B is 2,250 pounds, and the shearing force for any point between B and C is 250 pounds. Also, you can see that the shearing force at D is $-2{,}750$ pounds. (A *negative sign* means that the shearing force exerted by the left part of the beam on the right part is downward.)

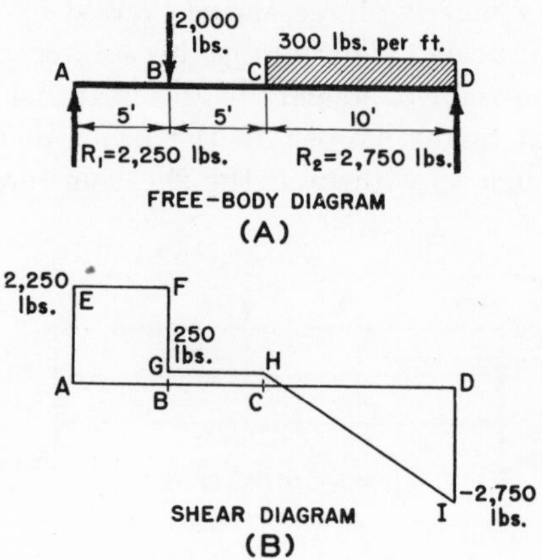

Fig. 30. Shear in a Beam

There are two points for you to notice in Fig. 30. For one, the shear diagram is a horizontal line between points A and B, and, also, a horizontal line between points B and C. Since there is no force applied to the beam between A and B and no force between B and C, it is *always* true that the shear diagram is a horizontal line for any length of the beam where there is no force. Remember this for later use.

Notice also in Fig. 30 that the shear diagram is a straight sloping line (HI) between C and D, and that there is a uniformly distributed load on the beam between C and D. Here is another general truth. The shear diagram is a straight sloping line for any length of the beam where there is only a uniformly distributed load. The sloping line changes at any point where a concentrated force is applied. (This will be covered in an example.)

The easiest way to draw a shear diagram is to start by drawing a base line such as *ABCD* in Fig. 30*B*. Then, move across the beam from left to right, plotting the forces as they occur. Plot a concentrated force vertically, upward or downward, just as it acts. *Plot a uniformly distributed load as a sloping line* and draw a horizontal line for any part of the beam where no force is applied. This procedure results in a diagram which shows the value of the shearing force at each point along the beam.

Illustrative Example 1. Fig. 31A shows the free-body diagram of a beam which carries a concentrated load and a uniformly distributed load. Draw the shear diagram.

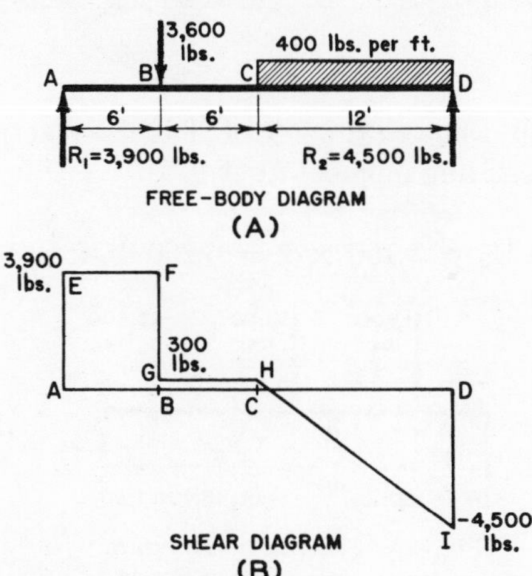

Fig. 31. How to Draw a Shear Diagram

Solution:

Fig. 31B shows the completed diagram. The following procedure is used.

1. Draw the base line $ABCD$
2. Starting at A, plot the reaction R_1 upward to locate point E. The shear at E is 3,900 lbs.
3. From E, draw a horizontal line to F
4. From F, plot the 3,600-lb. load downward to G. The shear at G is

$$3{,}900 - 3{,}600 = 300 \text{ lbs.}$$

5. From G, draw a horizontal line to H, where the uniformly distributed load starts
6. From H, draw the sloping line HI for the uniformly distributed load. The distributed load is 400 lbs. per ft. for a length of 12 ft., a total load of $400 \times 12 = 4{,}800$ lbs. The shear at I is

$$300 - 400 \times 12 = 300 - 4{,}800 = -4{,}500 \text{ lbs}$$

7. Plot the reaction R_2 upward from I to D to finish the shear diagram.

The shear diagram for a concentrated load or reaction in the middle of a uniformly distributed load is given in the following example.

Illustrative Example 2. Fig. 32A shows the free-body diagram of a beam with a concentrated load and a uniformly distributed load. Draw the shear diagram.

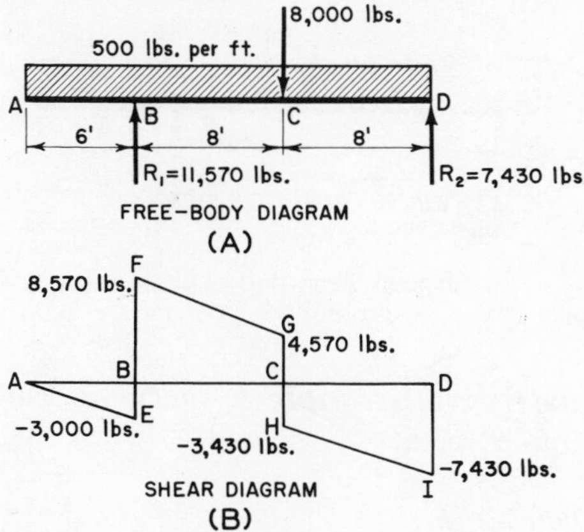

Fig. 32. Construction of Shear Diagram

Solution:

Fig. 32B shows the shear diagram, drawn as follows:

1. Draw the base line $ABCD$
2. Starting at A, draw the sloping line AE for the uniformly distributed load. The shear at E is

$$-500 \times 6 = -3{,}000 \text{ lbs.}$$

3. From E, plot the reaction R_1 upward to F. The shear at F is

$$-3{,}000 + 11{,}570 = 8{,}570 \text{ lbs.}$$

4. From F, draw the sloping line FG. The shear at G is

$$8{,}570 - 500 \times 8 = 8{,}570 - 4{,}000 = 4{,}570 \text{ lbs.}$$

5. From G, plot the 8,000-lb. load downward to H. The shear at H is

$$4{,}570 - 8{,}000 = -3{,}430 \text{ lbs.}$$

6. From H, draw the sloping line HI. The shear at I is

$$-3{,}430 - 500 \times 8 = -3{,}430 - 4{,}000 = 7{,}430 \text{ lbs.}$$

7. Plot the reaction R_2 upward from I to finish the shear diagram at D.

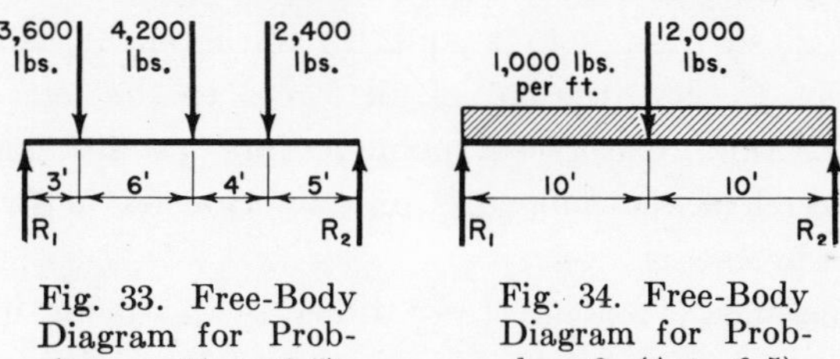

Fig. 33. Free-Body Diagram for Problem 1 (Art. 6-5)

Fig. 34. Free-Body Diagram for Problem 2 (Art. 6-5)

Practice Problems (Art. 6-5). Several free-body diagrams will be given in the following problems. Draw the shear diagram for each problem.

1. Fig. 33. 2. Fig. 34. 3. Fig. 35. 4. Fig. 36.

6-6. Bending Moment in Beams.

The best way to learn a subject is to learn one part at a time. The next important part is bending mo-

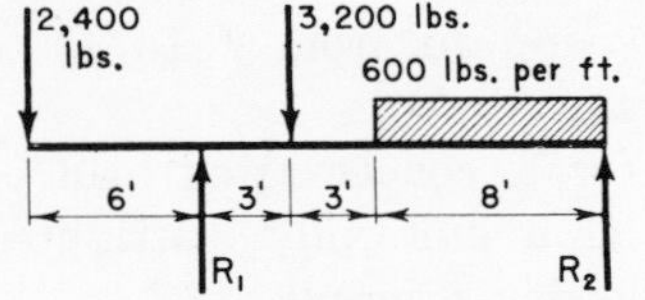

Fig. 35. Free-Body Diagram for Problem 3 (Art. 6-5)

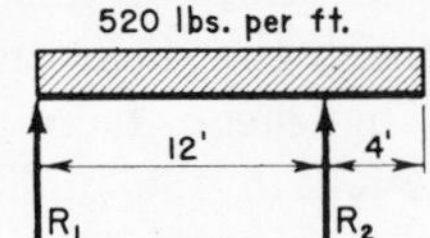

Fig. 36. Free-Body Diagram for Problem 4 (Art. 6-5)

ment, because the most important stress in a beam is due to bending moment. (Stress will be discussed later.) Fig. 37*A* shows a beam with the loads and reactions given and Fig. 37*B* shows how the beam bends under the loads. (The amount of the bending is exaggerated here. Beams do not bend that much if they are properly designed.) The beam bends be-

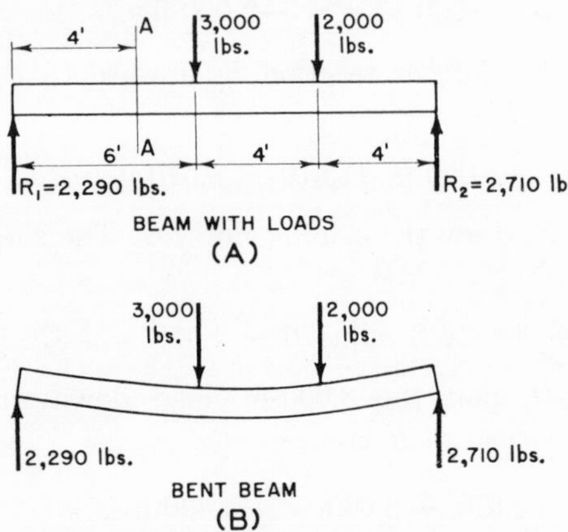

Fig. 37. Bending of Beam under Loads

cause of the moment of the forces which are applied to the beam. There is a bending moment at each section of the beam, for instance section *AA* in Fig. 37*A*, and the amount the beam bends depends upon the bending moment. The bending moment at any section, such as *AA*, is equal to the moment, with respect to that section, of all forces to the left of the section. Clockwise moments are *positive* and counterclockwise moments are *negative*, as in previous problems.

You should not have any difficulty in calculating bending moment if you have studied the first part of this book. For the bending moment at any point, you add the moments of all of the forces to the left of that point, taking that point as the moment center. Each time you calculate moment, a force in pounds will be multiplied by a distance in feet. The result will be expressed in pound feet (lb. ft. or # ft.).

Illustrative Example 1. Calculate the bending moments at points *A*, *B*, and *C* in Fig. 38.

Solution:

1. The only force to the left of *A* is the reaction R_1, so the bending moment at *A* is

$$M_a = 3{,}100 \times 2 = 6{,}200 \text{ lb. ft.}$$

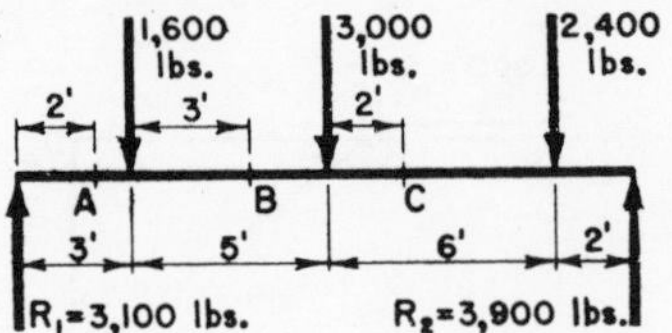

Fig. 38. Free-Body Diagram of Beam under Three Loads

2. Point *B* is 6 ft. from the left end of the beam and there are two forces to the left of *B*. Then,

$$\begin{aligned} M_b &= 3{,}100 \times 6 - 1{,}600 \times 3 \\ &= 18{,}600 - 4{,}800 = 13{,}800 \text{ lb. ft.} \end{aligned}$$

3. Point *C* is 10 ft. from the left end of the beam. There are three forces to the left of *C*.

$$\begin{aligned} M_c &= 3{,}100 \times 10 - 1{,}600 \times 7 - 3{,}000 \times 2 \\ &= 31{,}000 - 11{,}200 - 6{,}000 = 13{,}800 \text{ lb. ft} \end{aligned}$$

A beam with a uniform load will be given in the following problems. Remember to take all of the forces to the left of the point when you calculate the bending moment. If only part of the uniform load is to the left of the point, then take only that part when you calculate the bending moment.

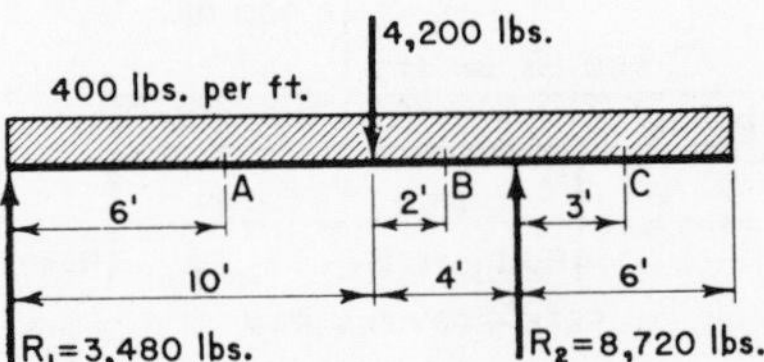

Fig. 39. Free-Body Diagram for Example 2 (Art. 6-6)

Illustrative Example 2. Calculate the bending moments at points *A*, *B*, and *C* in Fig. 39.

Solution:

1. The reaction R_1 is to the left of *A*, and so is a

6-foot length of the uniform load. The total amount of the uniform load in the 6-ft. length is 400 × 6 = 2,400 lbs., and the *moment arm* is the distance from A to the center of the 6-ft. length; that is, 3 ft. Then,

$$M_a = 3{,}480 \times 6 - 400 \times 6 \times 3$$
$$= 20{,}900 - 7{,}200 = 13{,}700 \text{ lb. ft.}$$

2. Point B is 12 ft. from the left end of the beam. To the left of point B there are the reaction R_1, the concentrated load of 4,200 lbs. and a 12-ft. length of the uniform load.

$$M_b = 3{,}480 \times 12 - 4{,}200 \times 2 - 400 \times 12 \times 6$$
$$= 41{,}800 - 8{,}400 - 28{,}800 = 4{,}600 \text{ lb. ft.}$$

3. Point C is 17 ft. from the left end of the beam. Take all of the forces to the left of C. Do not forget R_2.

$$M_c = 3{,}480 \times 17 - 4{,}200 \times 7 + 8{,}720$$
$$\times 3 - 400 \times 17 \times 8.5 = 59{,}200$$
$$- 29{,}400 + 26{,}200 - 57{,}800$$
$$= - 1{,}800 \text{ lb. ft.}$$

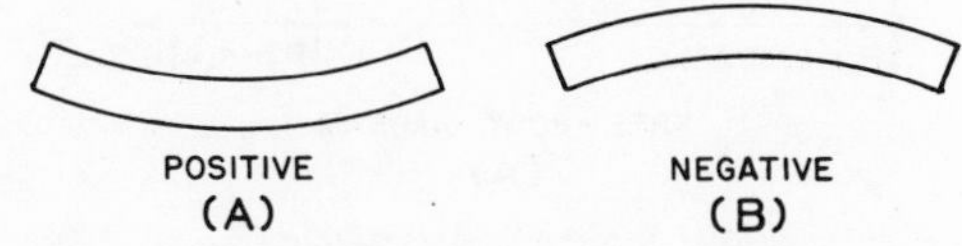

Fig. 40. Effects of Positive and Negative Bending Moments

We found a negative bending moment at point C in the last example. Fig. 40A shows how a beam bends when the bending moment is positive, and Fig. 40B shows how a beam bends when the bending moment is negative.

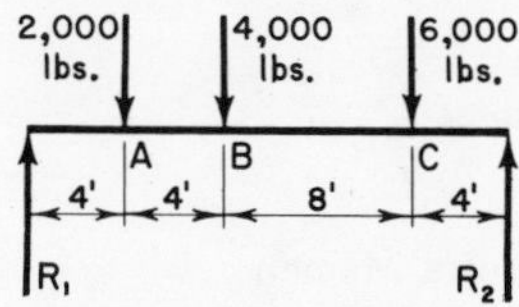

Fig. 41. Free-Body Diagram for Problem 1 (Art. 6-6)

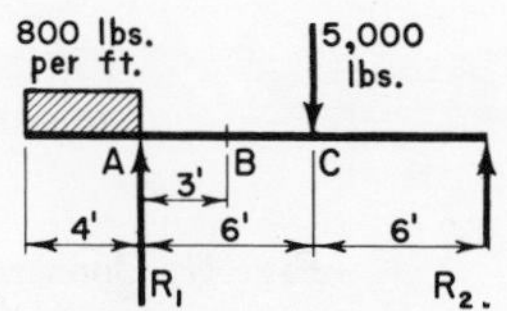

Fig. 42. Free-Body Diagram for Problem 2 (Art. 6-6)

Practice Problems (Art. 6-6). Find the bending moments at points A, B, and C in each of the following figures.

1. Fig. 41. 2. Fig. 42. 3. Fig. 43. 4. Fig. 44.

6-7. Moment Diagrams.

A *moment diagram* is a diagram which shows the value of the bending moment at each point along the beam. You can see a sample in Fig. 45. Fig. 45A shows the free-body diagram of a beam, and Fig. 45B shows the moment diagram, which is con-

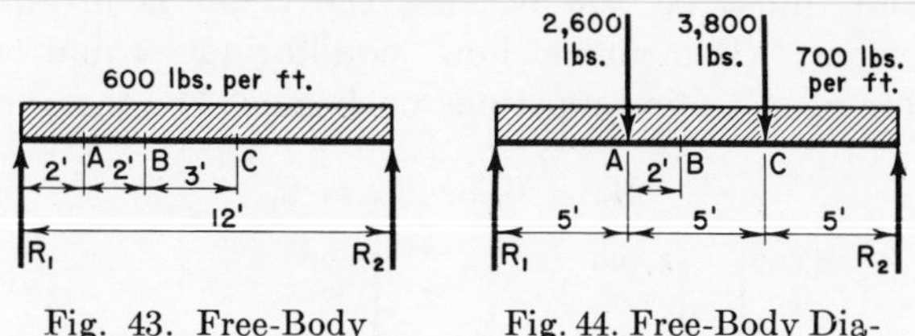

Fig. 43. Free-Body Diagram for Problem 3 (Art. 6-6)

Fig. 44. Free-Body Diagram for Problem 4 (Art. 6-6)

structed in the following manner: (1) draw a base line like $ABCD$ in Fig. 45B; (2) calculate the bending moments at several points along the beam; (3) plot the values calculated for bending moments; and (4) draw lines through the plotted points.

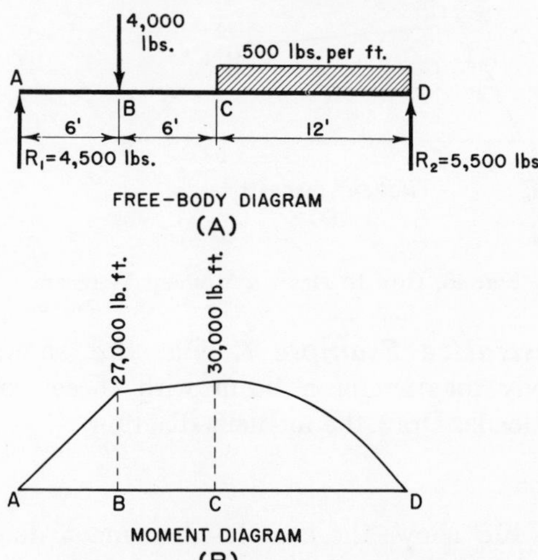

Fig. 45. Sample Moment Diagram

In Fig. 45B, notice that the moment diagram is a straight line between points A and B, and, also, a straight line between B and C. Notice, too, that there is no load on the beam between A and B, and no load between B and C. Now it is always true that the moment diagram is a straight line for any part of a beam where there is no load. You can use this fact to save time. In Fig. 45, for example, you could plot the bending moments at B and C, then you could draw straight lines fr m A to the plotted point at B and from there t the plotted point at C. You would not have to calculate any bending moments between A and B, nor between B and C.

Remember that the bending moment at any point is equal to the moment of all of the forces to the left of that point. There are no forces to the left of the left end of the beam, so the bending moment at the left end must be *zero*. All of the forces on the beam are to the left of the right end of the beam. The moment of all of the forces, with respect to any point, must be *zero* because the beam is in equilibrium. (Remember how equilibrium equations were used to find reactions on beams. For instance,

$$M_a = 0, \text{ or } M_d = 0.$$

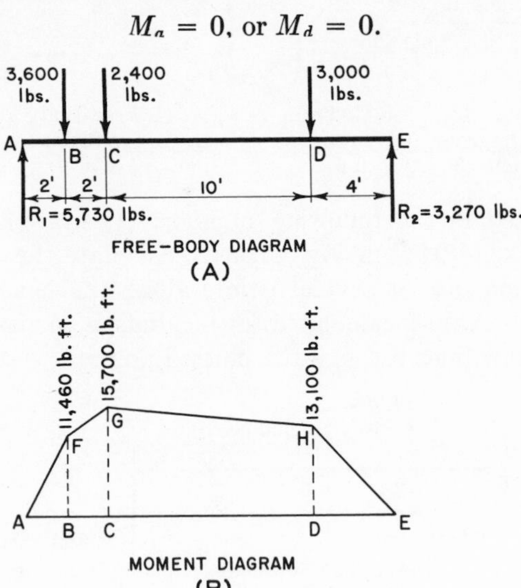

Fig. 46. How to Draw a Moment Diagram

Illustrative Example 1. Fig. 46*A* shows the free-body diagram of a beam with three concentrated loads. Draw the moment diagram.

Solution:

Fig. 46*B* shows the completed moment diagram. Proceed as follows:

1. Draw the base line *ABCDE*
2. The bending moment at *A* is *zero* because there are no forces to the left of *A*
3. The bending moment at *B* is

$$M_b = 5{,}730 \times 2 = 11{,}460 \text{ lb. ft.}$$

Plot this upward from *B* to locate point *F* and draw the straight line *AF*

4. The bending moment at *C* is

$$M_c = 5{,}730 \times 4 - 3{,}600 \times 2$$
$$= 22{,}900 - 7{,}200 = 15{,}700 \text{ lb. ft.}$$

Plot 15,700 lb. ft. upward from *C* to locate point *G* in the moment diagram. Draw the straight line *FG*.

5. The bending moment at *D* is

$$M_d = 5{,}730 \times 14 - 3{,}600 \times 12 - 2{,}400 \times 10$$
$$= 80{,}300 - 43{,}200 - 24{,}000 = 13{,}100 \text{ lb. ft.}$$

Plot 13,100 lb. ft. upward from *D* to locate point *H*. Draw the straight line *GH*.

6. The bending moment at *E* is zero because *E* is at the right end of the beam. Draw the straight line *HE* to finish the moment diagram.

The moment diagram is a straight line for any part of the beam where there are no forces, but the moment diagram is a parabola for any part of a beam where there is a uniformly distributed load. The best way to get the moment diagram in such a case is to calculate the bending moment at several points, plot these moments and then draw a smooth curve through the points. A good rule here is to calculate the bending moments at intervals of 1 foot if the uniform load extends over 10 feet or less; and to calculate the bending moments at intervals of 2 feet if the uniform load extends over more than 10 feet.

Illustrative Example 2. Fig. 47*A* shows the free-body diagram of a beam. Draw the moment diagram.

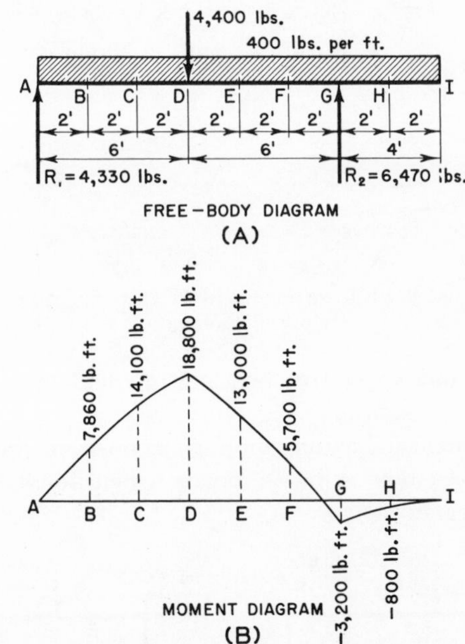

Fig. 47. Construction of a Momen Diagram

Solution:

Fig. 47*B* shows the completed moment diagram. Complete in the following manner.

1. Divide the beam into 2-ft. lengths as in Fig. 47*A* and draw the base line *ABCDEFGHI* in Fig. 47*B*.
2. The bending moment at *A* is *zero* (Why?)
3. The bending moment at *B* is

$$M_b = 4{,}330 \times 2 - 400 \times 2 \times 1$$
$$= 8{,}660 - 800 = 7{,}860 \text{ lb.ft}$$

Plot this value of 7,860 lb. ft. upward from B.

4. The bending moment at C is

$$M_c = 4{,}330 \times 4 - 400 \times 4 \times 2$$
$$= 17{,}300 - 3{,}200 = 14{,}100 \text{ lb. ft.}$$

Plot 14,100 lb. ft. upward from C.

5. The bending moment at D is

$$M_d = 4{,}330 \times 6 - 400 \times 6 \times 3$$
$$= 26{,}000 - 7{,}200 = 18{,}800 \text{ lb. ft.}$$

Plot 18,800 lb. ft. upward from D.

6. The bending moment at E is

$$M_e = 4{,}330 \times 8 - 400 \times 8 \times 4 - 4{,}400 \times 2$$
$$= 34{,}600 - 12{,}800 - 8{,}800 = 13{,}000 \text{ lb. ft.}$$

Plot 13,000 lb. ft. upward from E.

7. The bending moment at F is

$$M_f = 4{,}330 \times 10 - 400 \times 10 \times 5 - 4{,}400 \times 4$$
$$= 43{,}300 - 20{,}000 - 17{,}600 = 5{,}700 \text{ lb. ft.}$$

Plot 5,700 lb. ft. upward from F.

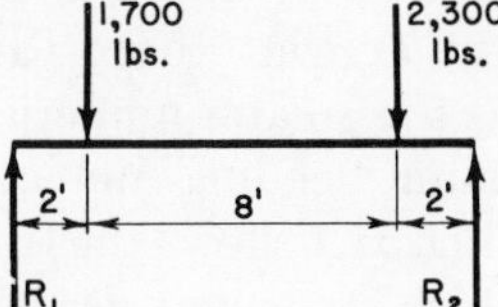

Fig. 48. Free-Body Diagram for Problem 1 (Art. 6-7)

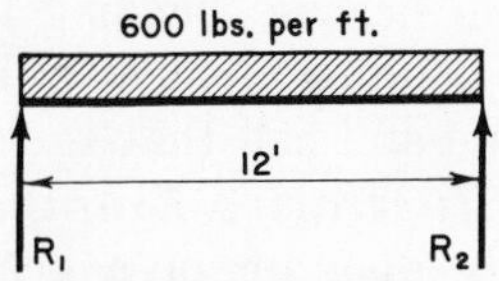

600 lbs. per ft.
12'
R1
R2

Fig. 49. Free-Body Diagram for Problem 2 (Art. 6-7)

8. The bending moment at G is

$$M_g = 4{,}330 \times 12 - 400 \times 12 \times 6 - 4{,}400 \times 6$$
$$= 52{,}000 - 28{,}800 - 26{,}400 = -3{,}200 \text{ lb. ft.}$$

Notice the minus sign and plot 3,200 lb. ft. *downward* from G.

9. The bending moment at H is

$$M_h = 4{,}300 \times 14 - 400 \times 14 \times 7 - 4{,}400 \times 8 + 6{,}470 \times 2$$
$$= 60{,}600 - 39{,}200 - 35{,}200 + 13{,}000$$
$$= -800 \text{ lb. ft.}$$

Plot 800 lb. ft. *downward* from H.

10. The bending moment at I is *zero* (Why?)

11. Connect the plotted points

Notice the *cusp* or sharp point at G.

The cusp in Fig. 47B is typical in beams which extend over a support. The bending moment is usually negative at such a point and there is a cusp in the moment diagram.

Practice Problems (Art. 6-7). Start with the free-body diagram in each of the following figures and draw the moment diagram.

1. Fig. 48. 2. Fig. 49. 3. Fig. 50. 4. Fig. 51.

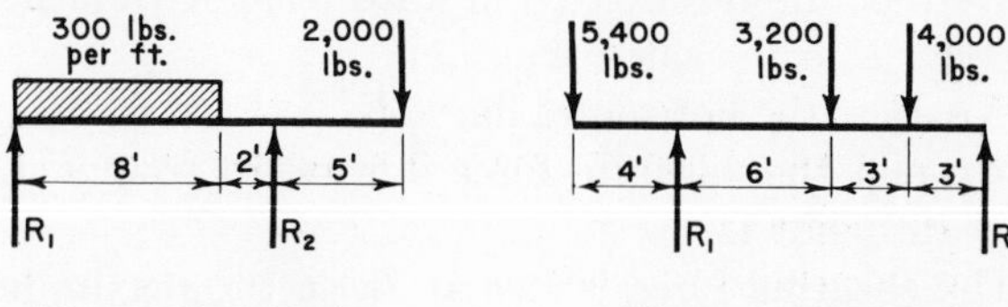

Fig. 50. Free-Body Diagram for Problem 3 (Art. 6-7)

Fig. 51. Free-Body Diagram for Problem 4 (Art. 6-7)

6-8. Maximum Bending Moment.

A moment diagram is useful to have because you can see how the bending moment varies across the beam; you can see, also, where the maximum bending moment occurs and how much it is. However, there are many occasions when you want to find the maximum bending moment without going to the trouble of drawing a moment diagram. Here is a simple rule that will help:

Rule. *The bending moment is maximum where the shearing force is zero.* If you locate the point in the beam where the shearing force is *zero* and calculate the bending moment at that point, you know that you have the maximum bending moment.

You do not have to draw the whole shear diagram to find the point where the shearing force is *zero.* You can start the shear diagram and continue with it until you find where the shearing force is *zero.* The maximum bending moment occurs at that point.

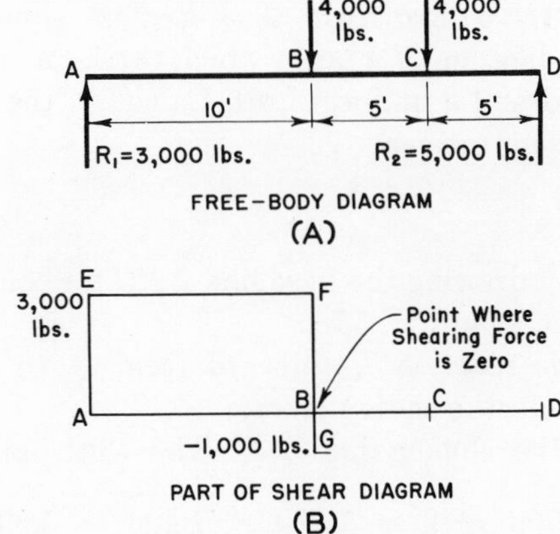

Fig. 52. Locating Point Where Shearing Force Is Zero

Illustrative Example 1. Fig. 52A shows a beam with two concentrated loads. Calculate the maximum bending moment.

Solution:

1. In Fig. 52*B*, draw the base line *ABCD* for the shear diagram.
2. We plot the reaction R_1 upward from *A* to locate point *E* in the shear diagram
3. We draw the horizontal line *EF*
4. We plot the 4,000-lb. force downward from *F* to locate point *G*
5. The shearing force is *zero* at *B*, so the maximum bending moment occurs at *B*. It is

$$Max.\ M = 3{,}000 \times 10 = 30{,}000 \text{ lb. ft.}$$

Sometimes the point of *zero* shearing force occurs in a stretch of uniform load. Then we have to solve an equation to locate the point.

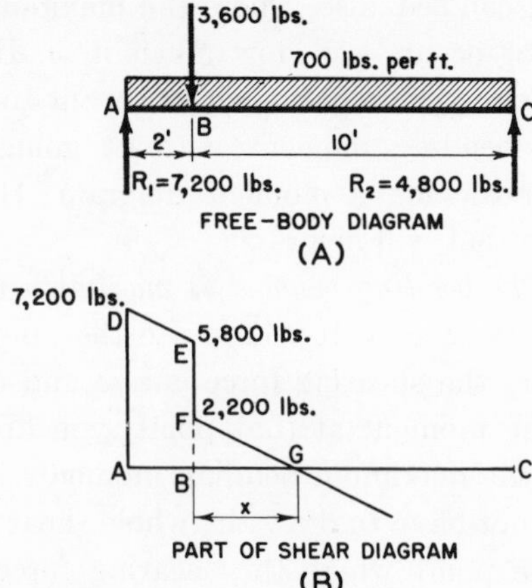

Fig. 53. Shear and Free-Body Diagrams of Beam Carrying a Concentrated Load and a Uniform Load

Illustrative Example 2. Fig. 53*A* shows the free-body diagram of a beam which carries a concentrated load and a uniform load. Calculate the maximum bending moment.

Solution:

1. Start by drawing the base line *ABC* for the shear diagram, as in Fig. 53*B*
2. Plot the reaction R_1 upward from *A* to locate point *D* in the shear diagram
3. Draw the sloping line *DE*. The shear at *E* is

$$7{,}200 - 700 \times 2 = 7{,}200 - 1{,}400 = 5{,}800 \text{ lbs.}$$

4. Plot the 3,600-lb. load downward from *E* to locate point *F*. The shear at *F* is

$$5{,}800 - 3{,}600 = 2{,}200 \text{ lbs.}$$

5. Draw the dotted line *FB*. You can locate *G* by writing an equation for the value of *G*. If the distance from *B* to *G* is x, then the shear at *G* is

$$2{,}200 - 700x = 0$$

Transposing the $700x$,

$$700x = 2{,}200$$

$$x = 3.14 \text{ ft.}$$

Point *G* is 3.14 ft. to the right of *B* and 5.14 ft. from the left end of the beam. Draw the sloping line *FG*.

6. The maximum bending moment occurs at point *G* because the shearing force is *zero* there. The maximum bending moment is

$$Max.\ M = 7{,}200 \times 5.14 - 700 \times 5.14 \times \frac{5.14}{2} - 3{,}600 \times 3.14$$
$$= 37{,}000 - 9{,}300 - 11{,}300 = 16{,}400 \text{ lb. ft.}$$

When a beam extends over a support, there is usually more than one point where the shearing force is *zero*. Then we must calculate the bending moment at each of these points. We find there is a maximum *positive* bending moment at one point and a maximum *negative* bending moment at the other. Take the bending moment which has the greater numerical value and call that the maximum bending moment.

Illustrative Example 3. Fig. 54*A* shows the free-body diagram of a beam which extends over the left support. Calculate the maximum bending moment.

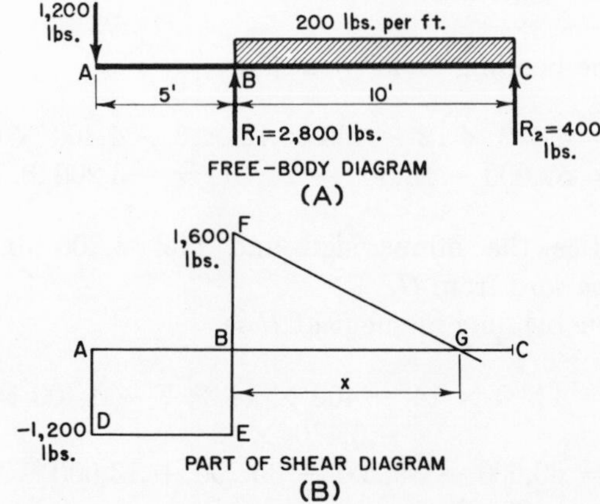

Fig. 54. Beam with Two Points Where Shearing Force Is Zero

Solution:

1. Start by drawing the base line *ABC* for the shear diagram as in Fig. 54*B*
2. Plot the 1,200-lb. load downward from *A* to locate point *D* in the shear diagram
3. Draw the horizontal line *DE*

4. Plot the reaction R_1 upward from E to locate point F. Notice that the shearing force is *zero* at B. The bending moment at B is

$$M_b = -1{,}200 \times 5 = -6{,}000 \text{ lb. ft.}$$

The shear at E is

$$-1{,}200 + 2{,}800 = 1{,}600 \text{ lbs.}$$

5. Continue with the shear diagram by drawing the sloping line FG. The shearing force is *zero* at G. To locate G,

$$V_g = 1{,}600 - 200x = 0$$

$$200x = 1{,}600$$

$$x = 8 \text{ ft.}$$

Point G is 8 ft. from B and is 13 ft. from the left end of the beam.

$$M_g = -1{,}200 \times 13 + 2{,}800 \times 8 - 200 \times 8 \times 4$$
$$= -15{,}600 + 22{,}400 - 6{,}400 = 400 \text{ lb. ft.}$$

6. The bending moment at B is $-6{,}000$ lb. ft.; and since this has a greater numerical value than the bending moment of 400 lb. ft. at G, the maximum bending moment is

$$Max.\ M = -6{,}000 \text{ lb. ft.}$$

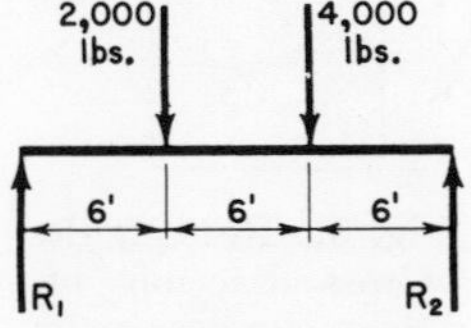

Fig. 55. Free-Body Diagram for Problem 1 (Art. 6-8)

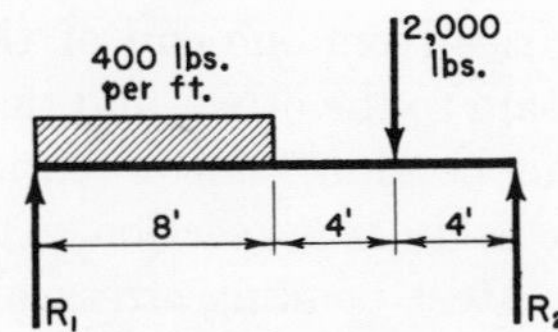

Fig. 56. Free-Body Diagram for Problem 2 (Art. 6-8)

Practice Problems (Art. 6-8). Calculate the maximum bending moment for the beam in each of the following figures.

1. Fig. 55. 2. Fig. 56. 3. Fig. 57. 4. Fig. 58.

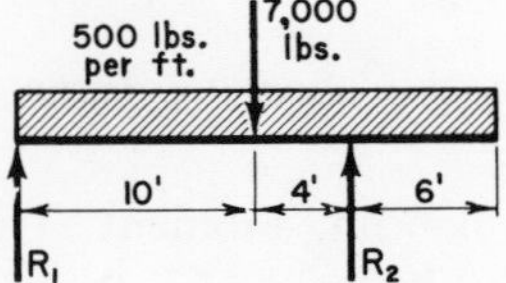

Fig. 57. Free-Body Diagram for Problem 3 (Art. 6-8)

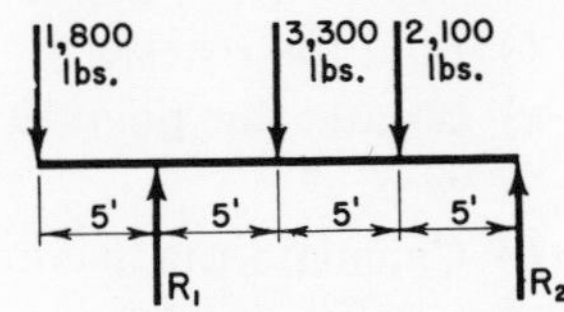

Fig. 58. Free-Body Diagram for Problem 4 (Art. 6-8)

6-9. Bending Stress.

The bending stress in a beam is due to bending moment, and is the usual basis for the design of a beam.

The deformation of a beam will be discussed briefly here. Fig. 59A shows a beam before the loads are applied and Fig. 59B shows the beam after the loads have been applied. Notice the deformation of the beam in Fig. 59B. There is the line AB which does not change length; above the line AB the material shortens, and below the line AB the material stretches. From our study of Chapter V we know that there must be *compressive stress* in the top part of the beam where the material shortens, and that there must be *tensile stress* in the lower part of the beam where the material stretches. There is no stress along the line AB, due to the bending moment, because the line AB does not change length.

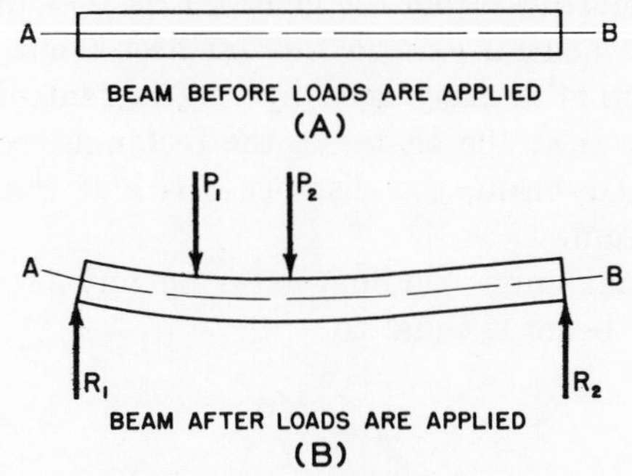

Fig. 59. Deformation of Beam under Loads

The next question is, "Where is the line AB?" The answer is, the line AB passes through the centroid of each cross section of the beam. Now look at Fig. 60A which shows the cross section of the beam and notice the centroid G. The horizontal line through the centroid is called the *neutral axis*. The bending stress is *zero* at the neutral axis and, at any other point in the cross section, the bending stress is proportional to the distance from the neutral axis. Fig. 60B shows how the stress varies over the cross section. Notice that the maximum compressive stress occurs at the top of the beam and the maximum tensile stress occurs at the bottom of the beam.

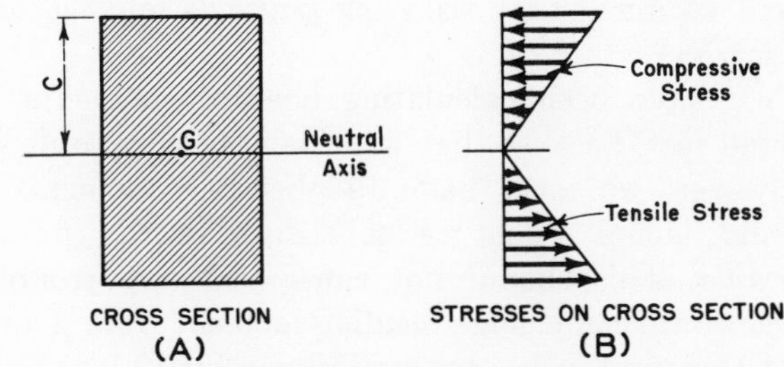

Fig. 60. Stresses in Beams

Now look again at Fig. 60*A* which shows the cross section of the beam. The neutral axis passes through the centroid of the cross section and the bending stress is proportional to the distance from the neutral axis. This means that the greatest bending stress occurs at the point in the cross section which is farthest from the neutral axis. The distance from the neutral axis to this farthest point in the cross section is designated by c. The centroid of a rectangle is at the center of the rectangle, so, for a rectangular beam, the distance c is half the depth of the beam.

The maximum bending stress on any cross section of a beam is equal to

$$S = \frac{Mc}{I}$$

where S is the *stress* in pounds per square inch; M is the *bending moment* in pound inches; c is the *distance* from the neutral axis to the farthest point in the cross section and is expressed in inches; and I is the *moment of inertia* of the area of the cross section with respect to the neutral axis; I is expressed in $in.^4$ This formula,

$$S = \frac{Mc}{I}$$

is called the *flexure formula*. It is probably used as much as any formula in engineering.

Remember that the neutral axis passes through the centroid of the cross section; also, that we have to use the moment of inertia of the cross section with respect to the neutral axis. Now you know why we spent so much time studying *centroids* and *moment of inertia*.

We have been calculating bending moments in pound feet, because that was the easy way to do it. However, we must have the bending moment in pound inches when we substitute in the *flexure formula*. This should not cause you any trouble, because we can change bending moment from pound feet to pound inches by multiplying by 12.

1 pound foot (lb. ft.) = 12 pound inches (lb. in.)

Illustrative Example 1. A beam of rectangular cross section, 6″ wide and 10″ deep, is subjected to a bending moment of 9,200 lb. ft. Calculate the maximum bending stress.

Solution:

Fig. 61 shows the cross section.

1. The bending moment is 9,200 lb. ft., but we must change this to lb. in.

$$M = 9{,}200 \times 12 = 110{,}400 \text{ lb. in.}$$

2. The centroid is at the center of the rectangle, so the distance c from the neutral axis to the farthest point in the cross section is half the depth of the beam.

$$c = 5''$$

3. The moment of inertia, with respect to the neutral axis is

$$I = \tfrac{1}{12}bh^3 = \tfrac{1}{12}(6)(10)^3 = 500 \text{ in.}^4$$

4. The maximum bending stress is

$$S = \frac{Mc}{I} = \frac{110{,}400' \times 5}{500} = 1{,}104 \text{ lbs. per sq. in.}$$

Now you see how the flexure formula works, but ordinarily the bending moment will not be given. Instead, you will have to start with the beam and go all the way through the problem. You already know that the bending moment varies from one end of the beam to the other, and that the bending stress varies in each cross section. The greatest bending stress occurs on the cross section where the bending moment is a maximum, so we have to calculate the maximum bending moment and use it in the flexure formula.

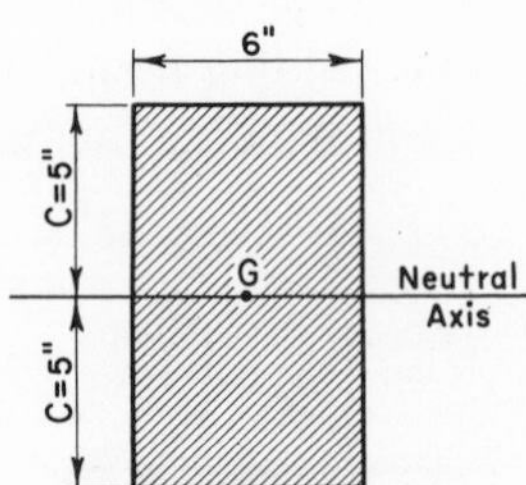

Fig. 61. Rectangular Cross Section of Beam for Example 1 (Art. 6-9)

The full procedure in calculating the maximum bending stress in a beam is:

a) Draw the free-body diagram
b) Find the reactions
c) Locate the point where the shearing force is *zero*
d) Calculate the maximum bending moment. This occurs where the shearing force is *zero*. Be sure that you have the bending moment in lb. in.
e) Locate the *neutral axis* of the cross section. The neutral axis passes through the centroid
f) Determine the distance c from the neutral axis to the farthest point in the cross section of the beam
g) Calculate the *moment of inertia* of the area

of the cross section with respect to the neutral axis

h) Substitute in the flexure formula,

$$S = \frac{Mc}{I}$$

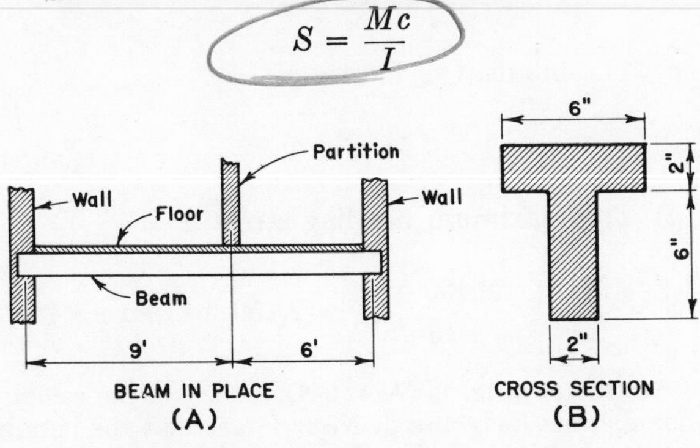

Fig. 62. Beam of Example 2 (Art. 6-9)

Illustrative Example 2. Fig. 62*A* shows a beam which supports a floor and a partition. The floor exerts a uniformly distributed load of 100 lbs. per ft. on the beam, and the partition exerts a concentrated force of 600 lbs. The beam is supported by walls at the ends. Fig. 62*B* shows the cross section of the beam. Calculate the maximum bending stress.

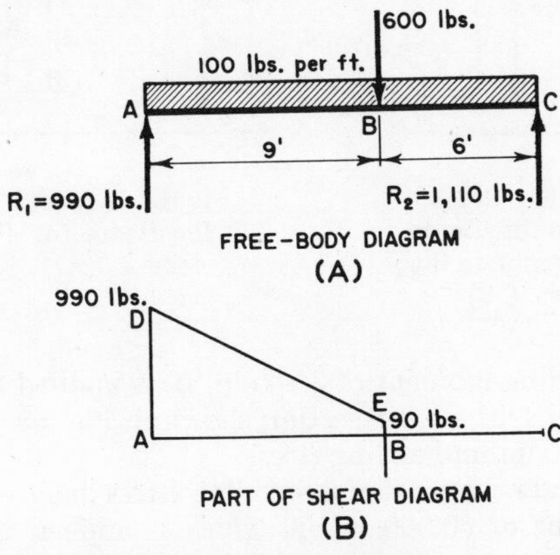

Fig. 63. Locating Point of Zero Shearing Force

Solution:

1. Fig. 63*A* shows the free-body diagram of the beam. The heavy line *ABC* represents the beam and is drawn first. Then the loads are drawn and finally the reactions R_1 and R_2
2. The reactions are calculated next
   a) We write the moment equation, $M_a = 0$, to find R_2

$$M_a = 600 \times 9 + 100 \times 15 \times 7.5 - 15R_2 = 0$$

$$15R_2 = 600 \times 9 + 100 \times 15 \times 7.5$$

$$= 5{,}400 + 11{,}250 = 16{,}650$$

$$R_2 = 1{,}110 \text{ lbs.}$$

   b) We write the moment equation, $M_c = 0$, to find the reaction R_1

$$M_c = 15R_1 - 600 \times 6 - 100 \times 15 \times 7.5 = 0$$

$$15R_1 = 600 \times 6 + 100 \times 15 \times 7.5$$

$$= 3{,}600 + 11{,}250 = 14{,}850$$

$$R_1 = 990 \text{ lbs.}$$

   c) We check the reactions by writing the equilibrium equation,

$$F_y = 0$$

$$F_y = 990 - 600 - 100 \times 15 + 1{,}110 = 0$$

$$2{,}100 - 600 - 1{,}500 = 0$$

$$0 = 0$$

The reactions check, which shows the solution is correct.

3. Fig. 63*B* shows part of the shear diagram
   a) Start by drawing the base line *ABC*
   b) Plot the reaction R_1 upward from *A* to locate point *D*. The shear at *D* is 990 lbs.
   c) Draw the sloping line *DE*. The shear at *E* is

$$990 - 100 \times 9 = 990 - 900 = 90 \text{ lbs.}$$

   d) Plot the 600-lb. load downward from *D*. The point of *zero* shearing force is at *B*
4. The maximum bending moment is at *B*. It is

$$Max.\ M = 990 \times 9 - 100 \times 9 \times 4.5$$
$$= 8{,}910 - 4{,}050 = 4{,}860 \text{ lb. ft.}$$

Change this to lb. in.

$$Max.\ M = 4{,}860 \times 12 = 58{,}400 \text{ lb. in.}$$

5. The neutral axis passes through the centroid of the cross section. Fig. 64*A* shows the area divided into two rectangles
   a) For the rectangle *A*,
      (1) $A_a = 6 \times 2 = 12$ sq. in.
      (2) $\bar{y}_a = 6 + \frac{1}{2} \times 2 = 6 + 1 = 7''$
   b) For the rectangle *B*,
      (1) $A_b = 2 \times 6 = 12$ sq. in.
      (2) $\bar{y}_b = \frac{1}{2} \times 6 = 3''$
   c) For the entire area,
      (1) $A = A_a + A_b = 12 + 12 = 24$ sq. in.
      (2) $M_x = A_a\bar{y}_a + A_b\bar{y}_b = 12 \times 7 + 12 \times 3 = 84 + 36 = 120 \text{ in.}^3$
      (3) $\bar{y} = \dfrac{M_x}{A} = \dfrac{120}{24} = 5''$

The neutral axis is 5″ above the bottom of the cross section.

6. The distance from the neutral axis to the bottom of the section is 5″ and the distance from the neutral axis to the top of the section is 3″. The greater distance is 5″, so

$$c = 5''$$

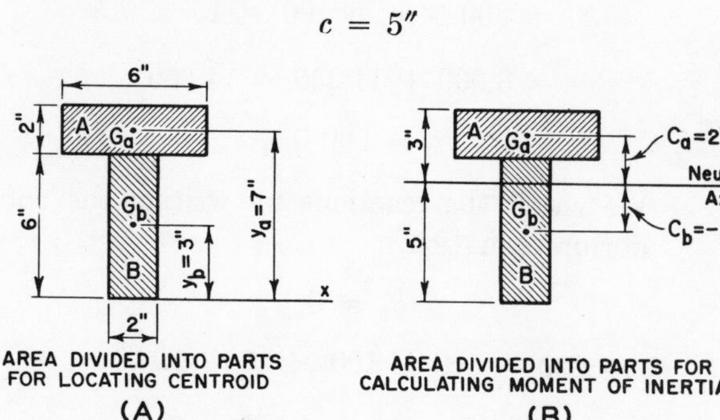

Fig. 64. Cross Section of Beam Divided into Two Rectangles

7. The next step is to calculate the moment of inertia of the cross section with respect to the neutral axis. Work from Fig. 64*B*
   a) For the rectangle *A*,
   (1) The moment of inertia with respect to a horizontal axis through the centroid is

$$I_{ag} = \tfrac{1}{12}bh^3 = \tfrac{1}{12} \times 6\,(2)^3 = 4 \text{ in.}^4$$

   (2) $A_a = 6 \times 2 = 12$ sq. in.
   (3) $c_a = 3 - \frac{1}{2} \times 2 = 3 - 1 = 2''$
   (4) The moment of inertia with respect to the neutral axis is

$$I_a = I_{ag} + A_a c_a^2 = 4 + 12\,(2)^2 = 4 + 48 = 52 \text{ in.}^4$$

   b) For the rectangle *B*,
   (1) The moment of inertia with respect to a horizontal axis through the centroid is

$$I_{bg} = \tfrac{1}{12}bh^3 = \tfrac{1}{12} \times 2\,(6)^3 = 36 \text{ in.}^4$$

   (2) $A_b = 2 \times 6 = 12$ sq. in.
   (3) $c_b = -(5 - \frac{1}{2} \times 6) = -(5 - 3) = -2''$.
   (4) The moment of inertia with respect to the neutral axis is

$$I_b = I_{bg} + A_b c_b^2 = 36 + 12\,(-2)^2$$
$$= 36 + 48 = 84 \text{ in.}^4$$

   c) For the entire area, the moment of inertia with respect to the neutral axis is

$$I = I_a + I_b = 52 + 84 = 136 \text{ in.}^4$$

8. Now calculate the maximum bending stress
   a) The maximum bending moment is

$$M = 58{,}400 \text{ lb. in.}$$

   b) The distance from the neutral axis to the farthest point in the cross section is

$$c = 5''$$

   c) The moment of inertia is

$$I = 136 \text{ in.}^4$$

   d) The maximum bending stress is

$$S = \frac{Mc}{I} = \frac{58{,}400 \times 5}{136} = 2{,}150 \text{ lbs. per sq. in.}$$

Practice Problems (Art. 6-9). Now you can calculate bending stress for yourself. *Never* forget that the bending moment must be in lb. in. when you substitute in the flexure formula.

1. A bending moment of 14,300 lb. in. is applied to a circular bar 2.5″ in diameter. Calculate the maximum bending stress.
2. A square bar, 1.5″ on a side, is subjected to a bending moment of 1,180 lb. ft. Calculate the maximum bending stress.

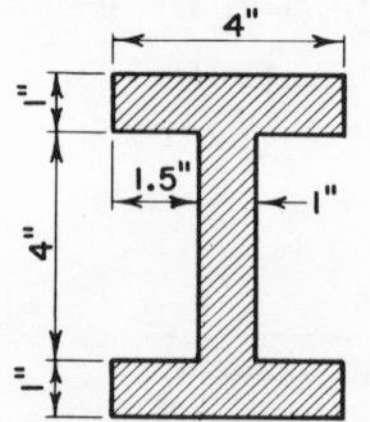

Fig. 65. Cross Section of Beam for Problem 3 (Art. 6-9)

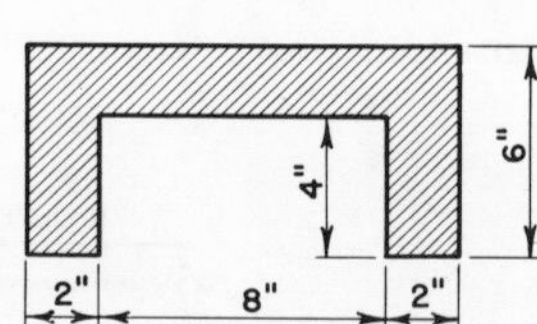

Fig. 66. Cross Section for Beam for Problem 4 (Art. 6-9)

3. A bending moment of 3,160 lb. ft. is applied to a beam which has the cross section shown in Fig. 65. Calculate the maximum bending stress.
4. Calculate the maximum bending stress due to a bending moment of 60,000 lb. in. which is applied to a beam having the cross section shown in Fig. 66.

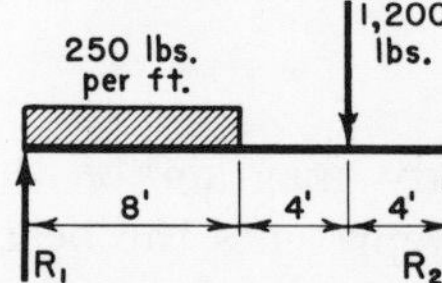

Fig. 67. Free-Body Diagram for Problem 5 (Art. 6-9)

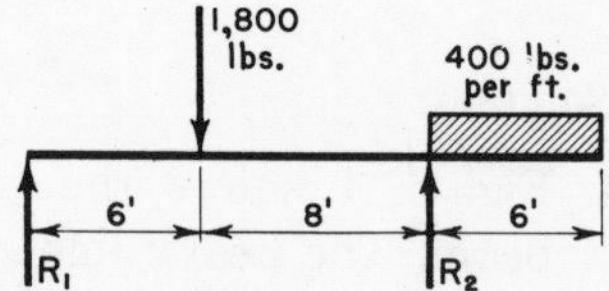

Fig. 68. Free-Body Diagram for Problem 6 (Art. 6-9)

5. Fig. 67 shows the free-body diagram of a rectangular beam, 6″ wide and 10″ deep. What is the maximum bending stress?
6. Fig. 68 shows the free-body diagram of a rectangular beam, 4″ wide and 12″ deep. Find the maximum bending stress.

7. Fig. 69A shows a beam which supports a roof and a chain hoist. The roof exerts a uniformly distributed load of 600 lbs. per ft. on the beam; the chain hoist and the object being lifted weigh 1,200 lbs. Fig. 69B shows the cross section of the beam. Find the maximum bending stress.

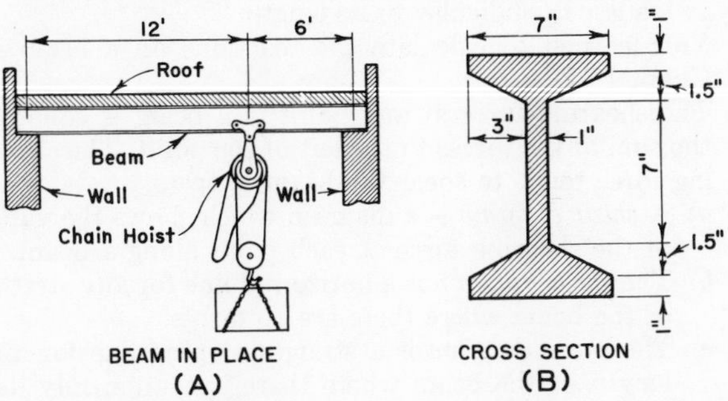

Fig. 69. Beam Supporting Roof and Chain Hoist, Problem 7 (Art. 6-9)

8. Fig. 70A shows a beam which supports a corridor floor. The floor exerts a uniformly distributed load of 1,000 lbs. per ft. on the beam. Fig. 70B shows the cross section of the beam. What is the maximum bending stress?

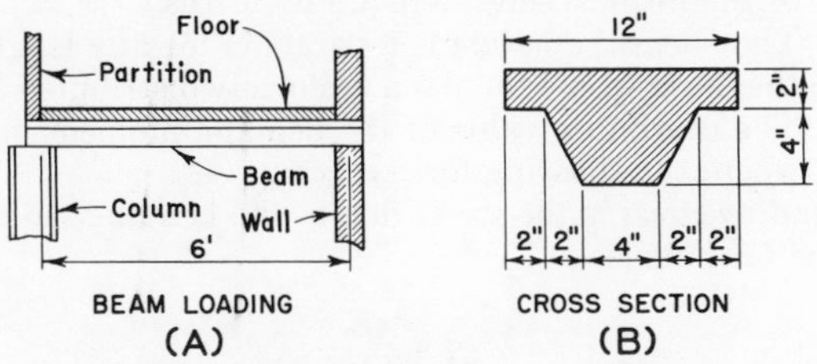

Fig. 70. Beam for Problem 8 (Art. 6-9)

6-10. Shearing Stress in Rectangular Beams.

Now that you know how to calculate bending stress, the next step will be to learn how to calculate the maximum shearing stress in a rectangular beam. Fig. 71A shows a beam with the forces acting on it. You know there is a shearing force at any cross section such as AA and you know how to calculate this shearing force. Fig. 71B shows the part of the beam to the right of the section AA and shows the shearing force V which is exerted on this part of the beam. (V is equal to the sum of the forces to the left of section AA.)

Fig. 71C shows the cross section of a rectangular beam having the width b and the altitude h. The shearing force V is distributed over the cross section but is not distributed uniformly. Fig. 71D shows how the shearing stress varies from top to bottom of the beam; the shearing stress is *zero* at the top and bottom of the beam, and the maximum shearing stress occurs at the neutral axis. The maximum shearing stress is

$$Max.\ S_s = \frac{3}{2}\frac{V}{bh}$$

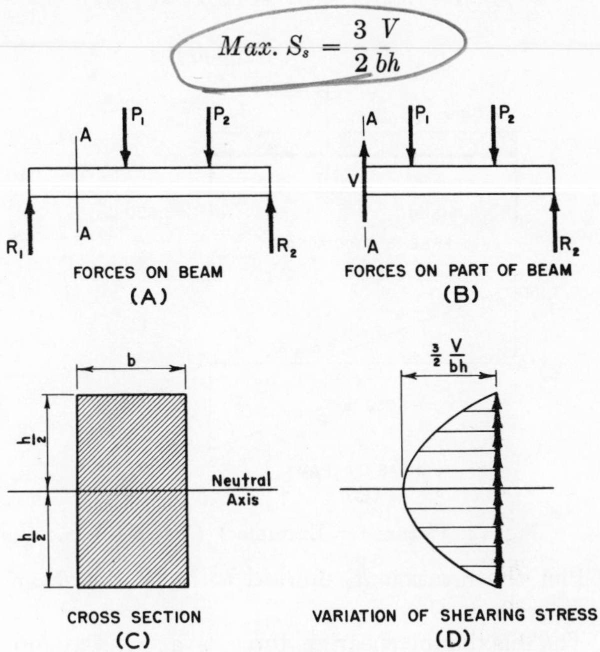

Fig. 71. Shearing Stress in Rectangular Beam

As you see, the shearing stress varies from top to bottom of the beam. Also, the shearing stress varies along the beam because the shearing force V changes. If we want to calculate the greatest shearing stress in the beam, we must use the maximum shearing force V in the formula. The maximum shearing force V can be obtained from the shear diagram, as you know, and the shearing force may be positive or negative; we take the greatest numerical value to use in the formula.

Illustrative Example 1. Fig. 72A shows the free-body diagram of a rectangular beam, 6″ wide and 10″ deep. Calculate the maximum shearing stress.

Solution:

1. Fig. 72B shows the shear diagram. Start it by drawing the base line ABC
2. Plot the reaction R_1 *upward* from A to locate D. The shear at D is 3,150 lbs.
3. Draw the sloping line DE. The shear at E is

$$3{,}150 - 300 \times 10 = 3{,}150 - 3{,}000 = 150 \text{ lbs.}$$

4. Plot the 2,000-lb. load downward from E to locate F. The shear at F is

$$150 - 2{,}000 = -1{,}850 \text{ lbs.}$$

5. Draw the sloping line FG. The shear at G is

$$-1{,}850 - 300 \times 6 = -1{,}850 - 1{,}800$$

$$= -3{,}650 \text{ lbs.}$$

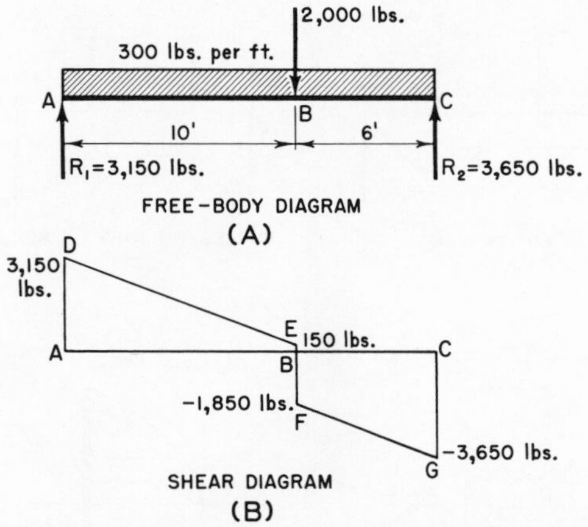

Fig. 72. Picture for Example 1 (Art. 6-10)

6. Plot the reaction R_2 upward to finish the shear diagram at C
7. The maximum shearing force is at G. Pay no attention to the minus sign

$$Max.\ V = 3{,}650 \text{ lbs.}$$

8. The maximum shearing stress in the beam is

$$Max.\ S_s = \frac{3}{2}\frac{V}{bh} = \frac{3}{2}\frac{3{,}650}{6 \times 10} = 91.3 \text{ \#/in.}^2$$

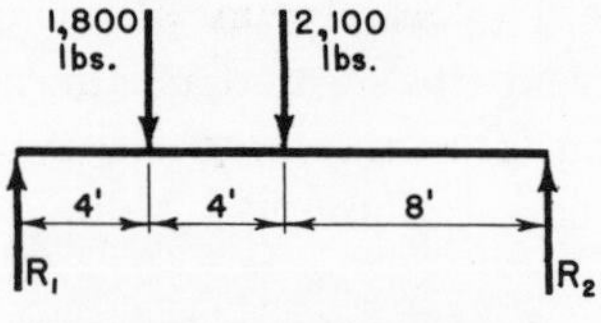

Fig. 73. Free-Body Diagram for Problem 1 (Art. 6-10)

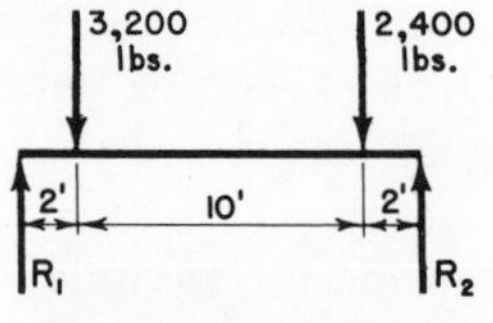

Fig. 74. Free-Body Diagram for Problem 2 (Art. 6-10)

Practice Problems (Art. 6-10). Practice calculating the maximum shearing stress in a rectangular beam.

1. The beam represented in Fig. 73 is rectangular, 4″ wide and 8″ deep. Find the maximum shearing stress.
2. Calculate the maximum shearing stress in a rectangular beam, 4″ by 10″, for the loading shown in Fig. 74.

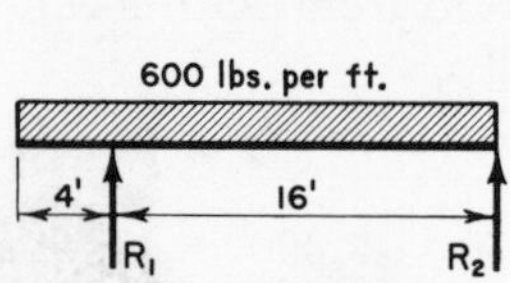

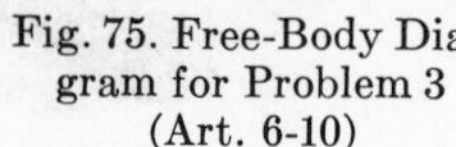

Fig. 75. Free-Body Diagram for Problem 3 (Art. 6-10)

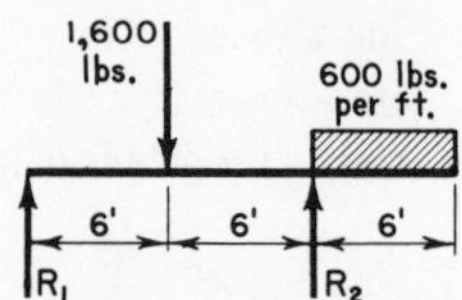

Fig. 76. Free-Body Diagram for Problem 4 (Art. 6-10)

3. A rectangular beam, 6″ by 10″, is subjected to the loads shown in Fig. 75. What is the maximum shearing stress?
4. Fig. 76 shows the free-body diagram of a rectangular beam, 6″ square. Calculate the maximum shearing stress.

SUMMARY OF CHAPTER VI

1. A *beam* is a *slender structural member* which is subjected to loads perpendicular to its length.
2. You learned to calculate the reactions on a beam in Chapter II.
3. The shearing force at any point in a beam is equal to the sum of the forces to the left of the point. The shearing force tends to shear the beam in two.
   a) A *shear diagram* is a diagram which shows the value of the shearing force at each point along a beam.
   b) The *shear diagram* is a horizontal line for any stretch of the beam where there are no forces.
   c) The *shear diagram* is a straight sloping line for any length of the beam where there is a uniformly distributed load.
4. The bending moment at any point, in a beam, is equal to the moment, with respect to that point, of all of the forces to the left of the point. The bending moment tends to bend the beam.
   a) A *moment diagram* is a diagram which shows the value of the bending moment at each point along a beam.
   b) The *moment diagram* is a straight line for any stretch of the beam where there are no forces.
   c) The *moment diagram* is a parabola for any length of the beam where there is a uniformly distributed load.
   d) The maximum value of the bending moment occurs where the shearing force is *zero*.
5. *Bending stress* is the stress due to the bending moment. The formula is

$$S = \frac{Mc}{I}$$

   a) M is the bending moment, expressed in lb. in.
   b) I is the moment of inertia of the cross section of the beam, taken with respect to the neutral axis.
   c) The neutral axis passes through the centroid of the cross section.
   d) The distance c is the distance from the neutral axis to the farthest point in the cross section.
   e) A *positive bending moment* causes compression in the top of the beam and tension in the bottom.
   f) A *negative bending moment* causes tension in the top of the beam and compression in the bottom.
6. The maximum shearing stress in a rectangular beam is

$$S_s = \frac{3}{2}\frac{V}{bh}$$

   a) V is the shearing force.
   b) The width of the beam is b.
   c) The depth of the beam is h.

Review Questions

Check your knowledge by answering these review questions.

1. What is a *beam?*
2. How do you find the *reactions* on a beam?

3. What is the *shearing force* in a beam?
4. What is a *shear diagram?*
5. What is a *bending moment?*
6. What is a *moment diagram?*
7. What is the *centroid of an area?*
8. How do you locate the *centroid of a composite area?*

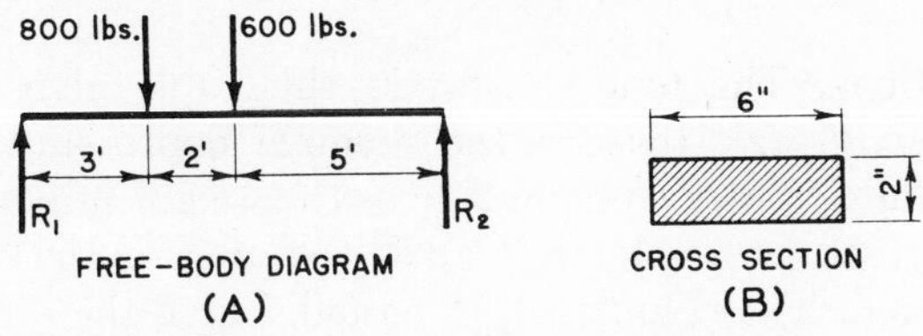

Fig. 77. Beam for Problem 1 (Review Problems)

9. What is *moment of inertia* of area?
10. How do you find the moment of inertia of a composite area?
11. How do you draw a *shear diagram?*
12. How do you draw a *moment diagram?*

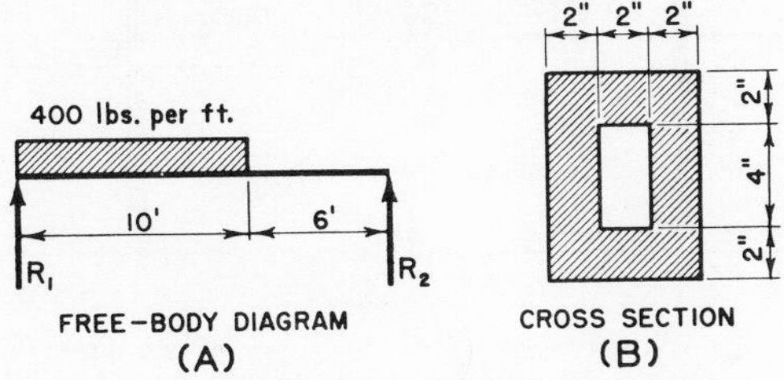

Fig. 78. Beam for Problem 2 (Review Problems)

13. Where does the *maximum bending moment* occur in a beam?
14. What is *bending stress?*
15. Give the *formula for bending stress.*
16. In what units should the bending moment be expressed when you calculate bending stress?
17. Is bending stress *tension, compression,* or *shear?*
18. Give the formula for the maximum shearing stress in a rectangular beam.

Review Problems

You can review this chapter by working these problems. In each case, the free-body diagram and the cross section is given. Follow instructions from there.

1. Fig. 77.
   a) Draw the *shear diagram.*
   b) Draw the *moment diagram.*
   c) Calculate the *maximum bending stress.*
   d) Calculate the *maximum shearing stress.*
2. Fig. 78.
   a) Draw the *shear diagram.*
   b) Draw the *moment diagram.*
   c) Calculate the *maximum bending stress.*

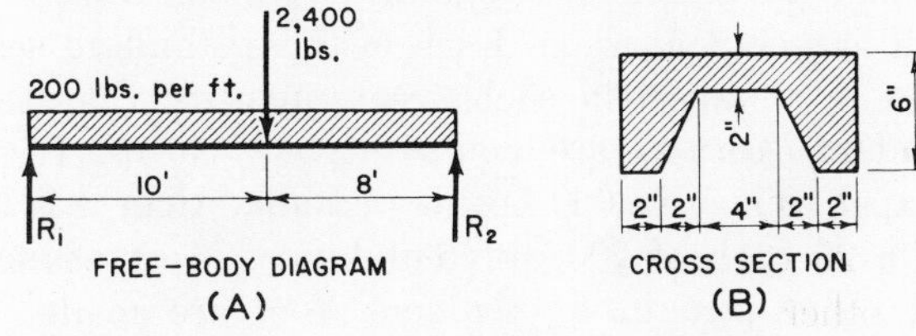

Fig. 79. Beam for Problem 3 (Review Problems)

3. Fig. 79.
   a) Draw the *shear diagram.*
   b) Draw the *moment diagram.*
   c) Calculate the *maximum bending stress.*

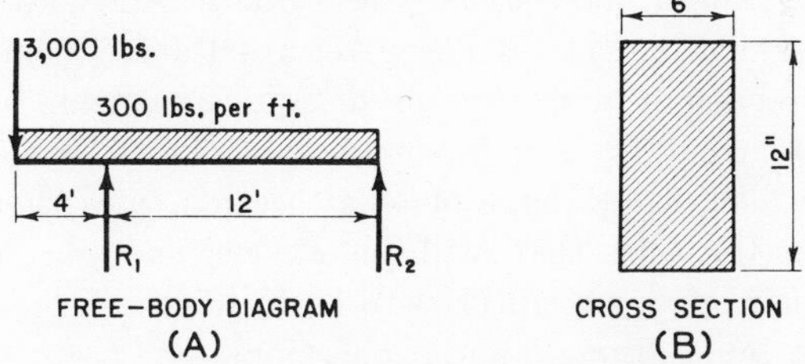

Fig. 80. Beam for Problem 4 (Review Problems)

4. Fig. 80.
   a) Draw the *shear diagram.*
   b) Draw the *moment diagram.*
   c) Calculate the *maximum bending stress.*
   d) Calculate the *maximum shearing stress.*

Chapter VII

BEAMS OF STANDARD SECTION

Purpose of This Chapter. The purpose of this chapter is to teach you the types of standard sections which are ordinarily used for beams in buildings and bridges, and how to design beams of these types.

There are a number of standard sections of beams, both in steel and wood. Each of these standard sections is produced in such great quantity that the standard sections are comparatively cheap. It is cheaper to make 5,000 beams just alike than it is to make 25 each of 200 different kinds. Most beams, and other structural members, too, are made of standard section in order to take advantage of the economy of mass production.

There are a large number of different shapes of standard steel sections and each shape is made in many different sizes. Wood beams are usually rectangular. There are too many sections to study all that are available, so let's take a representative group.

The usual procedure in designing a beam is to decide what type of beam to use; that is, wood or steel; also, what shape of steel section, and then to select the size that will be strong enough. Your problem in this chapter is to learn how to select the beam by studying standard sections.

7-1. Steel Side-Flange Sections.

One of the most common of the different types of standard steel section is the *wide-flange section.* Fig. 1 shows the cross section of a wide-flange beam. You are to notice the flanges, which are the top and bottom parts, and the web in the center. Notice, also, the dimensions of the section—the flange width, the flange thickness, and the depth of the section.

The centroid of the cross section in Fig. 1 is at G, at the intersection of the x and y axes.

The standard way of designating a particular wide-flange section is to give first the nominal depth of the section, then the symbol WF (to indicate that it is a *wide-flange section*), and finally the weight of the beam in pounds per foot of length. For example, 12 WF 58 designates a wide-flange section which has a nominal depth of 12″ and which weighs 58 pounds per foot of length.

You do not have to calculate the area of cross section for a wide-flange section, or the moment of inertia. This has already been done and you can get the figures from tables. Now look at Table I which gives the properties of a few samples of wide-flange sections. The first column in this table gives the *nominal size;* that is, the nominal depth and the nominal width. Column 2 gives the weight in pounds per foot, and column 3 gives the area of the cross section. The columns 4, 5, 6, and 7 give the dimension of the cross section.

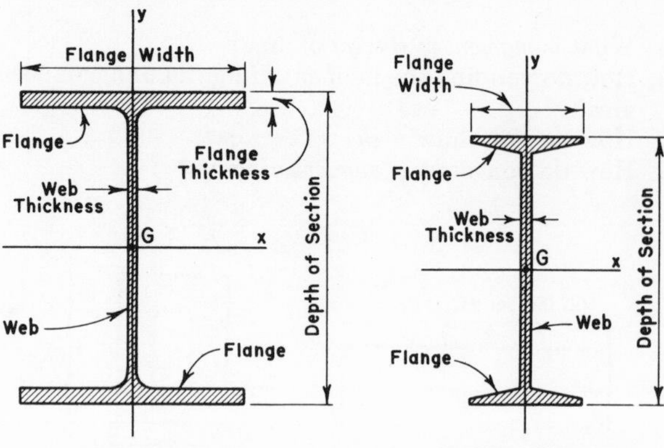

Fig. 1. Wide-Flange Section of Standard Steel Beam

Fig. 2. American Standard Steel-Beam Section

Column 8 of Table I gives the moment of inertia of the area of the cross section with respect to the x axis. Column 9 gives the section modulus $Z;$ you will be given the definition and use of modulus Z later. Column 10 gives the radius of gyration r which will be used in Chapter XII.

Columns 11, 12, and 13 give the properties of the cross section with respect to the y axis which will be used in Chapter XII.

The following illustrates the use of the table.

Illustrative Example 1. What is the web thickness of the wide-flange section, 16 WF 40?

Solution:

1. Look down column 1 to the sections which have a nominal depth of 16″. The second one weighs 40 lbs. per ft.
2. Look across to column 7. Read the web thickness as 0.307″

Illustrative Example 2. What is the standard designation for the wide-flange section which has a section modulus Z, with respect to the x axis, of 24.1 in.^{3}?

Solution:

1. Look down column 9 in Table I until you see 24.1

2. Look across to the left to column 1 and see that the nominal size is 10x5$\frac{3}{4}$. The depth is 10″
3. Look in column 2 to see that the weight per ft. is 23 lbs.
4. The standard designation is

10 WF 23

Practice Problems (Art. 7-1). Now practice with Table I, so you will become familiar with it.

1. What is the moment of inertia, I_x, for 12 WF 45?
2. Find the flange width of 8 WF 17.
3. Find the area of cross section of 14 WF 68.
4. Which wide-flange section has a moment of inertia, I_y, of 207 in.^{4}?

7-2. American Standard Steel Beams.

Another common type of steel beam is the American standard beam. Fig. 2 shows a typical cross section. The American standard section is similar to the wide-flange section, but usually has a narrower flange and a thicker web than a wide-flange section of the same depth and weight.

The designation for an American standard beam gives first the depth in inches, then the letter **I** (American standard beams are usually called **I** beams), and finally the weight of the section in pounds per foot of length. For example, 15 **I** 50, designates an American standard beam which is 15″ deep and which weighs 50 pounds per foot.

Table II gives the properties of some samples of American standard beams. This table gives about the same information as Table I, so there is really nothing new to learn.

Practice Problems (Art. 7-2).

1. What is the flange width of 20 **I** 75?
2. Find I_x for 12 **I** 40.8.
3. What is Z, with respect to the x axis, for 6 **I** 12.5?
4. What is the standard designation of the American standard beam for which I_y = 3.8 in.^{4}?

7-3. Steel Angles.

Another standard steel section that is used a great deal is the *angle section*. Fig. 3 shows the cross section of an equal leg angle; you can see the dimensions in Fig. 3*A*. The standard method of designating an angle is to give first the symbol ∠ to indicate that it is an angle, then the lengths of the legs and last the thickness. For example, the designation, ∠ 6x6x$\frac{1}{2}$, applies to an angle which has legs 6″ long and which is $\frac{1}{2}$″ thick.

TABLE I. PROPERTIES OF SAMPLE WIDE-FLANGE SECTIONS

Nominal Size	Wt. per Ft.	Area of Section	Depth of Section	Flange		Web Thickness	X Axis			Y Axis		
				Width	Thickness		I	Z	r	I	Z	r
In. 1	Lbs. 2	Sq. In. 3	In. 4	In. 5	In. 6	In. 7	In.^{4} 8	In.^{3} 9	In. 10	In.^{4} 11	In^3 12	In. 13
24x12	120	35.29	24.31	12.09	0.930	0.556	3635	299	10.15	254	42.0	2.68
24x12	100	29.43	24.00	12.00	0.775	0.468	2987	249	10.08	204	33.9	2.63
24x9	80	23.54	24.00	9.00	0.727	0.455	2230	186	9.73	82.4	18.3	1.87
18x11$\frac{3}{4}$	105	30.86	18.32	11.79	0.911	0.554	1853	202	7.75	231	39.2	2.73
18x7$\frac{1}{2}$	55	16.19	18.12	7.53	0.630	0.390	890	98.2	7.41	42.0	11.1	1.61
16x11$\frac{1}{2}$	88	25.87	16.16	11.50	0.795	0.504	1223	151.3	6.87	185.2	32.2	2.67
16x7	40	11.77	16.00	7.00	0.503	0.307	516	64.4	6.62	26.5	7.60	1.50
14x16	370	108.8	17.94	16.48	2.66	1.66	5454	608	7.08	1986	241.0	4.27
14x14$\frac{1}{2}$	95	27.94	14.12	14.55	0.748	0.465	1064	150.6	6.17	384	52.8	3.71
14x10	68	20.00	14.06	10.04	0.718	0.418	724	103	6.02	121.2	24.1	2.46
14x6$\frac{3}{4}$	30	8.81	13.86	6.73	0.383	0.270	289.6	41.8	5.73	17.5	5.2	1.41
12x10	58	17.06	12.19	10.01	0.641	0.359	476.1	78.1	5.28	107.4	21.4	2.51
12x8	45	13.24	12.06	8.04	0.576	0.336	351	58.2	5.15	50.0	12.4	1.94
12x6$\frac{1}{2}$	28	8.23	12.00	6.50	0.420	0.240	213.5	35.6	5.09	17.5	5.4	1.46
10x10	100	29.43	11.12	10.35	1.118	0.685	625	112.4	4.61	207	39.9	2.65
10x5$\frac{3}{4}$	23	6.77	10.00	5.75	0.390	0.240	120.6	24.1	4.22	11.3	3.9	1.29
8x6$\frac{1}{2}$	27	7.93	8.03	6.53	0.448	0.273	94.1	23.4	3.44	20.8	6.4	1.62
8x5$\frac{1}{4}$	17	5.00	8.00	5.25	0.308	0.230	56.4	14.1	3.36	6.7	2.6	1.16
6x6	20	5.90	6.20	6.02	0.367	0.258	41.7	13.4	2.66	13.1	4.4	1.50
5x5	13.5	3.98	4.86	4.99	0.292	0.230	17.1	7.02	2.07	6.05	2.43	1.23

Courtesy of the American Institute of Steel Construction

Table II. Properties of Sample American Standard Beams

Nominal Size	Wt. per Ft.	Area of Section	Depth of Section	Width of Flange	Web Thickness	X Axis			Y Axis		
						I	Z	r	I	Z	r
In. 1	Lbs. 2	Sq. In. 3	In. 4	In. 5	In. 6	In.^{4} 7	In.^{3} 8	In. 9	In.^{4} 10	In.^{3} 11	In. 12
24x7	100	29.25	24.00	7.25	0.747	2372	197.6	9.05	48.4	13.4	1.29
20x6¼	75	21.90	20.00	6.39	0.641	1264	126.3	7.60	30.1	9.40	1.17
18x6	65	18.98	18.00	6.17	0.629	878	97.5	6.80	23.4	7.60	1.11
15x6	70	20.38	15.00	6.18	0.770	660	87.9	5.69	28.8	9.30	1.19
15x5½	50	14.59	15.00	5.64	0.550	481	64.2	5.74	16.0	5.70	1.05
12x5¼	55	16.04	12.00	5.60	0.810	319	53.2	4.46	17.3	6.20	1.04
12x5¼	40.8	11.84	12.00	5.25	0.460	269	44.8	4.77	13.8	5.30	1.08
12x5	35	10.20	12.00	5.08	0.428	227	37.8	4.72	10.0	3.90	0.99
10x4¾	35	10.22	10.00	4.94	0.594	145.8	29.2	3.78	8.50	3.40	0.91
10x4¾	25.4	7.38	10.00	4.66	0.310	122.1	24.4	4.07	6.90	3.00	0.97
8x4	23	6.71	8.00	4.17	0.441	64.2	16.0	3.09	4.40	2.10	0.81
8x4	18.4	5.34	8.00	4.00	0.270	56.9	14.2	3.26	3.80	1.90	0.84
7x3¾	20	5.83	7.00	3.86	0.450	41.9	12.0	2.68	3.10	1.60	0.74
7x3¾	15.3	4.43	7.00	3.66	0.250	36.2	10.4	2.86	2.70	1.50	0.78
6x3⅜	17.25	5.02	6.00	3.57	0.465	26.0	8.70	2.28	2.30	1.30	0.68
6x3⅜	12.5	3.61	6.00	3.33	0.230	21.8	7.30	2.46	1.80	1.10	0.72
5x3	14.75	4.29	5.00	3.28	0.494	15.0	6.00	1.87	1.70	1.00	0.63
5x3	10	2.87	5.00	3.00	0.210	12.1	4.80	2.05	1.20	0.82	0.65
4x2¾	8.5	2.46	4.00	2.72	0.253	6.30	3.20	1.60	0.83	0.61	0.58
3x2⅜	6.5	1.88	3.00	2.41	0.251	2.70	1.80	1.19	0.51	0.43	0.52

Courtesy of the American Institute of Steel Construction

Table III. Properties of Sample Equal Angles

Size	Thickness	Weight per Ft.	Area of Section	X and Y axes				Z axis
				I	Z	r	$\bar{x}$ and $\bar{y}$	r
In. 1	In. 2	Lbs. 3	Sq. In. 4	In.^{4} 5	In.^{3} 6	In. 7	In. 8	In. 9
8x8	1	51.0	15.00	89.0	15.8	2.44	2.37	1.56
8x8	⅝	32.7	9.61	59.4	10.3	2.49	2.23	1.58
6x6	⅞	33.1	9.73	31.9	7.60	1.81	1.82	1.17
6x6	½	19.6	5.75	19.9	4.60	1.86	1.68	1.18
5x5	¾	23.6	6.94	15.7	4.50	1.51	1.52	0.97
5x5	7/16	14.3	4.18	10.0	2.80	1.55	1.41	0.98
4x4	11/16	17.1	5.03	7.20	2.60	1.19	1.25	0.78
4x4	⅜	9.8	2.86	4.40	1.50	1.23	1.14	0.79
3½x3½	9/16	12.4	3.62	4.00	1.70	1.05	1.08	0.68
3½x3½	¼	5.8	1.69	2.00	0.79	1.09	0.97	0.69
3x3	½	9.4	2.75	2.20	1.10	0.90	0.93	0.58
3x3	5/16	6.1	1.78	1.50	0.71	0.92	0.87	0.59
2½x2½	⅜	5.9	1.73	0.98	0.57	0.75	0.76	0.49
2½x2½	3/16	3.07	0.90	0.55	0.30	0.78	0.69	0.49

Courtesy of American Institute of Steel Construction

Fig. 3*B* shows the x, y, and z axes as they are usually placed for an angle section. The *centroid* is at G, at the intersection of the axes; the dimensions $\bar{x}$ and $\bar{y}$ show the location of G. The z axis is at 45° with the x axis; it will be used in Chapter XII.

Table III gives the properties of some samples of equal angles. This is similar to Tables I and II in this chapter. Column 1 gives the lengths of the legs and column 2 gives the thickness. You notice that

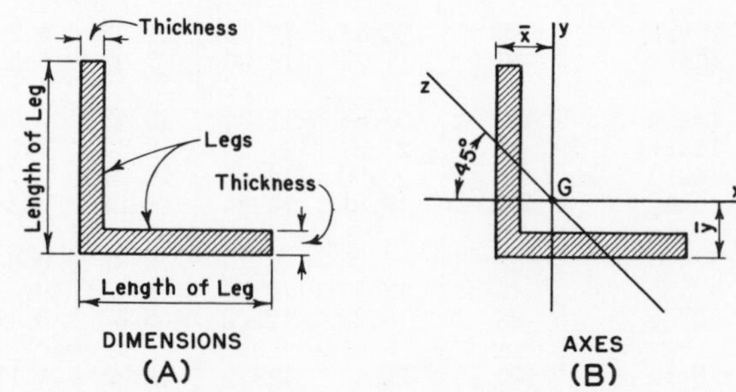

Fig. 3. Cross Section of an Equal-Angle Section

the x and y axes are together; because the moment of inertia I is the same for the x axis as for the y axis; also, z, r, and $\bar{x}$ or $\bar{y}$ are the same for one axis as for the other. The r for the z axis will be explained later.

Practice Problems (Art. 7-3). The following problems will help you become familiar with Table III.

1. How much does the angle, ∠4x4x$\frac{11}{16}$, weigh?
2. Find I_x for ∠3x3x$\frac{5}{16}$.
3. Locate the centroid of ∠5x5x$\frac{3}{4}$.
4. Pick out the angle for which $Z = 1.7$ in.^{3}

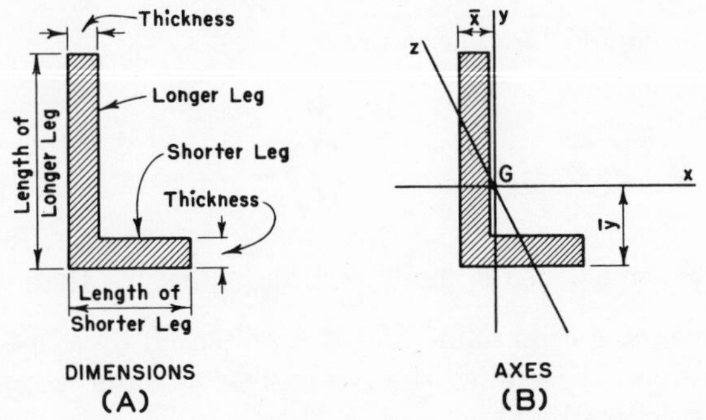

Fig. 4. Cross Section of an Unequal-Angle Section

Angles are made with unequal legs too. Fig. 4 shows the cross section of an unequal angle and Table IV gives the properties of some sample unequal angles. The only way in which Table IV is different from Table III is that the properties are given separately for the x and y axes. This has to be, because the properties are not the same for the x axis as for the y axis.

The standard method of designating an unequal angle is to give first the symbol ∠ (for angle), then the length of the longer leg, next the length of the shorter leg, and finally the thickness. For example, ∠ 5x3x$\frac{11}{16}$ means an angle which has legs of 5″ and 3″, and which is $\frac{11}{16}$″ thick.

Practice Problems (Art. 7-3—*Continued*). Practice using Table IV.

1. What is the area of cross section of ∠7x4x$\frac{3}{8}$?
2. Find I_y for ∠4x3x$\frac{1}{4}$.
3. What is Z, with respect to the x axis, for ∠6x3x$\frac{1}{2}$?
4. For which unequal angle is I_y equal to 10.5 in.^{4}?

7-4. Standard Wood Sections.

Rectangular wood sections are made in standard sizes; Fig. 5 shows a cross section. The actual size of a wood beam is not the same as the nominal size. The nominal size is the size used to describe the beam, for instance 2x4, 4x8, and so forth. The actual size is the actual dimensions. For example, what is called a 2x4 (nominal size) is really 1$\frac{5}{8}$″x3$\frac{5}{8}$″ (actual size). The actual size must be used in calculating a stress or designing a beam, because the actual size represents the amount of wood which is really there.

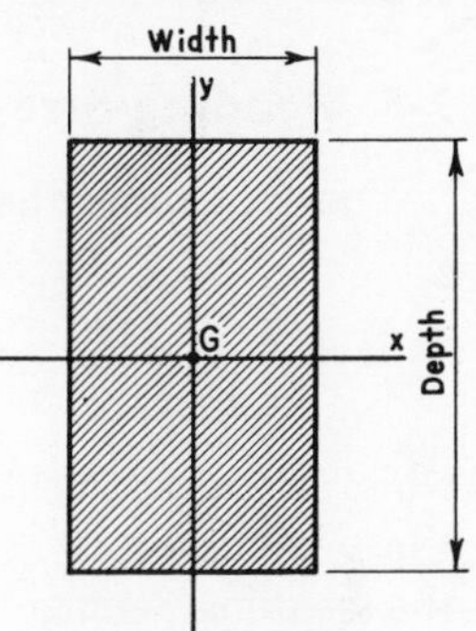

Fig. 5. Rectangular Wood Section

Table IV. Property of Sample Unequal Angles

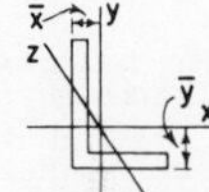

Size	Thickness	Weight per Ft.	Area of Section	X Axis				Y Axis				Z Axis
				I	Z	r	ȳ	I	Z	r	x̄	r
In. 1	In. 1	Lbs. 3	Sq. In. 4	In.^{4} 5	In.^{3} 6	In. 7	In. 8	In.^{4} 9	In.^{3} 10	In. 11	In. 12	In. 13
8x6	1	44.2	13.00	80.8	15.10	2.49	2.65	38.8	8.90	1.73	1.65	1.28
8x6	$\frac{1}{2}$	23.0	6.75	44.3	8.00	2.56	2.47	21.7	4.80	1.79	1.47	1.30
8x4	$\frac{7}{8}$	33.1	9.73	62.5	12.50	2.53	3.00	10.50	3.50	1.04	1.00	0.85
8x4	$\frac{7}{16}$	17.2	5.06	34.1	6.60	2.60	2.83	6.00	1.90	1.09	0.83	0.87
7x4	$\frac{15}{16}$	32.1	9.43	45.4	10.30	2.19	2.58	10.70	3.70	1.07	1.08	0.86
7x4	$\frac{3}{8}$	13.6	3.98	20.6	4.40	2.27	2.37	5.10	1.60	1.13	0.87	0.88
6x3$\frac{1}{2}$	$\frac{3}{4}$	22.4	6.56	23.3	6.10	1.89	2.18	5.80	2.30	0.94	0.93	0.75
6x3$\frac{1}{2}$	$\frac{1}{2}$	15.3	4.50	16.6	4.20	1.92	2.08	4.30	1.60	0.97	0.83	0.76
5x3	$\frac{11}{16}$	17.1	5.03	12.3	3.90	1.56	1.82	3.30	1.50	0.81	0.82	0.64
5x3	$\frac{5}{16}$	8.2	2.40	6.30	1.90	1.61	1.68	1.80	0.75	0.85	0.68	0.66
4x3	$\frac{5}{8}$	13.6	3.98	6.0	2.30	1.23	1.37	2.90	1.40	0.85	0.87	0.64
4x3	$\frac{1}{4}$	5.8	1.69	2.80	1.00	1.28	1.24	1.40	0.60	0.90	0.74	0.65
3x2	$\frac{7}{16}$	6.8	2.00	1.70	0.89	0.93	1.06	0.61	0.42	0.55	0.56	0.43
3x2	$\frac{1}{4}$	4.1	1.19	1.10	0.54	0.95	0.99	0.39	0.26	0.57	0.49	0.43

Courtesy of the American Institute of Steel Construction

Table V gives the properties of some samples of wood sections. Column 1 gives the nominal size, and column 2 gives the actual size. The smaller dimension is the width and the larger dimension is the depth (see Fig. 5 for width and depth). The rest of Table V is similar to previous tables.

Practice Problems (Art. 7-4). Work these problems so you will become familiar with Table V.

1. How big is a 10x14?
2. What is the area of cross section of a 2x8?
3. Find I_x for a 4x12.
4. What is Z, with respect to the y axis, for a 6x10?
5. Which section in Table V has an area closest to 35 sq. in?
6. Pick out a wood section for which I_y is equal to 104 in.^{4}

7-5. Bending Stress in Standard Sections.

You remember the *flexure formula*,

$$S = \frac{Mc}{I}$$

which we used to calculate bending stress. Here S is the bending stress in pounds per square inch; M is the bending moment in pound inches; c is the distance from the neutral axis to the farthest point in the cross section; and I is the moment of inertia of the area of the cross section with respect to the neutral axis. You can apply this formula to beams of standard section, but first rewrite it as

$$S = \frac{M}{\left(\frac{I}{c}\right)}$$

You should be able to prove

$$\frac{Mc}{I} \quad \frac{M}{\left(\frac{I}{c}\right)}$$

So much use is made of the quantity $\frac{I}{c}$ that it is given a special name and is represented by a special symbol. It is called the *section modulus* and is represented by Z. Thus,

$$Z = \frac{I}{c}$$

This is the Z that you saw in the tables of standard sections. Now we can substitute Z for $\frac{I}{c}$ in the flexure formula and write the flexure formula as

$$S = \frac{M}{Z}$$

Then, we just look up Z in the tables when we want to calculate bending stress in a standard section.

The tables give one value of Z with respect to the x axis and one value of Z with respect to the y axis. You may wonder which axis should be used. Fig. 6A shows the cross section of a rectangular beam; you are to notice the x and y axes. Fig. 6B shows a beam which has this cross section; notice here the x and y axes in the end cross section and notice that the loads are perpendicular to the x axis. Now when the beam is placed so that the loads are perpendicular to the x axis of the cross section, you use Z for the x axis in order to calculate the bending stress. When the beam is placed so the loads are perpendicular to

TABLE V. PROPERTIES OF SAMPLE WOOD SECTIONS

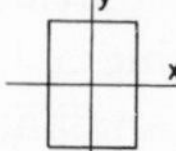

NOMINAL SIZE	ACTUAL SIZE	AREA OF SECTION	X AXIS			Y AXIS		
			I	Z	r	I	Z	r
In. 1	In. 2	Sq. In. 3	In.^{4} 4	In.^{3} 5	In. 6	In.^{4} 7	In.^{3} 8	In. 9
2x4	1⅝x3⅝	5.89	6.45	3.56	1.05	1.29	1.59	0.47
2x6	1⅝x5⅝	9.14	24.10	8.57	1.64	2.01	2.47	0.47
2x8	1⅝x7½	12.19	57.1	15.23	2.17	2.68	3.30	0.47
2x10	1⅝x9½	15.44	116.1	24.44	2.75	3.39	4.18	0.47
2x12	1⅝x11½	18.69	206	35.8	3.32	4.11	5.05	0.47
4x4	3⅝x3⅝	13.14	14.39	7.94	1.05	14.39	7.94	1.05
4x6	3⅝x5⅝	20.39	53.8	19.1	1.64	22.3	12.3	1.05
4x8	3⅝x7½	27.19	127.4	34.0	2.17	29.7	16.4	1.05
4x10	3⅝x9½	34.4	259	54.5	2.75	37.7	20.8	1.05
4x12	3⅝x11½	41.7	459	79.9	3.32	45.7	25.2	1.05
6x6	5½x5½	30.25	76.3	27.7	1.64	76.3	27.7	1.64
6x8	5½x7½	41.25	193.4	51.6	2.17	104	37.8	1.64
6x10	5½x9½	52.25	393	82.7	2.75	132	47.8	1.64
6x12	5½x11½	63.25	697	121.2	3.32	160	57.8	1.64
6x14	5½x13½	74.25	1128	167.1	3.90	187	67.8	1.64
8x8	7½x7½	56.25	264	70.3	2.17	264	70.3	2.17
8x10	7½x9½	71.25	536	112.8	2.75	333	89.0	2.17
8x12	7½x11½	86.25	951	165.3	3.32	403	107.8	2.17
8x14	7½x13½	101.25	1538	228	3.90	473	126.5	2.17
8x16	7½x15½	116.25	2327	300	4.48	543	145.3	2.17
10x10	9½x9½	90.25	679	143	2.75	679	143	2.75
10x12	9½x11½	109.25	1204	209	3.32	822	173	2.75
10x14	9½x13½	128.25	1948	289	3.90	964	203	2.75
10x16	9½x15½	147.25	2948	380	4.48	1108	233	2.75

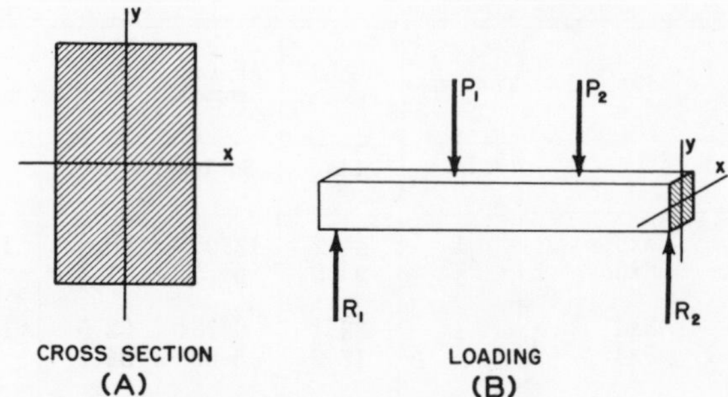

Fig. 6. Beam with Loads Perpendicular to X Axis

the y axis, you use Z for the y axis to calculate the bending stress.

Illustrative Example 1. A steel wide-flange beam, 10 WF 23, is loaded so the loads are perpendicular to the x axis. The maximum bending moment is 19,400 lb. ft. Calculate the maximum bending stress.

Solution:

1. The maximum bending moment must be converted to lb. in.

$$M = 19{,}400 \times 12 = 233{,}000 \text{ lb. in.}$$

2. Look up Z in column 9 of Table I.

$$Z = 24.1 \text{ in.}^3$$

3. The maximum bending stress is

$$S = \frac{M}{Z} = \frac{233{,}000}{24.1} = 9{,}680 \text{ lbs. per sq. in.}$$

It saves time to get the section modulus Z from the tables, instead of calculating it. Start with the loads and calculate the bending stress in a beam.

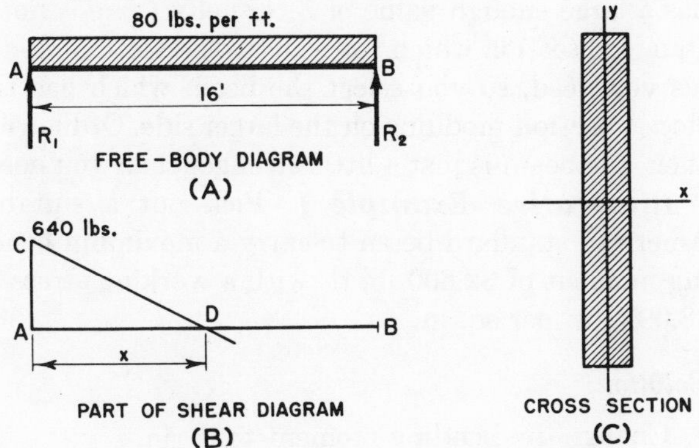

Fig. 7. Shear Diagram for Joist Problem

Illustrative Example 2. A 2x12 wood joist, 16′ long, is placed with the larger dimension vertical and is supported at the ends. The joist is subjected to a uniformly distributed load of 80 lbs. per ft. Calculate the maximum bending stress.

Solution:

1. Fig. 7*A* shows the free-body diagram
2. We can find the reactions by writing moment equations, or, since the loading is symmetrical, we can take each reaction as half of the total load. The total load is

$$80 \times 16 = 1{,}280 \text{ lbs.}$$

so the reactions are

$$R_1 = R_2 = \tfrac{1}{2} \times 1{,}280 = 640 \text{ lbs.}$$

3. Fig. 7*B* shows part of the shear diagram. We must locate the point where the shearing force is *zero* because that is the point where the maximum bending moment occurs.
   a) Start the shear diagram by drawing the base line *AB*
   b) Plot the reaction R_1 (640 lbs.) upward from *A* to locate point *C*. The shear at *C* is 640 lbs.
   c) Draw the sloping line *CD*. The shear at *D* is

$$640 - 80x = 0$$

and we can solve for x

$$80x = 640; \; x = 8 \text{ ft.}$$

4. The maximum bending moment occurs at *D*. It is equal to the moment of all forces to the left of *D*

$$Max.\ M = 640 \times 8 - 80 \times 8 \times 4$$
$$= 5{,}120 - 2{,}560 = 2{,}560 \text{ lb. ft.}$$

(If you do not understand the foregoing problem, review Chapter VI.) We convert this bending moment to lb. in. by multiplying by 12. Thus,

$$Max.\ M = 2{,}560 \times 12 = 30{,}700 \text{ lb. in.}$$

5. Fig. 7*C* shows the cross section of the joist. Notice that the loads are perpendicular to the x axis, so we must use Z for the x axis. In column 5 of Table V, find Z for a 2x12 standard wood section.

$$Z = 35.8 \text{ in.}^3$$

6. The maximum bending stress is

$$S = \frac{M}{Z} = \frac{30{,}700}{35.8} = 858 \text{ lbs. per sq. in.}$$

Practice Problems (Art. 7-5). You can calculate bending stress in standard sections. Z may be taken from the table. Unless it is specifically stated otherwise, each beam in the following problems is placed so the loads are perpendicular to the x axis.

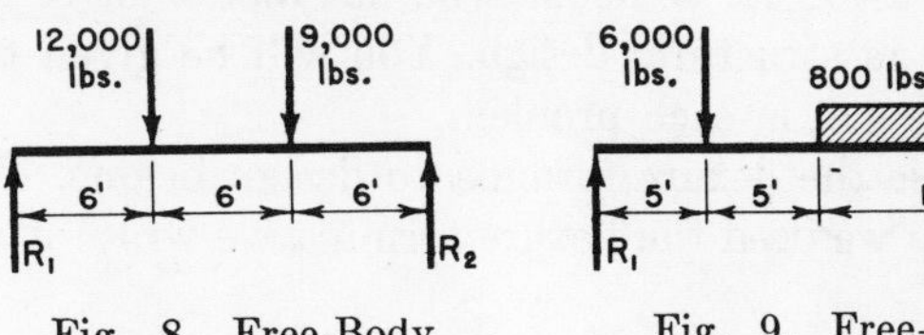

Fig. 8. Free-Body Diagram for Problem 1 (Art. 7-5)

Fig. 9. Free-Body Diagram for Problem 3 (Art. 7-5)

1. An American standard beam, 12 I 35, carries the loads shown in Fig. 8. Calculate the maximum bending stress.
2. A 2x10 wood joist, 12′ long, is supported at the ends and subjected to a uniformly distributed load of 100 lbs. per ft. Find the maximum bending stress.

3. A wide-flange beam, 8 WF 27, is to carry the loads shown in Fig. 9. What is the maximum bending stress?
4. A wide-flange beam, 14 WF 30, is 22 ft. long. The beam is supported at the ends and carries a concentrated load of 15,400 lbs. at a distance of 8 ft. from the left end. Find the maximum bending stress.
5. A 2x12 plank, 10 ft. long, forms part of a scaffold; the plank is supported at the ends and is placed with the short side vertical. A man who weighs 150 lbs. stands on the plank at a distance of 3 ft. from the left end, and a man who weighs 180 lbs. stands on the plank at a distance of 8 ft. from the left end. Calculate the maximum bending stress.
6. An American standard beam, 6 I 17.25, is 12 ft. long; it is supported at the left end, and at a distance of 3 ft. from the right end. The beam carries a uniformly distributed load of 400 lbs. per ft. over its entire length and a concentrated load of 1,800 lbs. at a distance at 4 ft. from the left end. What is the maximum bending stress?

7-6. Design of Beams of Standard Section.

Now you are ready to study the problem of designing a beam of standard section; to design a beam means to select the type of beam (for instance, steel wide-flange, American standard, rectangular wood beam, or some other type), and then to determine the size of the beam. Most beams in structures are of some type of standard section.

The selection of the type of beam does not depend as much on strength of materials as it does on other factors. We can select a strong enough beam of any type, and we use our knowledge of strength of materials to make sure that it is strong enough. However, there are other important factors besides strength of the beam. One of these factors is *economy*, and another is the problem of fastening the beam to its supports, and then fastening the beam to the objects supported. Sometimes, of course, it is easy to choose the type of beam; for example, beams used in residences are usually rectangular wood beams, while steel beams would probably be used in a fireproof structure; but, generally, the selection of the type of beam is a job for someone who has had a lot of experience in structural design. You will be given the type of beam in each problem.

We use the flexure formula to design beams. The last time we used the flexure formula we wrote it as,

$$S = \frac{M}{Z}$$

(S is *stress*, M is *bending moment*, and Z is *section modulus*.) Now multiply both sides of the formula by Z and divide by S. This will give you

$$\frac{S}{S} Z = \frac{M}{Z} \frac{Z}{S}$$

Next, cancel S on the left side of the equation and cancel Z on the right side. Then you will have

$$Z = \frac{M}{S}$$

You know that M is the maximum *bending moment* and that M must be expressed in pound inches; you know how to calculate it, too. Then, S is the working stress in bending; you know from Chapter V that the *working stress* is the stress which is considered safe for the material in service, and which we expect to be developed when the beam is loaded. You will be given the value of S for each problem and you can look in Table II of Chapter V for typical values of working stresses.

After you have calculated the maximum bending moment M (making sure that M is in pound inches), you divide M by the working stress S; this gives the section modulus Z.

$$Z = \frac{M}{S}$$

Then you look in the tables to pick out a beam which has a large enough value of Z. Usually there is not a standard section which has exactly the section modulus you need, so you select the beam which has the closest section modulus on the larger side. Ordinarily, then, the beam is just a little stronger than you need.

Illustrative Example 1. Pick out a suitable American standard beam to carry a maximum bending moment of 32,800 lb. ft. with a working stress of 18,000 lbs. per sq. in.

Solution:

1. Change the bending moment to lb. in.

$$M = 32{,}800 \times 12 = 394{,}000 \text{ lb. in.}$$

2. The working stress S is 18,000 lbs. per sq. in.
3. The section modulus needed is

$$Z = \frac{M}{S} = \frac{394{,}000}{18{,}000} = 21.8 \text{ in.}^3$$

4. Select the beam from Table II, and Z is with respect to the x axis. (These beams are always used this way.) Now look in column 8 and see the figure 24.4, which is as close to 21.8 as we can get and have a figure larger than 21.8; then look to the left to see that 24.4 is the section modulus of a beam which is 10″ deep and which weighs 25.4 lbs. per ft. This is the beam and the standard designation is

10 I 25.4

Now you know how to find the section modulus which is the key figure in the selection of a beam.

Practice Problems (Art. 7-6). Designing beams is best learned by doing it. Practice by solving the following problems.

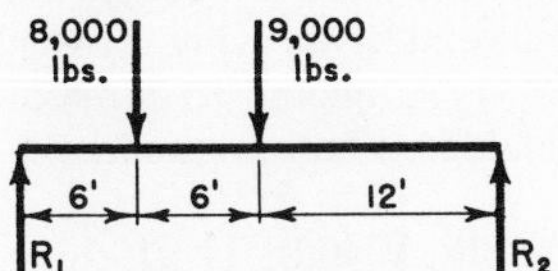

Fig. 10. Free-Body Diagram for Problem 2 (Art. 7-6)

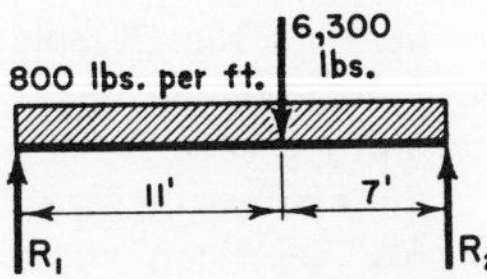

Fig. 11. Free-Body Diagram for Problem 3 (Art. 7-6)

1. A wood joist 16′ long is to be supported at the ends. The joist is to carry a uniformly distributed load of 60 lbs. per ft. over the entire length, and a concentrated load of 200 lbs. at a point 6′ from the left end. The working stress is 1,200 lbs. per sq. in. What size of joist should be used?
2. Select a wide-flange beam to carry the loads shown in Fig. 10. The working stress is 16,000 lbs. per sq. in.
3. An American standard beam is to carry the loads shown in Fig. 11 with a working stress of 20,000 lbs. per sq. in. Pick the beam.
4. Choose a rectangular wood beam to carry the loads shown in Fig. 12. The working stress is 1,600 lbs. per sq. in.
5. An American standard beam 20′ long is supported at the right end and at 6′ from the left end. The beam carries a concentrated load of 10,000 lbs. at the left end, and a concentrated load of 7,000 lbs. at 15′ from the left end. The working stress is 18,000 lbs. per sq. in. Select the beam.
6. A wide-flange beam 22′ long is to be supported at the ends. The beam is to carry a uniformly distributed load of 1,200 lbs. per ft. from the left end to a point 12′ from the left end, and a concentrated load of 9,000 lbs. 12′ from the left end. The working stress is 20,000 lbs. per sq. in. Choose the size of beam.

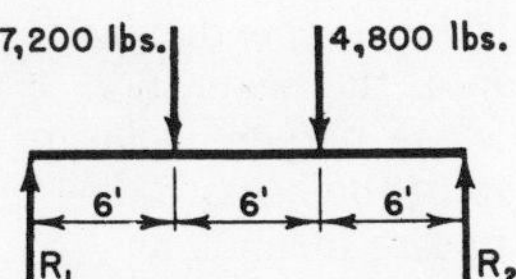

Fig. 12. Free-Body Diagram for Problem 4 (Art. 7-6)

7-7. Shearing Stress in Standard Sections.

You learned in Chapter VI to calculate the *shearing force* at any point in a beam and to represent the shearing force by V. The shearing force causes shearing stress in the cross section of the beam, and now you will learn how to calculate this stress in a beam of standard section. The shearing stress is distributed over the cross section of the beam, but the manner of distribution is complicated in any of the standard steel beams; so complicated that an exact formula is seldom used. Instead, a simple approximate formula is used, and gives good results. For standard steel beams, take the shearing stress as,

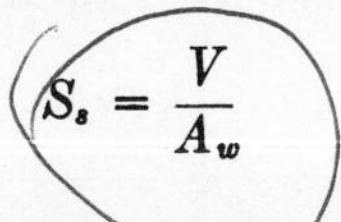

$$S_s = \frac{V}{A_w}$$

Here S_s is *shearing stress*, V is *shearing force*, and A_w is the area of the web of the beam.

The *web of a steel beam* is the vertical part. You can see several examples in Fig. 13. The web is a rectangle and so its area is the product of the thickness and the altitude. You should not encounter any trouble in calculating A_w.

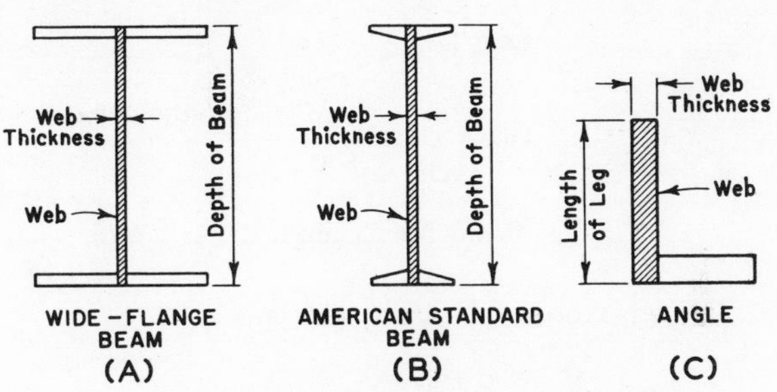

Fig. 13. Web Areas of Steel Beams

Usually, we want to find the maximum shearing stress in the beam. Then we must use the maximum shearing force V in the formula. You know by now that the shearing force varies from one end of the beam to the other, and you also know that you can look at the shear diagram and see what the maximum shearing force is. It does not matter whether the shearing force is *positive* or *negative.* The numerical value is the important part.

Illustrative Example 1. Fig. 14A shows the free-body diagram of a wide-flange beam, 12 WF 45. Calculate the maximum shearing stress.

Solution:

1. You can obtain the maximum shearing force V from the shear diagram in Fig. 14B. You know how to draw shear diagrams by now. Check this one to see that it is correct. The maximum shearing force occurs at the right end of the beam. It is

$$V = 9{,}400 \text{ lbs.}$$

Pay no attention to the negative sign.

2. Now find the area of the web
   a) In column 7 of Table I, read the web thickness as 0.336″

b) In column 4 of Table I, read the depth of the beam as 12.06″

c) The web area is the product of the thickness and the depth

$$A_w = 0.336 \times 12.06 = 4.06 \text{ sq. in.}$$

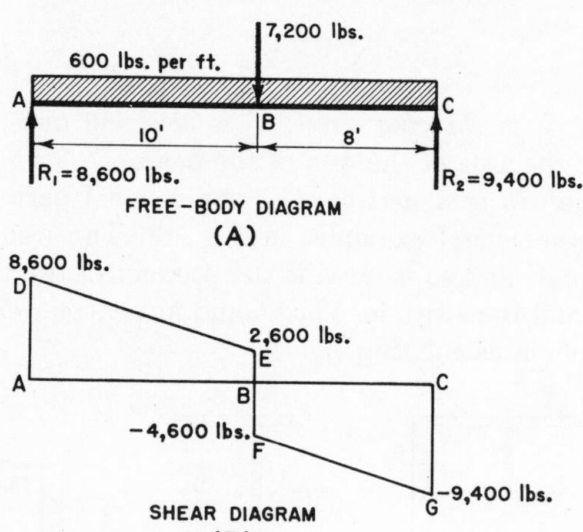

Fig. 14. Beam for Example 1 (Art. 7-7)

3. The maximum shearing stress is

$$S_s = \frac{V}{A_w} = \frac{9{,}400}{4.06} = 2{,}320 \text{ lbs. per sq. in.}$$

A rectangular wood beam is easy, too. You remember from Chapter VI that the maximum shearing stress in a rectangular beam is

$$S_s = \frac{3}{2}\frac{V}{bd}$$

Here b is the width of the beam and d is the depth, so the product bd is the area of the beam. We could write the formula as

$$S_s = \frac{3}{2}\frac{V}{A}$$

where A is the area of the beam. Now you can get the area of a standard wood beam from Table V and substitute in this formula.

Illustrative Example 2. A 4x10 wood beam is subjected to a maximum shearing force of 3,160 lbs. Calculate the maximum shearing stress.

Solution:

1. V is given as 3,160 lbs.
2. In column 3 of Table V, read the area as 34.4 sq. in.
3. The maximum shearing stress is

$$S_s = \frac{3}{2}\frac{V}{A} = \frac{3}{2}\frac{3{,}160}{34.4} = 138 \text{ lbs. per sq. in.}$$

Practice Problems (Art. 7-7).

1. A 2x8 wood beam is subjected to a maximum shearing force of 920 lbs. What is the maximum shearing stress?
2. Fig. 15 shows the free-body diagram of an American standard beam, 8 **I** 23. Find the maximum shearing stress.
3. A 4x12 wood beam is subjected to the loads shown in Fig. 16. Calculate the maximum shearing stress.
4. A wide-flange beam, 16 WF 88, is subjected to a maximum shearing force of 17,900 lbs. What is the maximum shearing stress?
5. An American standard beam, 12 **I** 40.8, is 21′ long and is supported at the ends. The beam is subjected to a concentrated load of 7,400 lbs., 6′ from the left end, and a concentrated load of 8,700 lbs., 14′ from the left end. Calculate the maximum shearing stress.
6. A wide-flange beam, 8 WF 27, is 18′ long. The beam is supported at the right end, and at 6′ from the left end. It carries a uniformly distributed load of 1,000 lbs. per ft. over the entire length and a concentrated load of 4,200 lbs. at the left end. Find the maximum shearing stress.

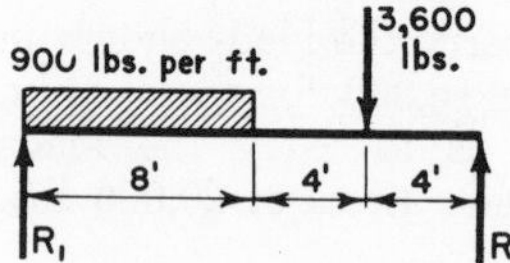

Fig. 15. Free-Body Diagram for Problem 2 (Art. 7-7)

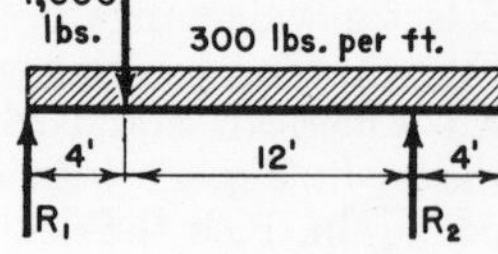

Fig. 16. Free-Body Diagram for Problem 3 (Art. 7-7)

SUMMARY OF CHAPTER VII

A review of the main points in this chapter follows.

1. Standard sections are used for most beams in bridges and buildings. You can find the properties of standard sections in tables.
2. We write the flexure formula as

$$S = \frac{M}{Z}$$

in order to calculate the bending stress in a beam of standard section. Z is the section modulus.

a) If the loads are perpendicular to the x axis of the cross section of the beam, take Z for the x axis.

b) If the loads are perpendicular to the y axis of the cross section of the beam, take Z for the y axis.

3. We write the flexure formula as

$$Z = \frac{M}{S}$$

to design a beam. We divide the maximum bending moment M by the working stress S to find the section modulus Z. Then we look in the tables to find a beam which has the required section modulus.

4. The shearing stress in a standard steel section is approximately equal to the shearing force V divided by the area of the web, A_w. The formula is

$$S_s = \frac{V}{A_w}$$

You find the dimensions of the web in the tables.

5. The maximum shearing stress in a rectangular beam is

$$S_s = \frac{3}{2}\frac{V}{A}$$

You can find the area A of any standard section in the tables.

Review Questions

Check your knowledge by answering these questions.

1. Name three types of standard steel section.
2. Why are standard sections economical?
3. What is the *section modulus of a beam?*
4. Which is greater, the *actual size* or the *nominal size* of a standard wood beam?
5. What is the section modulus used for?
6. How do you design a beam?
7. What is a *working stress?*
8. How do you calculate the shearing stress in a standard steel section?
9. How do you calculate the shearing stress in a standard wood section?

Review Problems

Review this chapter by working these problems before you go on with your study of the next chapter.

1. A 4x8 wood beam, 15′ long, is supported at the ends. The beam carries a concentrated load of 500 lbs. at 6′ from the left end, and a concentrated load of 750 lbs. at 10′ from the left end. Calculate the maximum bending stress and the maximum shearing stress.
2. Fig. 17 shows the free-body diagram of a wide-flange beam, 8 WF 27. Find the maximum bending stress and the maximum shearing stress.
3. An American standard beam, 15 **I** 70, is subjected to a maximum bending moment of 110,000 lb. ft. and a maximum shearing force of 32,800 lbs. Find the maximum bending stress and the maximum shearing stress.
4. Select a suitable American standard beam for the loading shown in Fig. 18. The working stress in bending is 18,000 lbs. per sq. in.

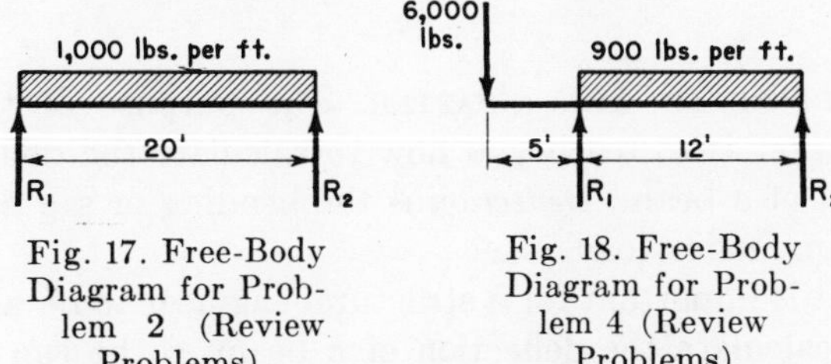

Fig. 17. Free-Body Diagram for Problem 2 (Review Problems)

Fig. 18. Free-Body Diagram for Problem 4 (Review Problems)

5. A pair of equal angles, placed as shown in Fig. 19, is used as a beam. The angles are 6′ long and are supported at the ends; they are subjected to a uniformly distributed load of 420 lbs. per ft. Select a suitable size for the angles using a working stress of 16,000 lbs. per sq. in. in bending.

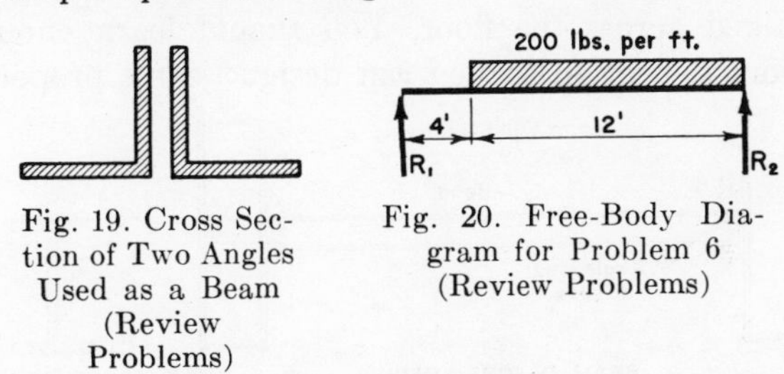

Fig. 19. Cross Section of Two Angles Used as a Beam (Review Problems)

Fig. 20. Free-Body Diagram for Problem 6 (Review Problems)

6. Pick out a rectangular wood beam for the loading shown in Fig. 20. The working stress in bending is 1,200 lbs. per sq. in.

CHAPTER VIII

DEFLECTION OF A BEAM

PURPOSE OF THIS CHAPTER. The purpose of this chapter is to teach you how to calculate the deflection of a beam. *Deflection* is the bending or sag of a beam under load.

It is important for a structural engineer to be able to calculate the deflection of a beam, so he can be sure to design a beam which will not deflect too much. A beam may be strong enough to carry the loads, but may still deflect too much to be suitable. For example, it would be possible to design a floor system which would not fall down under the loads, but which would deflect several inches whenever a person walked across the floor. You should learn enough about deflection so you can design beams properly.

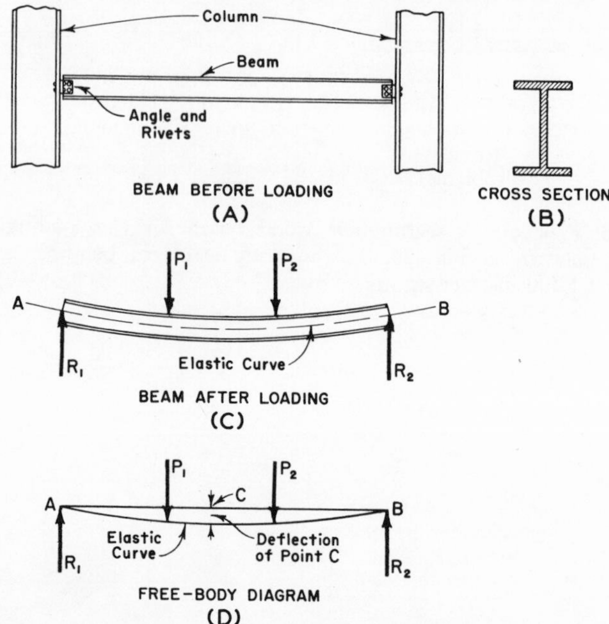

Fig. 1. Deflection of a Beam After Loading

8-1. What Deflection Is.

Fig. 1 illustrates the meaning of *deflection*. Fig. 1A shows a steel beam before the loads are applied, and Fig. 1B shows the cross section; the line AB in Fig. 1C goes through the centroid of each cross section of the beam. The beam is riveted to steel angles at the ends and the angles are riveted to steel columns. Fig. 1C shows the beam as it looks when it is supporting the loads. You should remember a picture like this in Chapter VI, when we studied bending stress; the upper part of the beam shortens and is in compression; the lower part of the beam stretches and is in tension. There is no change of length and no stress along the line AB; this line is called the *elastic curve of the beam.*

Fig. 1D shows the free-body diagram of the beam. The heavy line AB is the center line of the beam before the loads are applied, and the curved line is the elastic curve; the loads cause the beam to bend; the center line is called the *elastic curve* after the beam is bent. Any point C moves downward as the beam bends; the distance that the point moves is called its *deflection.*

Some points in a beam deflect more than other points. Usually, we are interested in the point that deflects the most; that is, we want to calculate the *maximum deflection* of the beam. The formulas which you can use for this purpose will be given. Some of these formulas will be exact and some will be only approximate. However, even the approximate formulas will be close enough for practical purposes. The derivation of the formulas will not be given, because that would take too much space, but you will be shown how to use the formulas.

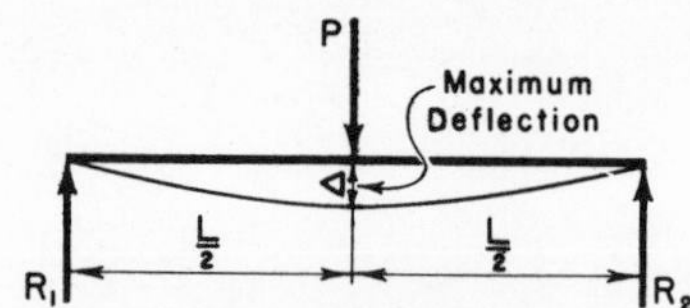

Fig. 2. Beam with Concentrated Load

8-2. Maximum Deflection of a Beam with a Concentrated Load at the Center.

One of the simplest formulas is for a beam which is supported at the ends and carries a concentrated load at the center. Fig. 2 shows a beam with this loading; here we use the symbol P for the load and the symbol L for the length of the beam. The maximum deflection is represented by Δ (Greek letter *delta*); it occurs at the center of the beam and is

$$\Delta = \frac{1}{48}\frac{PL^3}{EI}$$

where E is the *modulus of elasticity* of the material in tension and compression, and I is the *moment of inertia* of the cross section of the beam. Watch the units in this equation: take P in *pounds*, L in *inches*, E in *pounds per square inch*, and I in *in.*[4], if you want to get Δ in inches.

Illustrative Example 1. An American standard beam, 12 **I** 40.8, is 16′ long and is supported at the ends. The beam is subjected to a concentrated load of 18,000 lbs. at the center. Calculate the maximum deflection.

Solution:

1. The load P is 18,000 lbs.
2. The length L is 16′ and this must be expressed in inches

$$L = 16 \times 12 = 192''$$

3. The *modulus of elasticity* of steel is (see Table I, Chapter V)

$$E = 30{,}000{,}000 \text{ lbs. per sq. in.}$$

4. Look up I in column 7 of Table II, in Chapter VII

$$I = 269 \text{ in.}^4$$

5. The maximum deflection is

$$\Delta = \frac{1}{48}\frac{PL^3}{EI} = \frac{1}{48}\frac{18{,}000 \times (192)^3}{30{,}000{,}000 \times 269} = 0.329''$$

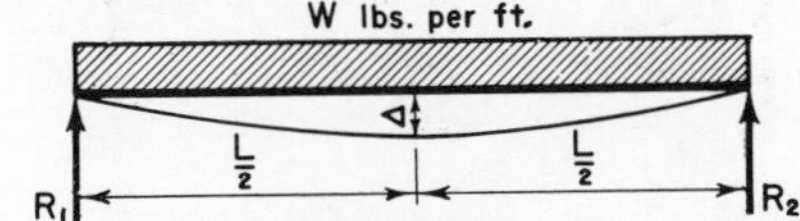

Fig. 3. Beam with Uniform Load

8-3. Maximum Deflection of a Beam with a Uniformly Distributed Load.

Fig. 3 shows a beam with a uniformly distributed load. Represent the load in pounds per foot by w (small letter) and the total load by W (capital letter). The maximum deflection occurs at the center and is

$$\Delta = \frac{5}{384}\frac{WL^3}{EI}$$

Notice here that W is the total load in pounds. You know how to obtain L, E, and I.

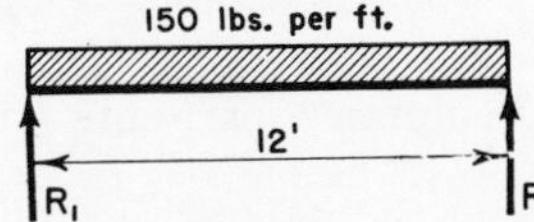

Fig. 4. Loading for Example 1 (Art. 8-3)

Illustrative Example 1. A 2x10 wood joist is subjected to the load shown in Fig. 4. The modulus of elasticity is 1,600,000 lbs. per sq. in. Calculate the maximum deflection.

Solution:

1. The total load W is equal to the load w in pounds per foot times the length of the beam.

$$W = 150 \times 12 = 1{,}800 \text{ lbs.}$$

2. The length L is 12′. In inches, this is

$$L = 12 \times 12 = 144''$$

3. $E = 1{,}600{,}000$ lbs. per sq. in.
4. Look up I in column 4 of Table V in Chapter VII

$$I = 116.1 \text{ in.}^4$$

5. The maximum deflection is

$$\Delta = \frac{5}{384}\frac{WL^3}{EI} = \frac{5}{384}\frac{1{,}800\ (144)^3}{1{,}600{,}000 \times 116.1} = 0.375''$$

Practice Problems (Art. 8-3). Calculate the following deflections so you will become familiar with the procedure.

1. A wide-flange beam, 8 **WF** 17, 14′ long, is supported at the ends and subjected to a uniformly distributed load of 1,100 lbs. per ft. Calculate the maximum deflection.
2. A 4x8 wood beam, 10′ long, is supported at the ends and subjected to a concentrated load of 1,500 lbs. at the center. $E = 1{,}400{,}000$ lbs. per sq. in. Find the maximum deflection.
3. An American standard beam, 10 **I** 35, is 20′ long and is supported at the ends. The beam carries a concentrated load of 12,000 lbs. at the center. What is the maximum deflection?

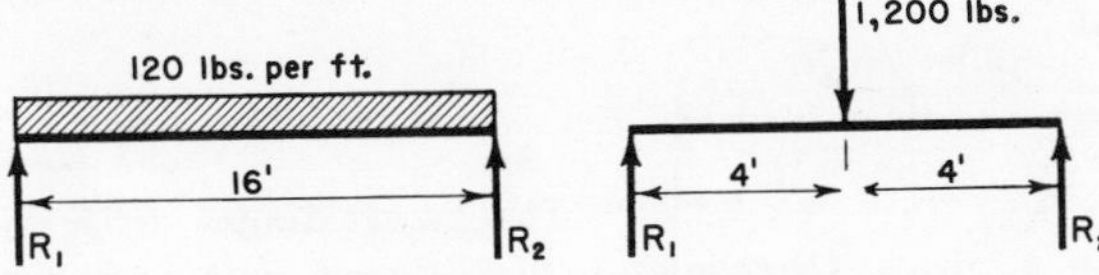

Fig. 5. Free-Body Diagram for Problem 4 (Art. 8-3)

Fig. 6. Free-Body Diagram for Problem 5 (Art. 8-3)

4. A 2x12 wood joist carries the load shown in Fig. 5. $E = 1{,}600{,}000$ lbs. per sq. in. Calculate the maximum deflection.
5. An American standard beam, 3 **I** 6.5, is subjected to the loading shown in Fig. 6. Find the maximum deflection.

8-4. A Collection of Formulas for Beam Deflections.

You will be given a collection of formulas for beam deflections. These formulas give you the deflections due to concentrated and uniformly distributed loads placed in different positions on beams. Table I presents seven special cases of beam loadings and gives formulas for deflections. The problem now is to learn to use the table. Then, later, you will be shown how

TABLE I. BEAM DEFLECTIONS

Case 1. *Beam Supported at Ends with Concentrated Load at Center*

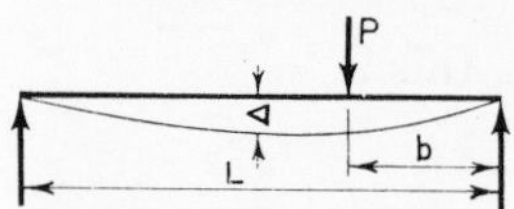

$$\Delta \text{ (at center)} = \frac{1}{48}\frac{PL^3}{EI}$$

This is maximum deflection.

Case 2. *Beam Supported at Ends with Concentrated Load at Any Point*

(Take b as distance from load to closest support.)

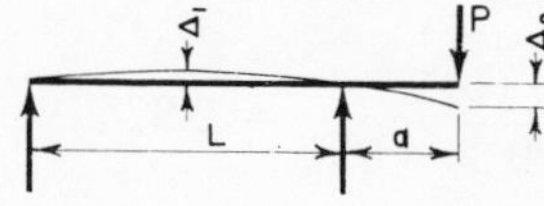

$$\Delta \text{ (at center)} = \frac{1}{16}\frac{Pb}{EI}(L^2 - \tfrac{4}{3}b^2)$$

This is approximately equal to the maximum deflection.

Case 3. *Beam Overhanging One Support with Concentrated Load at End of Overhang*

Δ_1 (halfway between supports)

$$= \frac{1}{16}\frac{PaL^2}{EI}$$

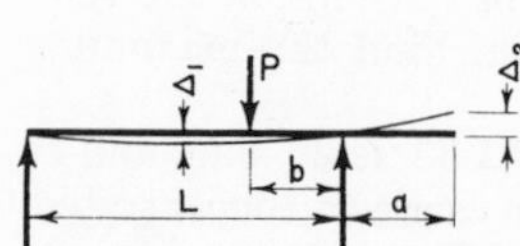

This is approximately equal to the maximum deflection between supports.

$$\Delta_2 = \frac{1}{3}\frac{Pa^2}{EI}(L + a)$$

Case 4. *Beam Overhanging One Support with Concentrated Load at Any Point between Supports*

(Take b as distance from load to closest support for Δ_1.)

Δ_1 (halfway between supports)

$$= \frac{1}{16}\frac{Pb}{EI}(L^2 - \tfrac{4}{3}b^2)$$

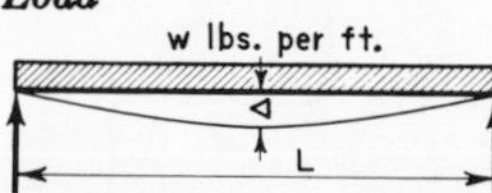

This is approximately equal to the maximum deflection between supports.

$$\Delta_2 = \frac{1}{6}\frac{Pab}{EIL}(L - b)(2L - b)$$

Case 5. *Beam Supported at Ends with Uniformly Distributed Load*

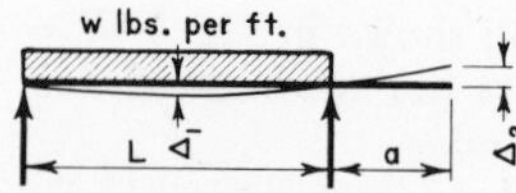

$$\Delta \text{ (at center)} = \frac{5}{384}\frac{WL^3}{EI}$$

This is maximum deflection.

Case 6. *Beam Overhanging One Support with Uniformly Distributed Load between Supports*

Δ_1 (halfway between supports)

$$= \frac{5}{384}\frac{WL^3}{EI}$$

This is the maximum deflection between supports.

$$\Delta_2 = \frac{1}{24}\frac{WL^2a}{EI}$$

Case 7. *Beam Overhanging One Support with Uniformly Distributed Load on Overhang*

Δ_1 (halfway between supports)

$$= \frac{1}{32}\frac{Wa^2L}{EI}$$

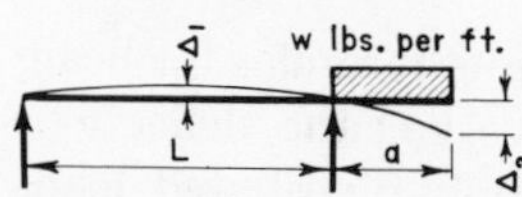

This is approximately equal to the maximum deflection between supports.

$$\Delta_2 = \frac{1}{6}\frac{W_a}{EIL}(a^2L + \tfrac{3}{4}a^3)$$

to apply these formulas to almost any beam-loading problem you need to solve.

The first beam in Table I is a beam supported at the ends with a concentrated load at the center, discussed at the beginning of this chapter.

Case 2 of Table I is a beam which is supported at the ends and which carries a concentrated load at any point. Take b as the distance from the load to the closest support. Then, as you see in the table, the deflection at the center is

$$\Delta = \frac{1}{16}\frac{Pb}{EI}(L^2 - \tfrac{4}{3}b^2)$$

(You must take L and b in inches in this formula; then the deflection Δ is in inches.) The maximum deflection does not occur at the center for this loading. However, this formula is simple and gives a result which is approximately equal to the maximum deflection; the error is usually less than 2 per cent, and this is close enough for practical purposes.

Illustrative Example 1. A wide-flange beam, 8 WF 27, is 18′ long and is supported at the ends. The beam carries a concentrated load of 9,800 lbs. at a distance of 6′ from the left end. Calculate the deflection at the center.

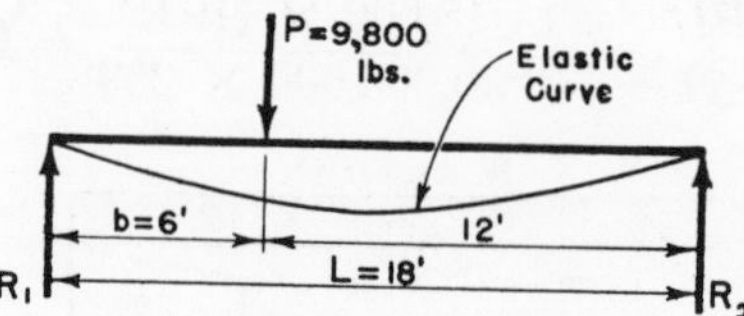

Fig. 7. Free-Body Diagram for Example 1 (Art. 8-4)

Solution:

Fig. 7 shows the free-body diagram of the beam.

1. The load P is 9,800 lbs.
2. The length b is the distance from the load to the closest support and this is 6′, but we must change b to inches

$$b = 6 \times 12 = 72''$$

3. The modulus of elasticity for a steel beam is

$$E = 30{,}000{,}000 \text{ lbs. per sq. in.}$$

4. Look up I in column 8 of Table I in Chapter VII

$$I = 94.1 \text{ in.}^4$$

5. The length L is 18′. Change L to inches

$$L = 18 \times 12 = 216''$$

6. The deflection at the center is

$$\Delta = \frac{1}{16}\frac{Pb}{EI}(L^2 - \tfrac{4}{3}b^2)$$

$$= \frac{1}{16}\frac{9{,}800 \times 72}{30{,}000{,}000 \times 94.1}[(216)^2 - \tfrac{4}{3}(72)^2]$$

$$= 0.620''$$

Case 3 in Table I is a beam which overhangs one support and which carries a concentrated load at the end of the overhang.

Here you are given two formulas. One is for the upward deflection Δ_1, halfway between the supports and the other formula is for the downward deflection Δ_2 at the end of the overhang. The formulas contain the length L between the supports and the distance a from the end of the overhang to the support.

Case 4 of Table I is a beam which overhangs one support and which carried a concentrated load at any point between the supports. Here L is the distance between supports and a is the length of the overhang. Again two formulas are given, one for the downward deflection Δ_1, halfway between the supports, and the other for the upward deflection Δ_2, at the end of the overhang. Notice that you are to take b as the distance from the load to the closest support when you calculate Δ_1; however, when you calculate Δ_2, take b as the distance from the load to the support which is next to the overhang. The formula for Δ_2 looks a little complicated, so study carefully the following example.

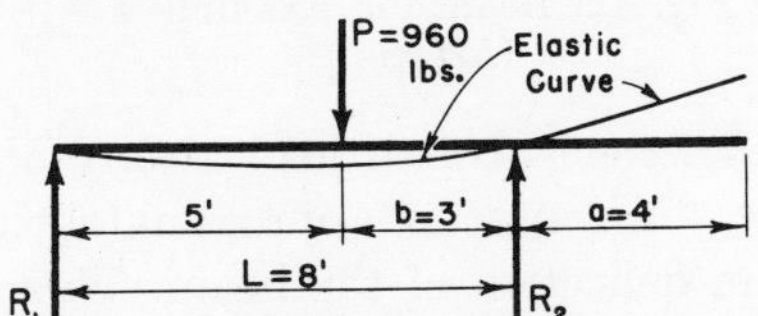

Fig. 8. Free-Body Diagram for Example 2 (Art. 8-4)

Illustrative Example 2. A 2x8 wood beam, 12′ long, is supported at the left end, and at a distance of 4′ from the right end. The beam carries a concentrated load of 960 lbs. at a distance of 5′ from the left end. E = 1,600,000 lbs. per sq. in. Calculate the maximum deflection.

Solution:

Fig. 8 shows the free-body diagram of the beam.

1. The load P is 960 lbs.
2. Notice that b = 3′, but we must express b in inches

$$b = 3 \times 12 = 36''$$

3. The distance a is 4′

$$a = 4 \times 12 = 48''$$

4. E = 1,600,000 lbs. per sq. in.
5. Look up I in column 4 of Table V, in Chapter VII

$$I = 57.1 \text{ in.}^4$$

6. The length L between supports is 8′

$$L = 8 \times 12 = 96''$$

7. The upward deflection at the end of the overhang is

$$\Delta_2 = \frac{1}{6}\frac{Pab}{EIL}(L - b)(2L - b)$$

$$= \frac{1}{6}\frac{960 \times 48 \times 36}{1{,}600{,}000 \times 57.1 \times 96}(96 - 36)(2 \times 96 - 36)$$

$$= 0.295''$$

8. The downward deflection at a point halfway between the supports is

$$\Delta_1 = \frac{1}{16}\frac{Pb}{EI}(L^2 - \tfrac{4}{3}b^2)$$

$$= \frac{1}{16}\frac{960 \times 36}{1{,}600{,}000 \times 57.1}[(96)^2 - \tfrac{4}{3}(36)^2] = 0.169''$$

9. The deflection Δ_2 is greater than Δ_1, so Δ_2 is the maximum deflection. It is

$$\textit{Max. deflection} = 0.295''$$

You can see that Case 5, of Table I, is a beam supported at the ends and subjected to a uniformly distributed load which we have studied previously.

The last two cases in Table I are beams with uniformly distributed loads. You have had enough experience in calculating deflections to understand them. The main things to notice are that W (capital letter) is the total load and all of the dimensions are to be taken in inches.

You notice that in Cases 2, 3, 4, and 7 of Table I, we gave you formulas for the deflection at a point halfway between the supports of the beam; and, in each of these cases, we told you this deflection was approximately equal to the maximum deflection, for any point between the supports. The difference between the formulas we gave you and the maximum deflection is never more than about two per cent; this small difference is not important in practical problems. It means that you may calculate the deflection to be, 0.51″, when the maximum deflection is 0.52″, but do not worry about the variance. The important part of the work is not to get such an answer as 0.112″ or 2.38″ when it ought to be 0.52″. An error of no more than two per cent is satisfactory for structural work, so you can use these formulas with confidence when you want to calculate the maximum deflection of a beam. The real gain from using the formulas in Table I will show up in the next section.

Practice Problems (Art. 8-4). Practice calculating beam deflections by working the following problems.

1. A wide-flange beam, 12 WF 45, is 20′ long, the beam is supported at the left end, and at a point 6′ from the right end. The beam carries a uniformly distributed load of 1,500 lbs. per ft. over the portion between the supports. Calculate the deflection of a point halfway between the supports, and at the end of the overhang.
2. A 6x12 wood beam, 16′ long, is supported at the right end, and at a point 5′ from the left end; the beam carries a concentrated load of 3,000 lbs. at the end of the overhang. E = 1,200,000 lbs. per sq. in. Calculate the deflection at the end of the overhang and at a point halfway between the supports.
3. An American standard beam, 7 I 20, is subjected to the loading shown in Fig. 9. Calculate the deflections at A and B.

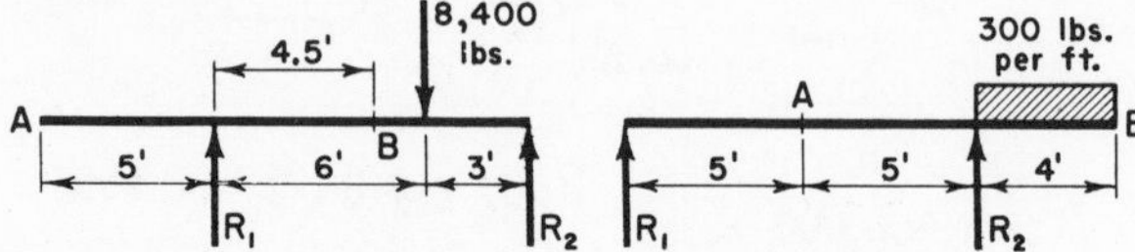

Fig. 9. Free-Body Diagram for Problem 3 (Art. 8-4)

Fig. 10. Free-Body Diagram for Problem 4 (Art. 8-4)

4. Fig. 10 shows the loading for a 2x12 wood beam. E = 1,500,000 lbs. per sq. in. Find the deflections at A and B.

8-5. Beam Deflection by Superposition.

In this section you will be shown a method of calculating an approximate value of the maximum deflection of a beam with several loads. This method is

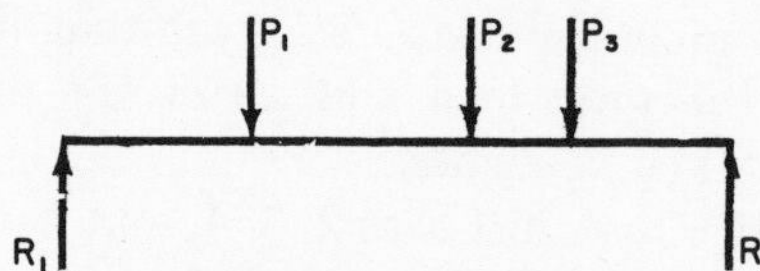

Fig. 11. Free-Body Diagram of Beam Carrying Three Loads

called *superposition* and, as we use it here, the word *superposition* means *putting together*.

Fig. 11 shows a beam with three loads, P_1, P_2, and P_3. We can use this beam as an example in explaining the method of superposition. Suppose we want to calculate the maximum deflection of the beam. Now we have, in Case 2 of Table I, a formula which gives the deflection at the center of a beam

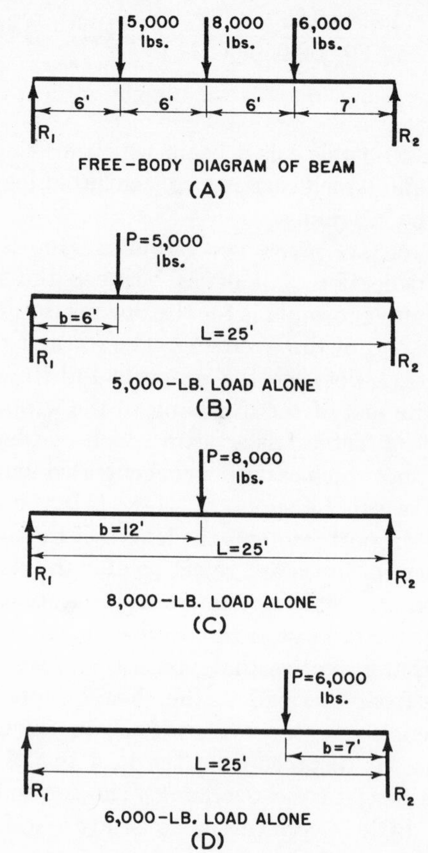

Fig. 12. Beam for Example 1 (Art. 8-5)

which carries a concentrated load at any point; this deflection at the center is approximately equal to the maximum deflection of the beam. We could use this formula to calculate the deflection that would occur at the center if P_1 were the only load on the beam. Next, we could calculate the deflection that would occur at the center if P_2 were the only load on the beam, and then we could calculate the deflection that would occur at the center if P_3 were the only load on the beam. This would give us the deflection at the center due to each of the loads acting separately and, if we added the deflections, the result would be the deflection at the center with all three of the loads applied to the beam.

Each of the separate deflections at the center that we calculate in this method of superposition is approximately equal to the maximum deflection due to the particular load. When we add the deflections, the result is so close to the maximum deflection of the beam, under the three loads, the difference is not worth worrying about.

Illustrative Example 1. Fig. 12*A* shows the loading for an American standard beam, 12 I 40.8. Calculate the maximum deflection.

Solution:

1. First, get the information which will be needed in every part of the problem.
   a) $E = 30{,}000{,}000$ lbs. per sq. in.
   b) Look up I in column 7 of Table II, in Chapter VII

$$I = 269 \text{ in.}^4$$

   c) The length L is 25′; change the length to inches

$$L = 25 \times 12 = 300''$$

2. For the 5,000-lb. load, draw the picture in Fig. 12*B*. Take the formula from Case 2, in Table I
   a) The load P is 5,000 lbs.
   b) The distance b is the distance from the load to the nearest support

$$b = 6 \times 12 = 72''$$

   c) The deflection at the center, due to the 5,000 lbs. load, is

$$\Delta = \frac{1}{16}\frac{Pb}{EI}\left(L^2 - \frac{4}{3}b^2\right)$$

$$= \frac{1}{16}\frac{5{,}000 \times 72}{30{,}000{,}000 \times 269}\left[(300)^2 - \frac{4}{3}(72)^2\right]$$

$$= 0.232''$$

3. For the 8,000 lb. load, we can use the picture in Fig. 12*C*
   a) $P = 8{,}000$ lbs.
   b) $b = 12'$; $b = 12 \times 12 = 144''$
   c) $\Delta = \frac{1}{16}\frac{Pb}{EI}\left(L^2 - \frac{4}{3}b^2\right)$

$$= \frac{1}{16}\frac{8{,}000 \times 144}{30{,}000{,}000 \times 269}\left[(300)^2 - \frac{4}{3}(144)^2\right]$$

$$= 0.556''$$

4. For the 6,000-lb. load, we work with the picture in Fig. 12D.
   a) $P = 6{,}000$ lbs.
   b) $b = 7'$; $b = 7 \times 12 = 84''$
   c) $\Delta = \frac{1}{16}\frac{Pb}{EI}\left(L^2 - \frac{4}{3}b^2\right)$

$$= \frac{1}{16}\frac{6{,}000 \times 84}{30{,}000{,}000 \times 269}\left[(300)^2 - \frac{4}{3}(84)^2\right]$$

$$= 0.315''$$

5. The total deflection is the sum of the deflections due to the separate loads.

$$\Delta = 0.232 + 0.556 + 0.315 = 1.103''$$

Table I gives enough formulas for deflection so that you can calculate the deflection due to each part of the load separately. Then you can add the separate deflections to get the total deflection.

Illustrative Example 2. Fig 13*A* shows the free-body diagram for a 4x12 wood beam. $E = 1{,}600{,}000$ lbs. per sq. in. Calculate the maximum deflection for a point between the supports.

Solution:

1. Obtain the general information first
   a) $E = 1{,}600{,}000$ lbs. per sq. in.
   b) Get I from column 4 of Table V, in Chapter VII, $I = 459$ in.^{4}

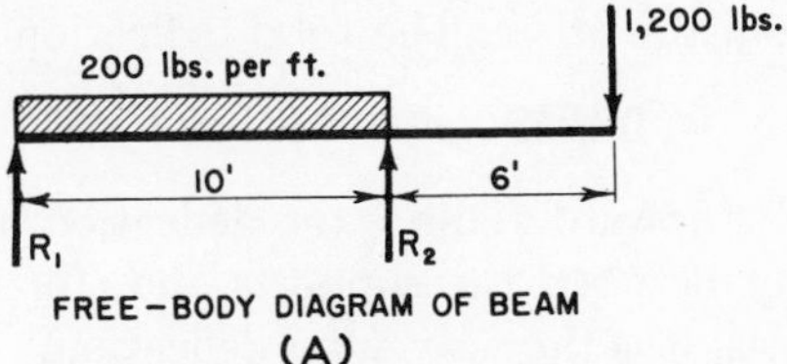

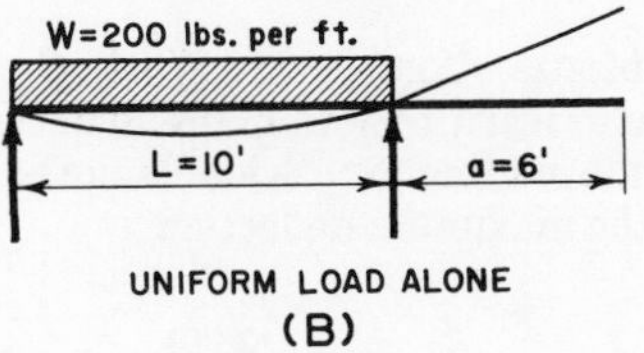

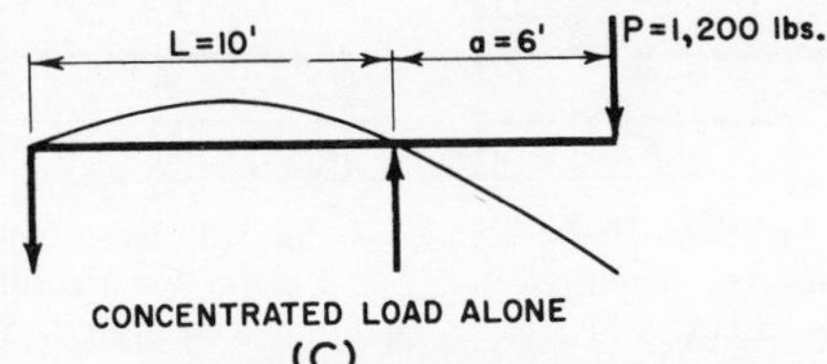

Fig. 13. Beam for Example 2 (Art. 8-5)

   c) The length L between supports is 10′

$$L = 10 \times 12 = 120''$$

   d) The length of the overhang is 6′

$$a = 6 \times 12 = 72''$$

2. For the uniform load alone, we use the picture in 13*B*. This is Case 6, in Table I.
   a) The total load is

$$W = 200 \times 10 = 2{,}000 \text{ lbs.}$$

b) The deflection at a point halfway between the supports is

$$\Delta = \frac{5}{384}\frac{WL^3}{EI} = \frac{5}{384}\frac{2{,}000(120)^3}{1{,}600{,}000 \times 459} = 0.0613''$$

Notice that this deflection is downward.

3. For the concentrated load alone, look at Fig. 13*C*. This is Case 3 of Table I
   a) $P = 1{,}200$ lbs.
   b) The deflection at a point halfway between the supports is

$$\Delta = \frac{1}{16}\frac{PaL^2}{EI} = \frac{1}{16}\frac{1{,}200 \times 72(120)^2}{1{,}600{,}000 \times 459} = 0.1058''$$

Notice that this deflection is upward.

4. For the total deflection, we combine the two deflections which we calculated separately. We have an upward deflection of 0.1058″ and a downward deflection of 0.0613″, so we must subtract one from the other. The total deflection is

$$\Delta = 0.1058 - 0.0613 = 0.045''$$

and it is upward. This is the deflection of a point halfway between the supports and, for practical purposes, it is the maximum deflection.

Practice Problems (Art. 8-5). Work the following problems in order to learn how to figure deflections.

1. Fig. 14 shows the loading for a wide-flange beam, 14 WF 68. Calculate the maximum deflection.

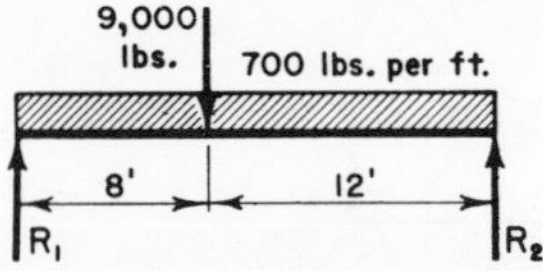

Fig. 14. Free-Body Diagram for Problem 1 (Art. 8-5)

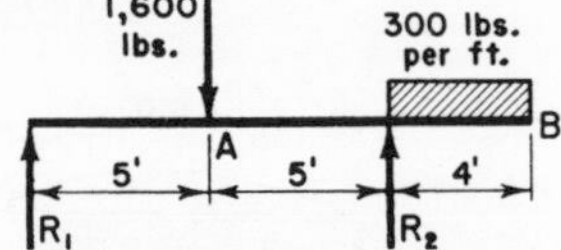

Fig. 15. Free-Body Diagram for Problems 2 and 3 (Art. 8-5)

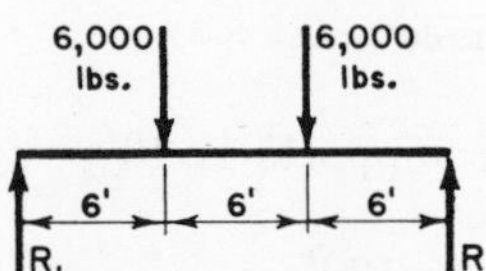

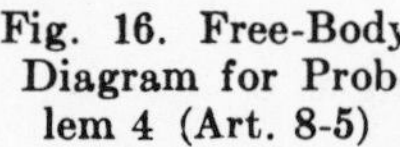
Fig. 16. Free-Body Diagram for Problem 4 (Art. 8-5)

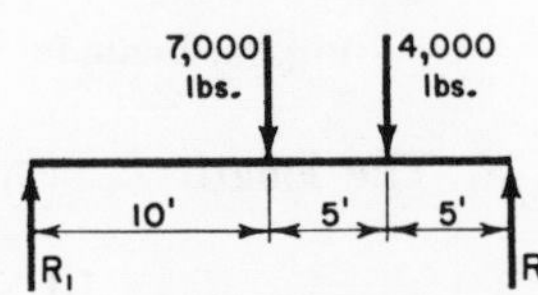

Fig. 17. Free-Body Diagram for Problem 5 (Art. 8-5)

2. A 4x10 wood beam carries the loads shown in Fig. 15. $E = 1{,}200{,}000$ lbs. per sq. in. Calculate the deflection at point *A*.
3. Fig. 15 shows the loading on an American standard beam, 6 I 12.5. Find the deflection at point *B*.
4. A wide-flange beam, 12 WF 28, carries the loads shown in Fig. 16. Find the maximum deflection.
5. Fig. 17 shows the loading for an American standard beam, 10 I 25.4. Calculate the maximum deflection.

SUMMARY OF CHAPTER VIII

The main points of this chapter are summarized here.

1. The line which passes through the centroid of each cross section of a beam is called the *elastic curve of the beam.* The elastic curve is straight before the loads are applied to the beam and is bent after the loads are applied.
2. The deflection of any point in a beam is the distance that this point moves as the beam bends.
3. Table I gives formulas for deflections for several types of beam loading.
   a) The lengths *L*, *a*, and *b* in these formulas are to be taken in inches.
   b) The load *W* is the total of the uniformly distributed load.
   c) The deflection Δ is in inches.
   d) A deflection at the center of a beam which is supported at two points is approximately equal to the maximum deflection between the supports.
4. When several loads are applied to a beam, the deflection can be calculated separately for each load. The separate deflections can be added to give the total deflection. This method is called *superposition.*

Review Questions

These questions may trip you if you have not studied this chapter thoroughly.

1. What is the *elastic curve of a beam?*
2. What is meant by the *deflection of a beam?*
3. What property of the material of which a beam is made affects the deflection? How?
4. What property of the beam cross section affects the deflection?
5. How is the method of superposition used to calculate the maximum deflection of a beam?

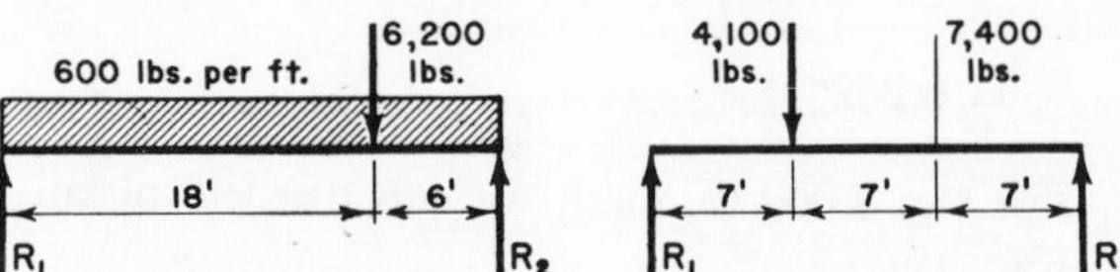

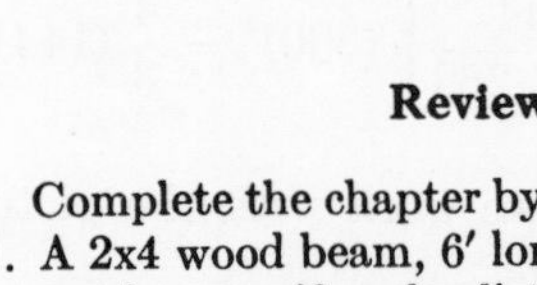

Fig. 18. Free-Body Diagram for Problem 3 (Review Problems)

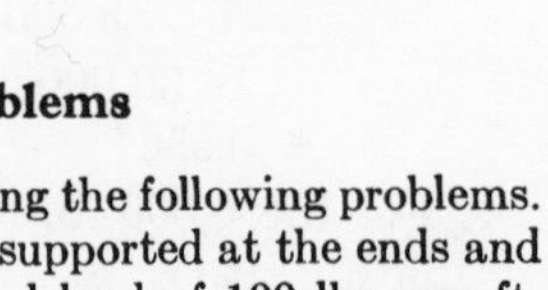

Fig. 19. Free-Body Diagram for Problem 4 (Review Problem)

Review Problems

Complete the chapter by solving the following problems.

1. A 2x4 wood beam, 6′ long, is supported at the ends and carries a uniformly distributed load of 100 lbs. per ft. $E = 1{,}200{,}000$ lbs. per sq. in. What is the maximum deflection?
2. A wide-flange beam, 10 WF 23, 15′ long, is supported at the ends and carries a concentrated load of 5,000 lbs. at the center. Find the maximum deflection.
3. Fig. 18 shows the loading for an American standard beam, 12 I 35. Calculate the maximum deflection.
4. What is the maximum deflection for a wide-flange beam, 12 WF 28, which carries the loads shown in Fig. 19.

CHAPTER IX

STATICALLY INDETERMINATE BEAMS

PURPOSE OF THIS CHAPTER. The purpose of this chapter is to study a type of beam which is a little different from the beams we have studied so far. This type of beam is called a *statically indeterminate beam.*

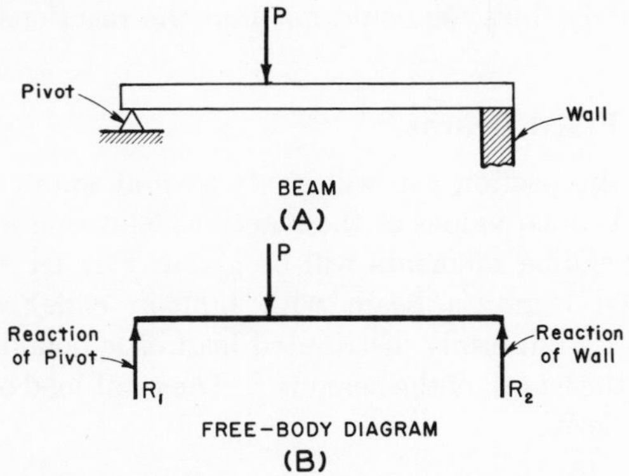

Fig. 1. Reactions of Pivot and Wall on Beam

In all of the beams studied in previous chapters, we have been able to calculate the reactions by writing moment equations, because there were only two reactions. However, when there are more than two reactions on the beam, you cannot find the reactions by writing moment equations. Such a beam is called a *statically indeterminate beam.*

Moment equations are equations of equilibrium (remember from Chapter II), and the equations of equilibrium are also called the *equations of statics* (because a body at rest is static). If the reactions on a beam can be calculated by using the equations of statics (as we have been doing), the beam is said to be *statically determinate;* that is, the reactions can be determined by means of the equations of statics. However, if the reactions on a beam cannot be calculated by means of the equations of statics, the beam is said to be statically indeterminate; that is, the reactions cannot be determined by means of the equations of statics.

In this chapter you will be shown how to recognize a statically indeterminate beam. Then you will be given diagrams and formulas from which you can calculate the reactions, shearing forces and bending moments on the types of beams which you are likely to encounter in engineering work. You will be able to calculate the stresses if you know the cross section of the beam, and you will be able to design a beam for any ordinary loading.

There are several theorems and basic methods for analyzing a statically indeterminate beam. However, it would take too much time and space to explain and teach you how to use these methods. Instead, you will be given the formulas and diagrams without deriving or proving them. You should accept the formulas as correct and learn to use them.

After the reactions have been found, a statically indeterminate beam is just like any other beam. You can calculate shearing forces and bending moments, and use the flexure formula to calculate a bending stress, or to design a beam.

9-1. Types of Supports and Reactions.

The first step in the study of indeterminate beams is to learn something about the different types of supports and the sort of reactions which these supports exert on beams. Fig. 1*A* shows a beam which is supported by a pivot at the left end, and a wall at the right end. Supports of these types only exert forces on the beam; Fig. 1*B* shows the forces in the free-body diagram of the beam.

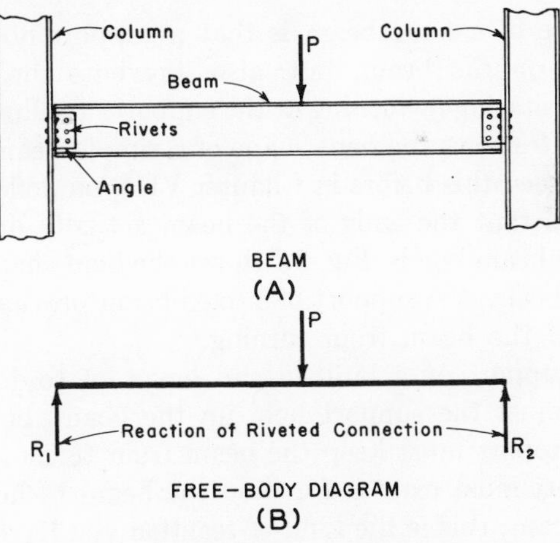

Fig. 2. Reactions of Riveted Connection on Beam

Fig. 2*A* shows a steel beam which is supported by riveted connections at the ends. The beam is riveted to short lengths of steel angles and, in turn, the angles are riveted to steel columns. There may be some room for argument about the reactions exerted by such riveted connections, but it is usually assumed that the only reaction is a force such as you see in the free-body diagram in Fig. 2*B*.

Beams which have supports of the types shown in Figs. 1 and 2 are called *simple beams.*

Fig. 3*A* shows a beam with built-in ends. A beam of this type is called a *fixed beam.* The distinguishing feature of a fixed beam is that a support not only holds up the beam, but, also, prevents the beam from rotating or turning at the support. To illustrate, Fig. 3*B* shows the bent shape of a simple beam; you have seen this before in Chapter VIII, on deflection. Notice that the ends of the beam actually do turn as the beam bends. Fig. 3*C* shows the bent shape of a fixed beam; the support of a fixed beam prevents the end of the beam from turning.

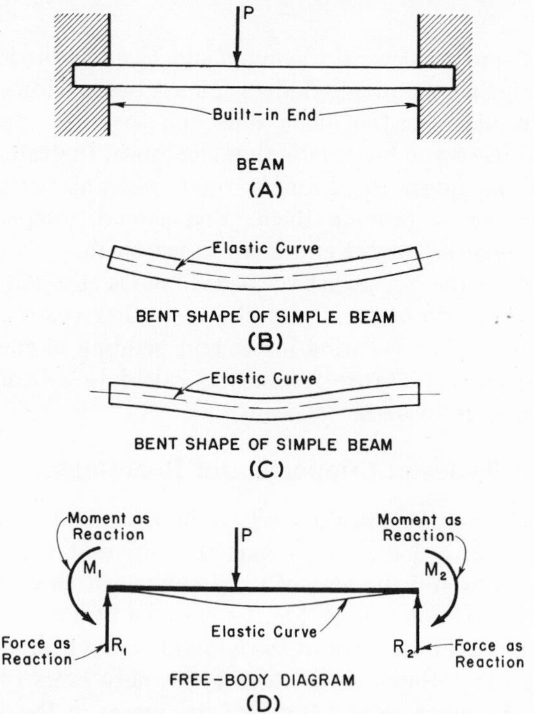

Fig. 3. Reactions on Fixed Beam

A support at a built-in end has a lot to do. Not only must the support hold up the beam, but also the support must keep the beam from turning. The support must exert a force on the beam to hold up the beam; this is the kind of reaction you have been working with. Also, the support must exert a moment on the beam to keep the end of the beam from turning. Fig. 3*D* shows the free-body diagram of the fixed beam of Fig. 3*A*. Here you see the forces R_1 and R_2 exerted by the supports and, also, the moments M_1 and M_2 exerted by the supports. Notice how these moments are represented. This method is not in use everywhere, but it is convenient. A force tends to move a body in a straight line, and so we represent a force by a straight arrow; a moment tends to turn a body and we represent a moment by a curved (turning) arrow.

We count the moments M_1 and M_2 in Fig. 3*D* as reactions along with the forces R_1 and R_2. This makes four reactions on the beam, so the beam is statically indeterminate.

The reactions on a beam consist of a force at each point where the beam is supported and a moment at each built-in end. If the total number of reactions is more than two, the beam is statically indeterminate. You could write moment equations indefinitely, but you could not find the reactions that way.

9-2. Fixed Beams.

In this section you will study several examples of fixed beams; values of the reactions, shearing forces, and bending moments will be given. Fig. 4*A* shows a fixed beam (a beam with built-in ends) which carries a uniformly distributed load of w pounds per foot; the length of the beam is L. The total load on the beam is W.

$$W = wL$$

Fig. 4*B* shows the free-body diagram of the fixed beam with the uniform load. Here you see the forces R_1 and R_2 at the ends of the beam and, also, the moments M_1 and M_2 at the ends. The values are

$$R_1 = \frac{W}{2}; \quad R_2 = \frac{W}{2}; \quad M_1 = \frac{WL}{12}; \quad M_2 = \frac{WL}{12}$$

In these formulas, W is the total load on the beam and is expressed in pounds; also R_1 and R_2 are in pounds. If you take the length L in feet, the moments M_1 and M_2 are in pound feet.

Fig. 4*C* shows the shear diagram of the beam. (The shearing force at any point in a beam is a force which tends to shear the beam in two at that point; the shearing force is equal to the sum of the forces to the left of the point. The shear diagram shows the value of the shearing force at each point along the beam.)

Notice in Fig. 4*C* that the maximum value of the shearing force is $W/2$ and the shearing force is *zero* at point B. Point B is at the center of the beam.

Fig. 4*D* shows the moment diagram of the beam. (The bending moment tends to bend the beam; the bending moment at any point is equal to the moment, with respect to that point, of all of the forces to the left of the point. The moment diagram shows the value of the bending moment at each point along the beam.) You can see in Fig. 4*D* that the bending moment at each end of the beam is

$$-\frac{WL}{12}$$

and the bending moment at the center is

$$\frac{WL}{24}$$

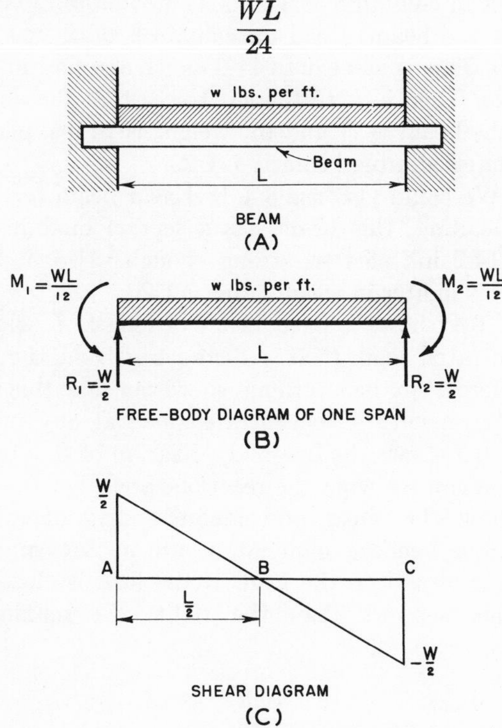

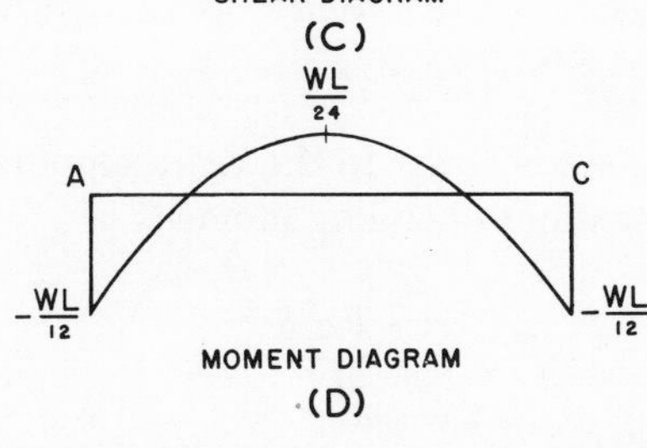

Fig. 4. Fixed Beam with Uniform Load

The maximum numerical value of the bending moment occurs at the end, and is

$$\frac{WL}{12}$$

This is the value in which you are interested, as it causes the maximum bending stress; pay no attention to the negative sign of the bending moment at the ends.

The bending stress in the beam is given by the flexure formula. You probably remember this formula,

$$S = \frac{M}{Z}$$

where M is the bending moment in pound inches, and Z is the section modulus of the cross section. You can find the section modulus of a standard section in the tables in Chapter VII.

Illustrative Example 1. A wide-flange beam 12 WF 28 is 20′ long and is built in at the ends. The beam carries a uniformly distributed load of 1,500 lbs. per ft. Calculate the maximum bending stress.

Solution:

1. The total load is

$$W = 1{,}500 \times 20 = 30{,}000 \text{ lbs.}$$

2. The length L is 20′
3. The maximum bending moment is (see Fig. 4*D*)

$$M = \frac{WL}{12} = \frac{30{,}000 \times 20}{12} = 50{,}000 \text{ lb. ft.}$$

This must be changed to lb. in.

$$M = 50{,}000 \times 12 = 600{,}000 \text{ lb. in.}$$

4. The section modulus is obtained from column 9 of Table I in Chapter VII.

$$Z = 35.6 \text{ in.}^3$$

5. The maximum bending stress is

$$S = \frac{M}{Z} = \frac{600{,}000}{35.6} = 16{,}600 \text{ lbs. per sq. in.}$$

Fig. 5*A* shows a fixed beam which carries a concentrated load at the center. The load is represented by P and the length by L.

Fig. 5*B* shows the free-body diagram of the beam. Here you see that the reactions consist of the forces R_1 and R_2 and the moments M_1 and M_2.

Figs. 5*C* and 5*D* show the shear and moment diagrams for the fixed beam with a concentrated load at the center. The bending moment is

$$\frac{PL}{8}$$

at the center, and

$$-\frac{PL}{8}$$

at each end. The numerical values of these bending moments are the same, so there is no doubt that the maximum bending moment is

$$\frac{PL}{8}$$

We can write the flexure formula as

$$S = \frac{M}{Z}$$

if we want to calculate a bending stress, or we can write the formula as

$$Z = \frac{M}{S}$$

if we want to design a beam. Here S is the *working stress.*

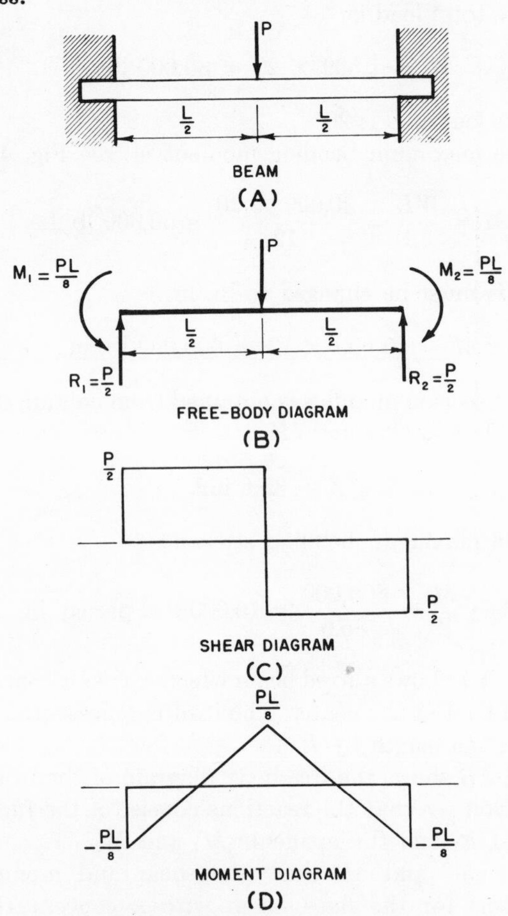

Fig. 5. Fixed Beam with Concentrated Load at Center

Illustrative Example 2. A fixed beam 16′ long is to carry a concentrated load of 8,700 lbs. at the center. Select a suitable American standard beam, using a working stress of 18,000 lbs. per sq. in.

Solution:

1. The load P is 8,700 lbs.
2. The length L is 16′
3. The maximum bending moment is (see Fig. 5*D*)

$$M = \frac{PL}{8} = \frac{8{,}700 \times 16}{8} = 17{,}400 \text{ lb. ft.}$$

$$M = 17{,}400 \times 12 = 209{,}000 \text{ lb. in.}$$

4. The working stress S is 18,000 lbs. per sq. in.
5. The section modulus required is

$$Z = \frac{M}{S} = \frac{209{,}000}{18{,}000} = 11.6 \text{ in.}^3$$

6. Look in column 8 of Table II, in Chapter VII, to pick the beam. Read up column 8 until you see 12.0. This is as near to 11.6 as we can find in the table. Then look to the left to see that the depth of the beam is 7″ and the weight is 20 lbs. per ft. Then a suitable beam is 7 **I** 20.
   a) We could also use 8 **I** 18.4 as a beam for this loading; this beam has a section modulus of 14.2 in.^{3} so it is strong enough. Also, it is a bit lighter in weight than 7 **I** 20.

Fig. 6*A* shows a fixed beam of length L with a concentrated load P at a distance a from the left end. Here a can be anything, so we can take this as a fixed beam with a concentrated load at any point.

Fig. 6*B* shows the free-body diagram of this beam and you can see what the reactions are. Figs. 6*C* and 6*D* show the shear and moment diagrams. The maximum bending moment occurs at the support which is closest to the load. If the load is closer to the left support than the right, the maximum bending moment is

$$\frac{Pab^2}{L^2}$$

but if the load is closer to the right support than the left, the maximum bending moment is

$$\frac{Pa^2b}{L^2}$$

It is best to take the lengths a, b, and L in feet to calculate one of these bending moments. This gives the bending moment in pound feet and you can multiply by 12 to convert it to pound inches.

Illustrative Example 3. A 4x10 wood beam is 12′ long and fixed at the ends. The beam carries a concentrated load of 2,100 lbs. at a distance of 3′ from the left end. Calculate the maximum bending stress.

Solution:

Fig. 7 shows the beam and load.

1. The load P is 2,100 lbs.
2. The length a is 3′
3. The length b is 9′
4. The length L is 12′
5. The load is closer to the left support than the

right, so the maximum bending moment occurs at the left end

$$M = \frac{Pab^2}{L^2} = \frac{2{,}100 \times 3\,(9)^2}{(12)^2} = 3{,}540 \text{ lb. ft.}$$

$$M = 3{,}540 \times 12 = 42{,}500 \text{ lb. in.}$$

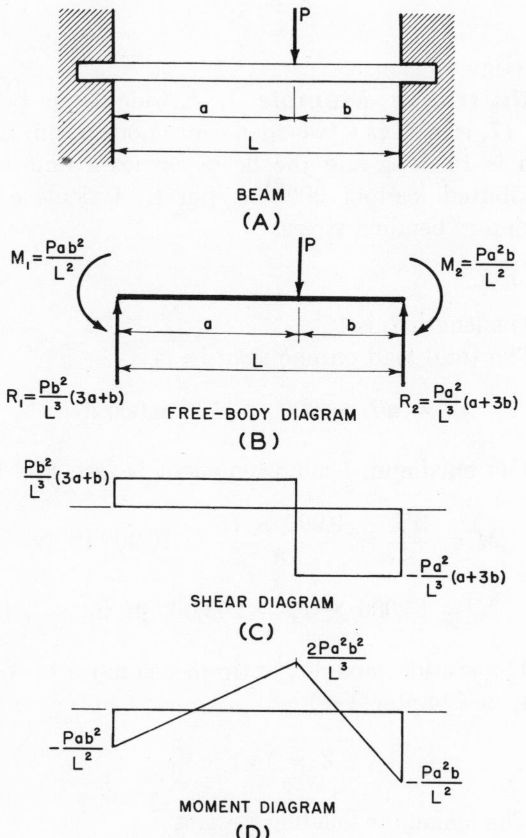

Fig. 6. Fixed Beam with Concentrated Load at Any Point

6. The section modulus is (see column 5 of Table V, in Chapter VII)

$$Z = 54.5 \text{ in.}^3$$

7. The maximum bending stress is

$$S = \frac{M}{Z} = \frac{42{,}500}{54.5} = 780 \text{ lbs. per sq. in.}$$

Here is a word of caution in using the formulas given in this section. The formula applies only to beams in which the cross section is the same from one end to the other. However, most beams in structures do have the same cross section from one end to the other, so the formulas should suit your needs.

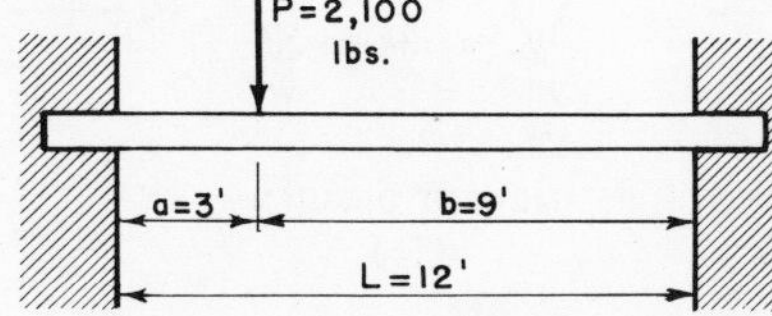

Fig. 7. Beam for Example 3 (Art. 9-2)

Practice Problems (Art. 9-2). These problems will help you remember fixed beams.

1. An American standard beam, 12 I 40.8, is 18′ long and is fixed at the ends. The beam carries a uniformly distributed load of 1,400 lbs. per ft. Calculate the maximum bending stress.
2. A 2x10 wood beam, which is 14′ long and which is fixed at the ends, is subjected to a concentrated load of 1,100 lbs. at the center. What is the maximum bending stress?
3. A fixed beam, 24′ long, carries a concentrated load of 9,200 lbs. at a distance of 15′ from the left end. Select a suitable wide-flange beam, using a working stress of 20,000 lbs. per sq. in.
4. A fixed beam, 10′ long, carries a concentrated load of 600 lbs. at a distance of 4′ from the left end. Select a suitable rectangular wood beam, using a working stress of 1,200 lbs. per sq. in.
5. A fixed beam, 16′ long, is to carry a uniformly distributed load of 2,100 lbs. per ft. Select a suitable American standard beam, using a working stress of 18,000 lbs. per sq. in.
6. A fixed beam, 14′ long, is to carry a concentrated load of 4,300 lbs. at the center. Select a suitable American standard beam, using a working stress of 16,000 lbs. per sq. in.
7. A wide-flange beam, 14 WF 30, is 21′ long and is a fixed beam. It is subjected to a concentrated force of 16,700 lbs. at a distance of 8′ from the left end. Calculate the maximum bending stress.

9-3. Continuous Beams.

Continuous beams make up an important class of statically indeterminate beams; they are important to the structural engineer because continuous beams are used so commonly in building and bridge structures.

A *continuous beam* is a beam which continues over more than two supports. For example, Fig. 8*A* shows a beam which is continuous over three supports and which carries a uniformly distributed load. The part of the beam between two adjacent supports is called a *span;* thus, the beam in Fig. 8*A* extends over two spans.

A beam has a reaction at each support, and supports of the type shown in Fig. 8*A* only exert forces. Nevertheless, there are three reactions on this beam, and so the beam is statically indeterminate. (Any beam which has more than two reactions is statically indeterminate; the reactions cannot be calculated by means of moment equations.)

The values of the reactions, for the beam in Fig. 8, cannot be worked without taking the time and space to develop certain theories, so the values will be given without proof. The reactions are shown in Fig. 8*B*.

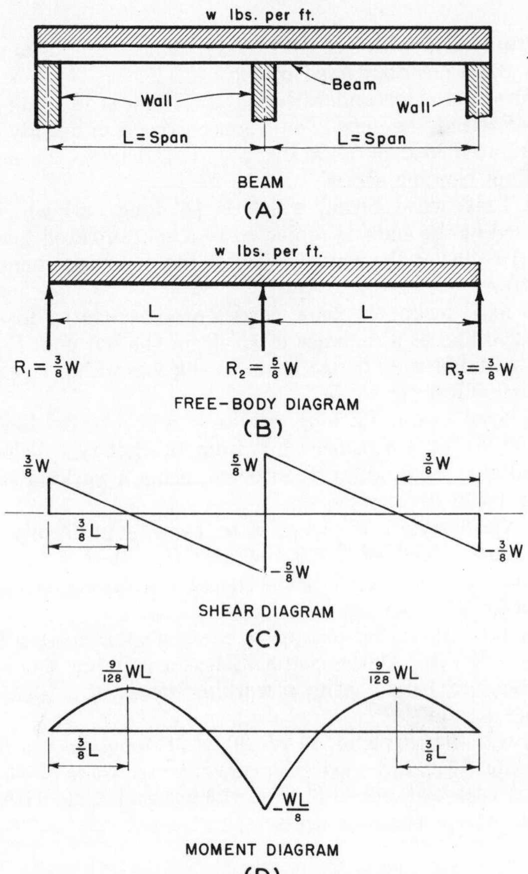

Fig. 8. Continuous Beam of Two Spans

You could draw the shear and moment diagrams for yourself, after you know the reactions; that is, you could if you applied what you learned in Chapter VI. However, the diagrams will be given to save your time. Fig. 8*C* shows the shear diagram and Fig. 8*D* shows the moment diagram.

In Figs. 8*C* and 8*D*, *W* is the total load on one span, and *L* is the length of a span; *w* is the load in lbs. per ft., so

$$W = wL$$

The bending moment has its maximum value at the center support of this continuous beam.

$$Max.\ M = -\frac{WL}{8}$$

This figure is probably the most important one for the beam, and is what you would use in the flexure formula if you wrote it as

$$S = \frac{M}{Z}$$

to calculate a stress or as

$$Z = \frac{M}{S}$$

to design a beam.

Illustrative Example 1. A wide-flange beam, 8 WF 17, is used as a two-span continuous beam. Each span is 15′ long and the beam carries a uniformly distributed load of 600 lbs. per ft. Calculate the maximum bending stress.

Solution:

1. The length *L* is 15′
2. The total load on one span is

$$W = wL = 600 \times 15 = 9{,}000 \text{ lbs.}$$

3. The maximum bending moment is (see Fig. 8*D*)

$$M = \frac{WL}{8} = \frac{9{,}000 \times 15}{8} = 16{,}900 \text{ lb. ft.}$$

$$M = 16{,}900 \times 12 = 203{,}000 \text{ lb. in.}$$

4. The section modulus is (from column 9 of Table I, in Chapter VII)

$$Z = 14.1 \text{ in.}^3$$

5. The maximum bending stress is

$$S = \frac{M}{Z} = \frac{203{,}000}{14.1} = 14{,}400 \text{ lbs. per sq. in.}$$

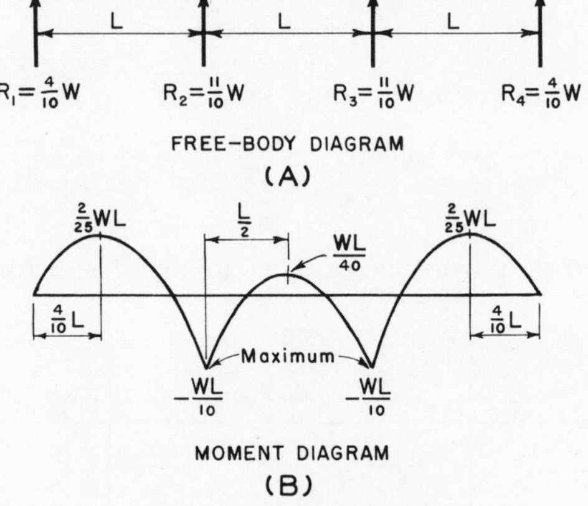

Fig. 9. Continuous Beam of Three Spans

You will now be given a considerable amount of information about continuous beams, but you will be expected to study this information until you understand it thoroughly. You should be able to understand the problems, because you have already worked

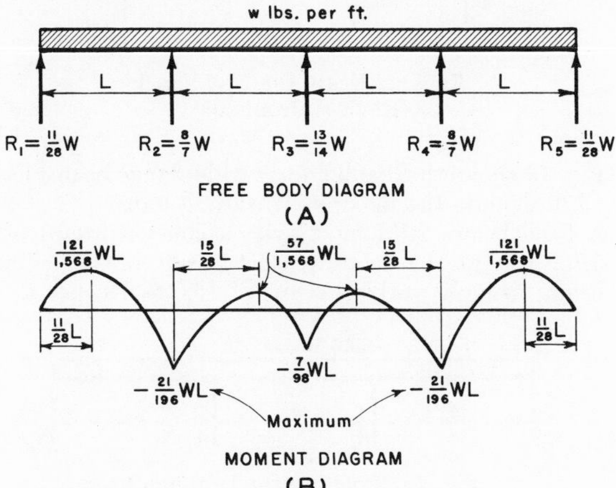

Fig. 10. Continuous Beam of Four Spans

with reactions and moment diagrams. Figs. 9, 10, and 11 show you the free-body diagrams and moment diagrams for three different continuous beams. In each case, the length of each span is L, the beam is subjected to a uniformly distributed load of w pounds per foot, and the total load in each span is W. The maximum bending moment for each beam is also shown. You should now be able to obtain the necessary information, from these figures, and use it.

Illustrative Example 2. A steel beam, 85′ long, is continuous over five spans of 17′ each. The beam carries a uniformly distributed load of 450 lbs. per ft. Calculate the maximum bending moment.

Solution:

1. The length of each span is $L = 17'$
2. The total load in each span is

$$W = wL = 450 \times 17 = 7{,}660 \text{ lbs.}$$

3. The maximum bending moment is

$$M = \frac{2}{19} WL = \frac{2}{19} \times 7{,}660 \times 17 = 13{,}700 \text{ lb. ft.}$$

(see Fig. 11*B*).

These formulas and moment diagrams are only correct for beams which have the same cross section from one end to the other. They are not right for beams which do not have the same cross section at all points. However, there is not much reason for you to design beams of varying cross section, so these formulas and moment diagrams should serve your purpose.

Practice Problems (Art. 9-3). Solving the following problems will help you to learn more about continuous beams.

1. An American standard beam, 10 I 25.4, is 64′ long and is used as a continuous beam over four equal spans; the beam carries a uniformly distributed load of 1,400 lbs. per ft. Calculate the maximum bending stress.
2. Select a suitable rectangular wood beam to be used as a continuous beam over three spans of 14′ each; the beam is to carry a uniformly distributed load of 290 lbs. per ft., and the working stress is 1,500 lbs. per sq. in.
3. Pick a suitable wide-flange beam to carry a uniformly distributed load of 1,900 lbs. per ft. over five equal spans of 16′ each. The working stress is 20,000 lbs. per sq. in.
4. Select a suitable American standard beam to carry a uniformly distributed load of 1,700 lbs. per ft. over two equal spans of 20′ each. The working stress is 18,000 lbs. per sq. in.
5. A 2x12 wood beam, 48′ long, is used as a continuous beam over four equal spans of 12′ each. The beam carries a uniformly distributed load of 200 lbs. per ft. Calculate the maximum bending stress.

SUMMARY OF CHAPTER IX

Here are the main points for you to remember about statistically indeterminate beams.

1. A reaction is a force or moment exerted at a point where a beam is supported.
   a) Any support which holds up a beam exerts a force on the beam.

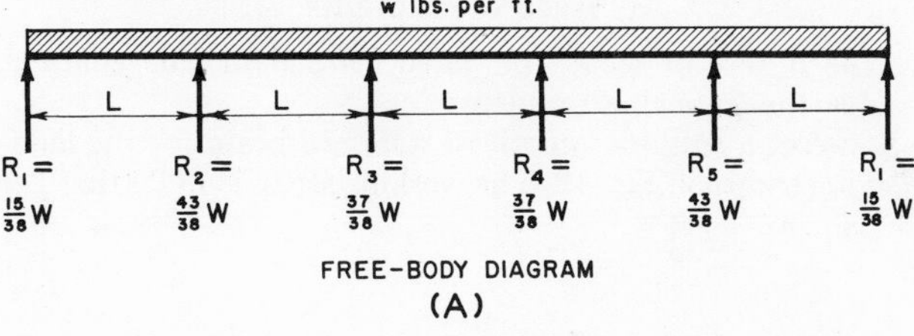

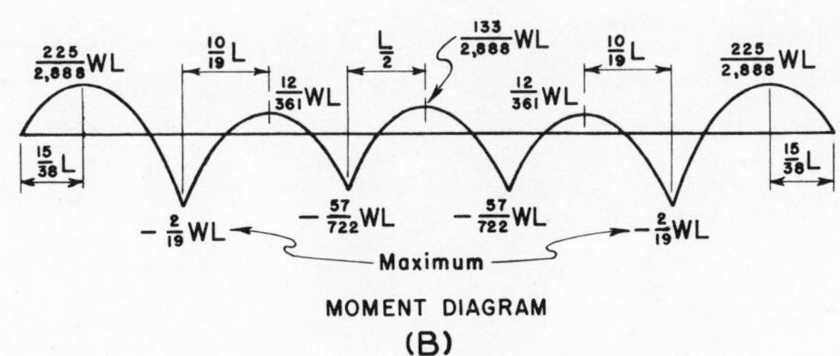

Fig. 11. Continuous Beam of Five Spans

   b) A built-in or fixed support exerts a moment on a beam in addition to a force.
   c) The total number of reactions on a beam is equal to the sum of the number of forces and the number of moments exerted on the beam by the supports.
2. If the total number of reactions (including both forces and moments) is more than two, the beam is statically

indeterminate; the reactions cannot be found by writing moment equations.

a) If the reactions are known, the bending moments can be calculated and the flexure formula can be applied.

b) You have been given the reactions and moment diagrams for a number of statically indeterminate beams.

You should be able now to use the reaction and moment diagrams.

3. The maximum bending moment in a statically indeterminate beam is usually negative, but you can disregard the negative sign for steel and wood beams. The important fact you should remember about the bending moment is its *numerical value.*

Review Questions

See if you can answer the following questions.

1. What is a *reaction?*
2. What is a *fixed end of a beam?*
3. What kinds of reactions are exerted on beams?
4. What kind of reaction does a riveted connection exert on a beam?
5. What kind of reaction is exerted at a built-in support?
6. What is a *statically indeterminate beam?*
7. How can you use the flexure formula for an indeterminate beam?
8. Does the maximum bending moment on a statically indeterminate beam usually occur at a support, or at a point between supports?
9. State the meaning of W and L in the formula,

$$M = \frac{WL}{10}$$

for the bending moment in a statically indeterminate beam.

Review Problems

As a test of what you have learned in this chapter, solve the following problems.

1. Select a suitable American standard beam for the loading shown in Fig. 12. The working stress is 18,000 lbs. per sq. in.
2. A 6x12 wood beam, 16′ long, is fixed at the ends and carries a uniformly distributed load of 430 lbs. per ft. Find the maximum bending stress.

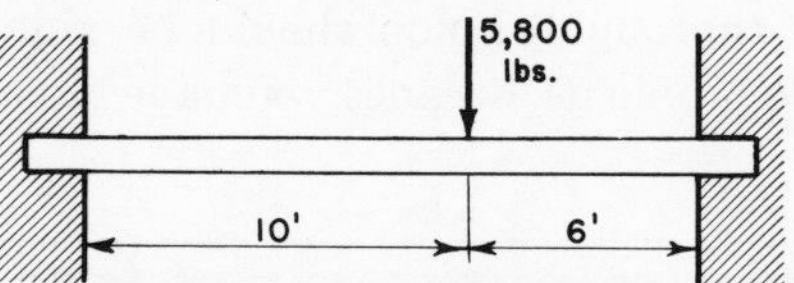

Fig. 12. Beam for Problem 1
(Review Problems)

3. Fig. 13 shows the loading for a wide-flange beam, 12 WF 45. Calculate the maximum bending stress.
4. A fixed beam, 20′ long, carries a concentrated load of 5,700 lbs. at the center. Select a suitable wide-flange beam, using a working stress of 16,000 lbs. per sq. in.

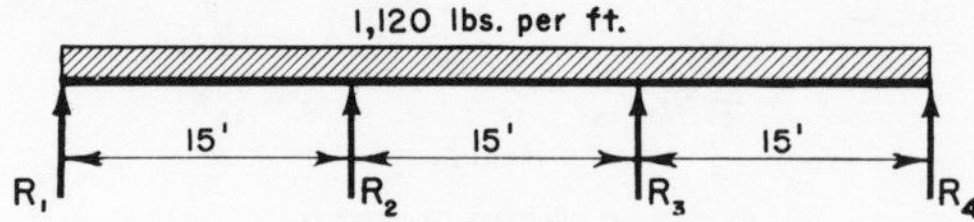

Fig. 13. Loading for Problem 3
(Review Problems)

5. Select a suitable rectangular wood beam for the loading shown in Fig. 14. Use a working stress of 1,400 lbs. per sq. in.

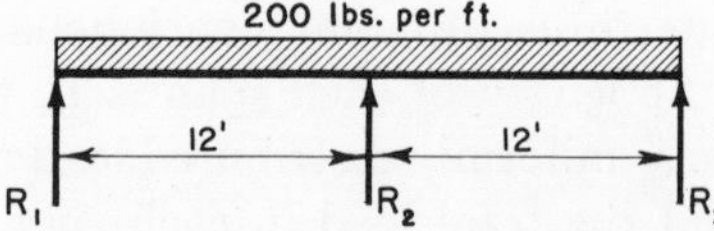

Fig. 14. Loading for Problem 5
(Review Problems)

6. An American standard beam, 10 I 35, which is 76′ long, is used as a continuous beam over four equal spans. The beam carries a uniformly distributed load of 880 lbs. per ft. What is the maximum bending stress?

CHAPTER X

REINFORCED-CONCRETE FLOOR SLABS

PURPOSE OF THIS CHAPTER. The purpose of this chapter is to study the stresses in a reinforced-concrete floor slab, and to learn how to design such a slab. Reinforced-concrete floor slabs are commonly used in buildings and bridges, so it is important for you to know what they are, and how to design them.

10-1. What Concrete Is.

Concrete is a mixture of four materials. These are: (1) *Cement.* This is usually Portland cement. You have probably seen Portland cement many times where buildings, sidewalks, and pavements were being constructed; (2) *Fine aggregate.* This is usually sand, although air-cooled blast-furnace slag is used sometimes; (3) *Coarse aggregate.* This is usually gravel or crushed stone; and (4) *Water.*

The materials of which concrete is made are dumped into the revolving drum of a concrete mixer, where they are mixed for a minute or more; and then the wet concrete is dumped into a form.

A *form* is a boxlike structure of wood or metal constructed in the shape the concrete is to take. Fig. 1 shows part of a wooden form for a concrete beam. The wet concrete is dumped into the form and is then spaded or vibrated to get the air out and make it fit tightly against the form, after which the concrete is allowed to dry for several days.

The concrete gains strength as it dries. When it has become strong enough the form is removed and the beam or floor slab is ready for use.

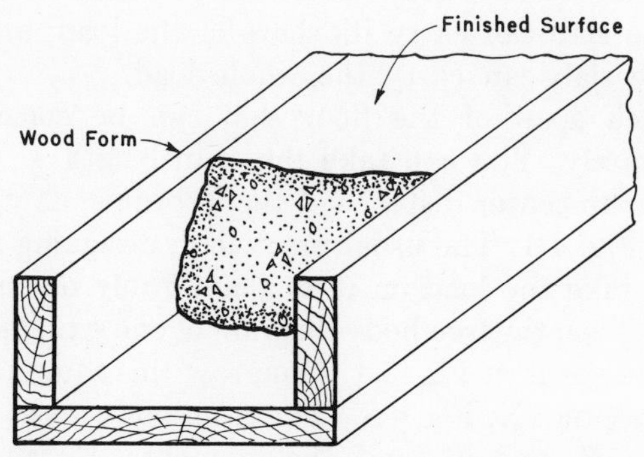

Fig. 1. Part of Form for Concrete Beam

Concrete is fairly strong in compression; the ultimate strength (breaking strength) in compression is usually between 2,500 and 5,000 pounds per square inch. However, concrete is not considered to be strong in tension. In fact, the usual practice is to assume that concrete has no strength at all in tension.

Concrete is ideal material for walls and columns because these structural members are usually stressed in compression.

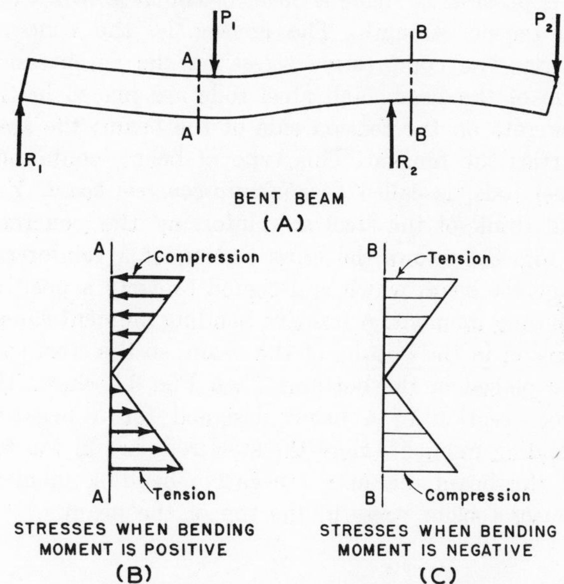

Fig. 2. Stresses in Wood or Steel Beam

10-2. What a Reinforced-Concrete Beam Is.

You should know from what we have studied so far that a beam bends when loads are applied to it. Fig. 2*A* shows the bent shape of a beam which carries the loads P_1 and P_2 and which is supported by the reactions R_1 and R_2. There is a *positive* bending moment at the cross section *AA* and a *negative* bending moment at the cross section *BB*. You learned, in Chapter VI, that a positive bending moment causes compressive stress in the top of the beam and tensile stress in the bottom of the beam; and, that a negative bending moment causes tensile stress in the top of the beam and compressive stress in the bottom of the beam.

Fig. 2*B* shows the stresses on the cross section *AA* of the beam; these are the stresses which would be developed in a steel or wood beam, or in a beam of any material which can withstand tension as well as compression. You can think of these stresses as exerted by the right-hand part of the beam, on the left-hand part, at the section AA; and you can see in Fig. $2B$ that there is compression in the top of the beam and tension in the bottom.

Fig. $2C$ shows the stresses on the cross section BB, where the bending moment is negative. Again, this is the way the stresses are distributed when the beam is made of a material that has tensile strength. Fig. $2C$ shows there is tension in the top of the beam, and compression in the bottom, when the bending moment is negative.

Now that we have reviewed the distribution of stress in a wood or steel beam, you may wonder how it is possible to make a beam of concrete which has no tensile strength. The answer is, the concrete carries the compressive stress on the compression side of the beam, and steel rods are placed in the concrete on the tension side of the beam; the steel carries the tension. This type of beam, containing steel rods, is called a *reinforced-concrete beam.* You can think of the steel as reinforcing the concrete.

Fig. $3A$ shows the cross section of a reinforced-concrete beam which is designed to carry a positive bending moment. A positive bending moment causes tension in the bottom of the beam, so the steel rods are placed in the bottom. Then Fig. $3B$ shows the cross section of a beam designed for a negative bending moment. Here the steel rods are in the top of the beam, because a negative bending moment causes tensile stress in the top of the beam.

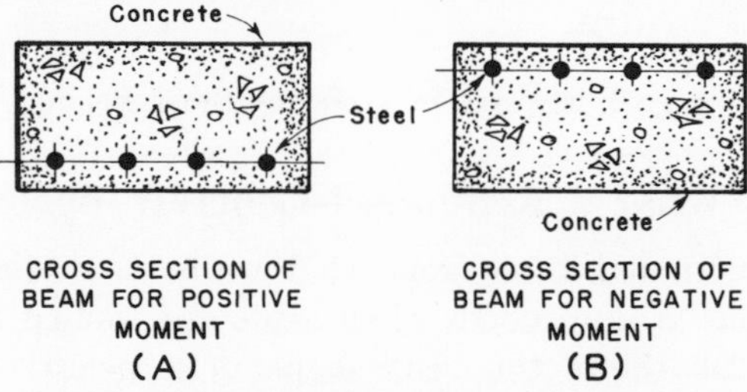

Fig. 3. Rectangular Reinforced-Concrete Beam

10-3. Concrete Floor Slabs.

The most common use of rectangular reinforced-concrete beams is in floor slabs. Fig. $4A$ shows a section through a concrete floor slab and the **T** beams which support the slab. The floor slab acts as a beam to support its own weight and the loads which are placed on the floor. The **T** beams support the floor slab and, in turn, the **T** beams are supported by girders and columns.

The floor slab is really a continuous beam with spans of length L. You should know from our studies of statically indeterminate beams in Chapter IX that the bending moment is positive near the center of each span, at points A, and here you can see that the reinforcing rods are in the bottom of the slab. The bending moment is negative at points B, over the supports, so the reinforcing rods are in the top of the slab at the supports.

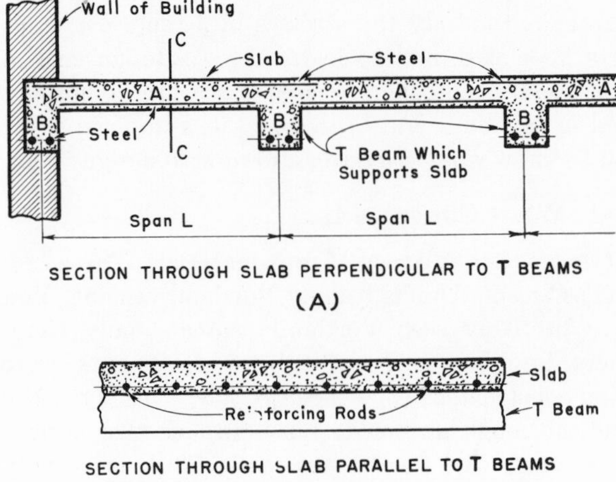

Fig. 4. Reinforced-Concrete Floor Slab

Fig. $4B$ shows a cross section of the floor slab taken parallel to the **T** beams which support the slab. This section is marked as CC in Fig. $4A$. The bending moment is positive at this section, so the reinforcing rods are in the bottom of the slab.

The floor slab in Fig. 4 is a rectangular reinforced-concrete beam with the cross section shown in Fig. $4B$; the width of the beam might be 20′ or more. However, we do not take the width of the beam as 20′ in designing the slab. Instead, we consider a strip 12″ wide. We make this strip strong enough to hold the loads which it must carry. Then, each strip of the slab can carry its share of the load, and the whole slab can carry the whole load.

Each span of the floor slab can be considered separately. You can take the span length L as the center-to-center distance of the **T** beams, as you see it in Fig. $4A$. The usual practice in designing a slab is to take the load on it as a uniformly distributed load. Then the free-body diagram of one span appears as you see it in Fig. $5A$. (You saw this same picture in Chapter IX, Fig. $4B$.) The reactions consist of the forces R_1 and R_2 and the moments M_1 and M_2. If the span is fixed (built in) at the ends, the forces R_1 and R_2 are each equal to $\frac{W}{2}$ and the moments M_1 and M_2 are each equal to $\frac{WL}{12}$. Here W is the total load on the span; w is the load in pounds per foot.

$$W = wL$$

The moment diagram for one span with fixed ends is shown in Fig. 5*B*. This is the same diagram that you saw in Fig. 4*D* of Chapter IX.

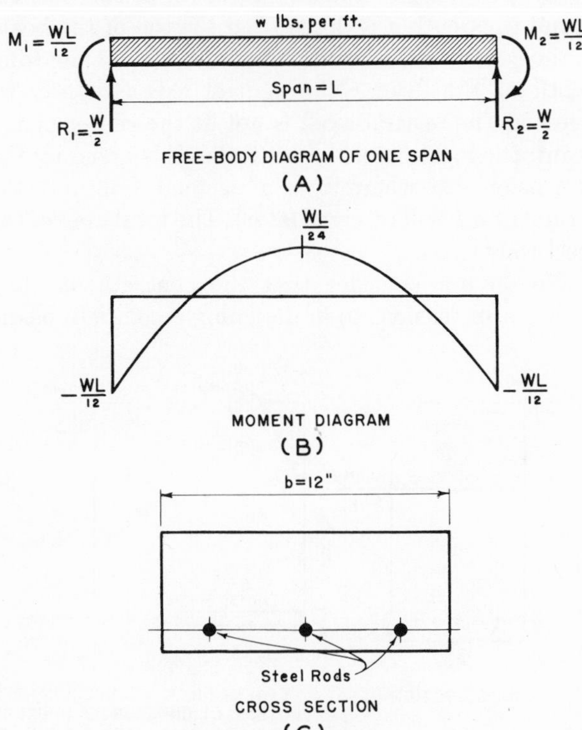

Fig. 5. Strip of Floor Slab

The load on a floor slab is usually given as so many pounds per square foot; for example, 125 pounds per square foot or 200 pounds per square foot. Then, when we take a strip 1′ wide, the load per foot of length of this strip is the same as the load per square foot on the slab. That is, w in Fig. 5*A* is the same as the load per square foot on the floor slab.

Fig. 5*C* shows the cross section of a 12″ strip of the floor slab. This is a rectangular beam of 12″ width. The problem of the designer is to determine the depth of the slab and the size and spacing of the steel rods.

10-4. Bending Moments in Floor Slabs.

A *floor slab* is a continuous beam. We can give you formulas for the bending moments in a 12″ strip of the slab so you will be able to design a floor slab. These formulas have some basis in theory but they depend also upon experience and judgment, so we have to regard them as *empirical* (*empirical* means based on experience and judgment). We cannot take the space to prove them for you. However, they do represent reasonable practice and you will be safe in using them.

Fig. 6 shows a section through a floor slab. The end spans are called *exterior spans* and the other spans are called *interior spans;* the spans are labeled in Fig. 6. The supports at points A in Fig. 6 are called *exterior supports* and the supports at B and C are called *interior supports*. The supports at B are called the *first interior supports* because they are the closest interior supports to the ends of the beam.

The bending moments at the supports (points A, B, and C in Fig. 6) are negative, which means that the reinforcing rods must be in the top of the slab. The bending moments at the centers of the spans (points D and E in Fig. 6) are positive, so, here, the reinforcing rods must be in the bottom of the slab.

If we take W as the total load on a span and L as the length of the span, then the bending moment at an exterior support (points A in Fig. 6) can be taken as

$$M = -\frac{WL}{16}$$

The bending moment at a first interior support (points B, in Fig. 6) can be taken as

$$M = -\frac{WL}{10}$$

and the bending moment at other interior supports (points C, in Fig. 6) can be taken as

$$M = -\frac{WL}{12}$$

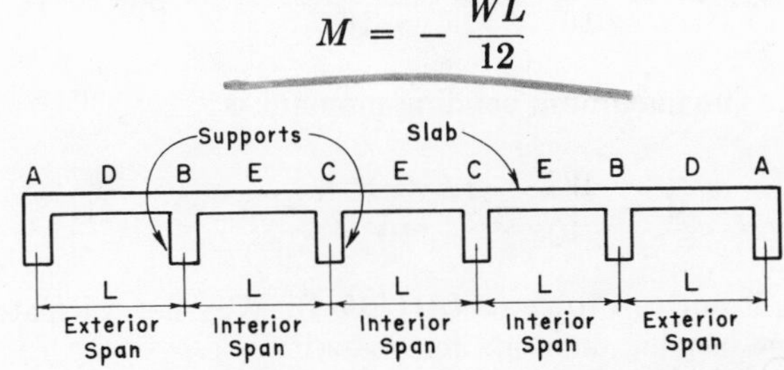

Fig. 6. Section through Floor Slab

Hereafter, we will call this *the moment at an interior support.*

The bending moment at the center of an exterior span (points D, in Fig. 6) can be taken as

$$M = \frac{WL}{10}$$

and the bending moment at the center of an interior span (points E, in Fig. 6) can be taken as

$$M = \frac{WL}{12}$$

These values of bending moment are not exact values as obtained by theory; rather, they represent judgment and experience, and allow for the fact that the actual conditions in the floor slab may not be the same as the assumed conditions.

If you take W in pounds and L in feet, you will get the bending moment M in pound feet. You can look back at the formulas of this section and see that the maximum numerical value of M is

$$\frac{WL}{10}$$

It would be a good idea to remember this.

Illustrative Example 1. A floor slab carries a uniformly distributed load of 200 lbs. per sq. ft. on spans of 8′. Calculate the bending moment at an exterior support and calculate the maximum bending moment.

Solution:

1. The load w is 200 lbs. per ft.
2. The span L is 8′
3. The total load on a 12″ strip is

$$W = wL = 200 \times 8 = 1{,}600 \text{ lbs.}$$

4. The bending moment at an exterior support is

$$M = -\frac{WL}{16} = -\frac{1{,}600 \times 8}{16} = -800 \text{ lb. ft.}$$

5. The maximum bending moment is

$$M = \frac{WL}{10} = \frac{1{,}600 \times 8}{10} = 1{,}280 \text{ lb. ft.}$$

Practice Problems (Art. 10-4). Why not calculate a few bending moments for yourself?

1. Calculate the bending moment at the center of an exterior span for a slab which carries a load of 230 lbs. per sq. ft. on spans of 9′.
2. What is the bending moment at an interior support of a slab which carries a load of 400 lbs. per sq. ft. on spans of 7′?
3. A floor slab is to carry a load of 160 lbs. per sq. ft. on spans of 10′. Calculate the bending moment at the center of an interior span.
4. A floor slab is to carry a load of 190 lbs. per sq. ft. on spans of 6′. Find the bending moment at the center of an exterior span.

10-5. Stresses and Moment in a Rectangular, Reinforced-Concrete Beam.

There are some new ideas and new symbols for you to learn in studying reinforced-concrete beams. Fig. 7A shows the cross section of a rectangular reinforced-concrete beam which is designed for a positive bending moment. The width of the beam is b, and the depth d is taken from the top of the beam to the center of the reinforcing rods; d is not the total depth of the beam. The neutral axis (there is no stress at the neutral axis) is not at the center of the beam; the location of the neutral axis is given by the dimension kd, where k is a decimal fraction (the formula for k will be given later). The total area of the steel rods is A_s.

We do not consider that the concrete has any strength in tension, so in designing a concrete beam,

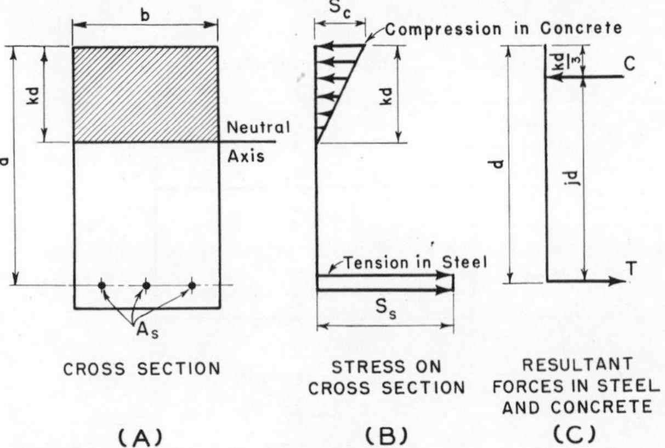

Fig. 7. Stresses and Forces in Reinforced-Concrete Beam

we only count that part of the concrete which is in compression. This is the part above the neutral axis and is shaded in Fig. 7A.

Fig. 7B shows how the stresses vary over the cross section of a reinforced-concrete beam. The compressive stress increases from *zero* at the neutral axis to a value of S_c at the top; S_c is the maximum stress in the concrete. We do not show any stress in the concrete below the neutral axis because that part of the concrete is in tension, and concrete does not possess tensile strength. However, the steel can take tension, and Fig. 7B shows the tensile stress in the steel; the amount of this tensile stress is S_s.

Fig. 7C shows the total force (C) in the concrete and the total force (T) in the steel. Here is how we calculate C. We have the compressive stress in the concrete increasing uniformly from *zero* to S_c, so the average stress in the concrete is $\frac{1}{2}S_c$. The area of concrete in compression is the shaded rectangle in

Fig. 7*A;* we call this area A_c and you can see that it is

$$A_c = b \times kd = kbd$$

The total force C in the concrete is the product of the area and the average stress, so

$$C = A_c \times \tfrac{1}{2}S_c = kbd \times \tfrac{1}{2}S_c = \tfrac{1}{2}kbd\ S_c$$

The force C is below the top of the beam by the distance $\frac{1}{3}kd$. (We will not prove this.)

The total force T in the steel is equal to the product of the area of the steel and the stress in the steel.

$$T = A_sS_s$$

Notice the distance jd in Fig. 7*C*. This is the distance between the forces C and T. You can see that jd is equal to the distance d minus the distance $\frac{1}{3}kd$; that is

$$jd = d - \tfrac{1}{3}kd = d\,(1 - k/3)$$

We can cancel d in this equation to get

$$j = 1 - k/3$$

j being a decimal fraction.

The two forces C and T must be equal so that the sum of the x components (have you forgotten x components?) of the forces on the cross section can be equal to *zero.* Thus,

$$\Sigma F_x = -C + T = 0$$

$$C = T$$

The bending moment M on the cross section is equal to the product of one of the forces C and T, and the distance jd. (A pair of equal, parallel, and opposite forces, such as C and T, is called a *couple.* Their moment about any point is equal to the product of one force and the distance between the forces.) So

$$M = Cjd = Tjd$$

We had

$$C = \tfrac{1}{2}kbdS_c$$

and this can be substituted in the equation $M = Cjd$ to give

$$M = Cjd = (\tfrac{1}{2}kbdS_c)\ jd = \tfrac{1}{2}kjbd^2S_c$$

Also, we had

$$T = A_sS_s$$

If this is substituted in the equation $M = Tjd$, the result is

$$M = Tjd = A_sS_s\,jd$$

These formulas will be used later.

10-6. Calculation of *k* and *j*.

The first step in designing a reinforced-concrete floor slab is to learn how to calculate the numbers k and j. We want to design a reinforced-concrete floor slab; that is, a slab of concrete and steel. There are reasonable working stresses for these materials, and we would like to stress each material up to its working stress but not beyond. (A working stress is the stress which the material can withstand safely in service.) Then, the stress S_c in the concrete and the stress S_s in the steel should be the working stresses for these materials. Remember this because S_c and S_s will be used in later problems.

You should remember that we studied modulus of elasticity in Chapter V. We calculated stress, which is force divided by area, or force per unit area. Also, we calculated strain, which is deformation divided by length; for example, the strain in a tension member is the stretch of the member divided by the length of the member. The *modulus of elasticity* of a material is equal to the stress divided by the strain. We represent the modulus of elasticity by E, and Table I of Chapter V gives values of E for some of the common materials of construction. We will represent the modulus of elasticity of steel by E_s and its value is

$$E_s = 30{,}000{,}000 \text{ pounds per square inches}$$

We will represent the modulus of elasticity of concrete by E_c; this varies between 2,000,000 and 5,000,000 pounds per square inches.

One of our formulas will contain the ratio of E_s to E_c. We will represent this ratio by n, so

$$n = \frac{E_s}{E_c}$$

Now we can give you a formula for the number k.

$$k = \frac{n\dfrac{S_c}{S_s}}{1 + n\dfrac{S_c}{S_s}}$$

Here S_c is the working stress in the concrete, S_s is the working stress in the steel, and n is the ratio of E_s to E_c. This formula gives the value of k for a beam in which the working stresses S_c and S_s are developed at the same time. We will design beams of this type, so remember the formula.

The number k is important for two reasons. For one reason this number shows us where the neutral axis is; the distance from the top of the beam to the neutral axis is kd, where d is the depth of the beam. Also, we need to find k in the process of designing a beam or slab.

Illustrative Example 1. A rectangular reinforced-concrete beam is to be made of concrete (for which the working stress is 900 lbs. per sq. in.) and steel (for which the working stress is 20,000 lbs. per sq. in.). The modulus of elasticity for the concrete is 2,000,000 lbs. per sq. in. Calculate k.

Solution:

1. The modulus of elasticity of the steel is

$$E_s = 30{,}000{,}000 \text{ lbs. per sq. in.}$$

2. The modulus of elasticity of the concrete is

$$E_c = 2{,}000{,}000 \text{ lbs. per sq. in.}$$

3. $$n = \frac{E_s}{E_c} = \frac{30{,}000{,}000}{2{,}000{,}000} = 15$$

4. The working stress for the concrete is

$$S_c = 900 \text{ lbs. per sq. in.}$$

5. The working stress for the steel is

$$S_s = 20{,}000 \text{ lbs. per sq. in.}$$

6. $$K = \frac{n\dfrac{S_c}{S_s}}{1 + n\dfrac{S_c}{S_s}} = \frac{15 \times \dfrac{900}{20{,}000}}{1 + 15 \times \dfrac{900}{20{,}000}}$$

$$= \frac{0.675}{1 + 0.675} = 0.402$$

The next unknown is j. This is simple, because

$$j = 1 - k/3$$

You can easily calculate j if you know k.

Illustrative Example 2. Calculate j for the beam of Example 1.

Solution:

1. $k = 0.402$, as found in Example 1

2. $j = 1 - \dfrac{k}{3} = 1 - \dfrac{0.402}{3} = 1 - 0.134 = 0.866$

Practice Problems (Art. 10-5 and Art. 10-6).

1. Calculate k and j for a rectangular concrete beam for which $S_c = 1{,}350$ lbs. per sq. in., $S_s = 20{,}000$ lbs. per sq. in., and $E_c = 3{,}000{,}000$ lbs. per sq. in.
2. A rectangular reinforced-concrete beam is to be made of concrete for which $S_c = 1{,}200$ lbs. per sq. in., and steel for which $S_s = 18{,}000$ lbs. per sq. in. $E_c = 3{,}000{,}000$ lbs. per sq. in. Find k and j.
3. Calculate k and j for a rectangular reinforced-concrete beam for which the working stress in concrete is to be 1,700 lbs. per sq. in., and the working stress in steel is 20,000 lbs. per sq. in. Take $n = 8$.
4. What will k and j be if

$$S_c = 1{,}000 \text{ lbs. per sq. in.}$$

$$S_s = 16{,}000 \text{ lbs. per sq. in.}$$

and

$$E_c = 2{,}500{,}000 \text{ lbs. per sq. in.}$$

10-7. How to Calculate the Depth of a Floor Slab.

Now that you know how to calculate k and j, our next step is to learn how to find the depth of a floor slab.

Fig. 8 shows the cross section of a 12″ strip of floor slab. We divide the slab into 12″ strips in making design calculations. Each strip is a rectangular reinforced-concrete beam for which the width b is 12″. Our problem now is to calculate the depth.

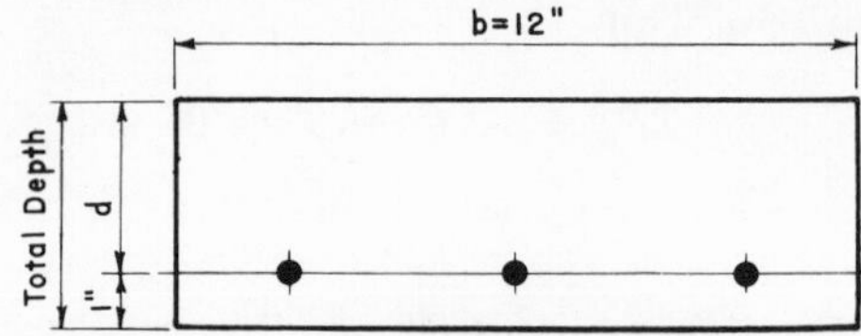

Fig. 8. Cross Section of Strip of Floor Slab

Notice that d in Fig. 8 is not the total depth of the beam but only the distance from the top of the beam to the center of the steel rods. The total depth of the beam is 1″ greater than d.

See Art. 10-5, where we had an equation,

$$M = \tfrac{1}{2}kjbd^2S_c$$

This equation is true for a rectangular reinforced-concrete beam of any size. For a 12″ strip of floor slab, the width b is 12″, so the equation can be written as

$$M = \tfrac{1}{2}kj(12)d^2S_c = 6kjd^2S_c$$

We want to find d, so let us solve the equation for d.

We can start by dividing the equation by $6KjS_c$ to get

$$\frac{M}{6kjS_c} = \frac{6kjd^2S_c}{6kjS_c}$$

Then we can cancel $6kjS_c$ on the right side of this last equation to get

$$\frac{M}{6kjS_c} = d^2, \quad \text{or} \quad d^2 = \frac{M}{6kjS_c}$$

Finally, we will take the square root of each side of the equation to get

$$d = \sqrt{\frac{M}{6kjS_c}}.$$

You know how to calculate k and j; S_c is the working stress for the concrete; M is the maximum bending moment in the slab and is

$$M = \frac{WL}{10}$$

as we pointed out to you in Art. 10-4. You may remember that we take this value for the bending moment at the center of an exterior span and at the first interior support. The bending moment is smaller than $\frac{WL}{10}$ at other points in the slab, so the slab could have less depth at other points. However, it is less trouble and is cheaper to make the slab the same depth throughout. (This procedure of using the maximum bending moment to calculate the depth is not the only one that can be followed, but it is a reasonable procedure and does result in a satisfactory design.)

The distance d is only the distance from the top of the slab to the center of the steel rods. You must add 1″ to d to find the total depth.

Illustrative Example 3. A floor slab is to carry a uniformly distributed load of 200 lbs. per sq. ft.; the distance between centers of the supports is 8′. The working stress for the concrete is 1,200 lbs. per sq. in. and the working stress for the steel is 20,000 lbs. per sq. in. The modulus of elasticity for the concrete is 3,000,000 lbs. per sq. in. What total depth of slab is required?

Solution:

1. To calculate k,

   a) $E_s = 30{,}000{,}000$ lbs. per sq. in.
   b) $E_c = 3{,}000{,}000$ lbs. per sq. in.
   c) $n = \frac{E_s}{E_c} = 10$
   d) $S_c = 1{,}200$ lbs. per sq. in.
   e) $S_s = 20{,}000$ lbs. per sq. in.
   f) $K = \dfrac{n\frac{S_c}{S_s}}{1 + n\frac{S_c}{S_s}} = \dfrac{10 \times \frac{1{,}200}{20{,}000}}{1 + 10 \times \frac{1{,}200}{20{,}000}} = 0.375$

2. To calculate j,

   a) $j = 1 - \frac{k}{3} = 1 - \frac{0.375}{3} = 0.875$

3. To calculate M,

   a) The load per foot of length is

   $$w = 200 \text{ lbs. per ft.}$$

   b) The total load is

   $$W = wL = 200 \times 8 = 1{,}600 \text{ lbs.}$$

   c) The maximum bending moment is

   $$M = \frac{WL}{10} = \frac{1{,}600 \times 8}{10} = 1{,}280 \text{ lb. ft.}$$

   $$M = 1{,}280 \times 12 = 15{,}400 \text{ lb. in.}$$

4. To calculate d,

   a) $d = \sqrt{\frac{M}{6kjS_c}}$

   $$= \sqrt{\frac{15{,}400}{6 \times 0.375 \times 0.875 \times 1{,}200}} = 2.56''$$

5. The total depth needed is

   $$d + 1 = 2.56 + 1 = 3.56''$$

Practice Problems (Art. 10-7). There is nothing hard about calculating the depth of a floor slab.

1. What total depth is needed for a floor slab which is supported by **T** beams 10′ apart and which is to carry a uniformly distributed load of 160 lbs. per sq. ft.? The working stresses are 1,000 lbs. per sq. in. for concrete and 18,000 lbs. per sq. in. for steel. E_c = 2,500,000 lbs. per sq. in.
2. Find the total depth required for a floor slab to carry a uniformly distributed load of 400 lbs. per sq. ft. with supports 7′ apart. E_c = 3,750,000 lbs. per sq. in.; S_c = 1,400 lbs. per sq. in.; S_s = 18,000 lbs. per sq. in.
3. A concrete floor slab is to be supported by beams which are 6′ apart, and the slab is to carry a uniformly distributed load of 250 lbs. per sq. ft. E_c = 2,000,000 lbs. per sq. in.; S_c = 800 lbs. per sq. in.; S_s = 16,000 lbs. per sq. in. Calculate the total depth necessary.

4. A floor slab that is to carry a load of 220 lbs. per sq. ft. is to be supported by beams which are 7.5′ apart. The working stresses are 20,000 lbs. per sq. in. for steel and 1,125 lbs. per sq. in. for concrete. The modulus of elasticity for the concrete is 2,500,000 lbs. per sq. in. What total depth is needed for the slab?

10-8. Rounding Off the Depth of the Slab.

The total depth needed usually comes out as an uneven number, such as 3.33″ or 3.77″. Concrete is made in its final shape by being dumped into forms and these forms are not made carefully enough to be accurate to one-hundredth of an inch. Consequently, the dimensions of concrete slabs and beams are usually given in multiples of ½″. Following this practice, we increase the calculated figure for the total depth to the next larger half-inch dimension. Thus, if the calculations showed that a total depth of 3.33″ was needed, the slab would be made 3.5″ thick. If the necessary depth, as calculated, was 3.77″, the slab would be made 4″ thick.

Practice Problems (Art. 10-8). What should be the actual thickness of a floor slab if the calculations show that the total depth needed is:

1. 2.88″
2. 3.41″
3. 4.16″
4. 3.39″

10-9. Calculation of Steel Area.

Now look again at what you know about concrete floor slabs and beams. We divide the floor slab into strips 12″ wide; then each of these strips is a rectangular beam. Fig. 9*A* shows the cross section. We take the depth of the beam as the distance from the top of the beam to the center of the steel rods.

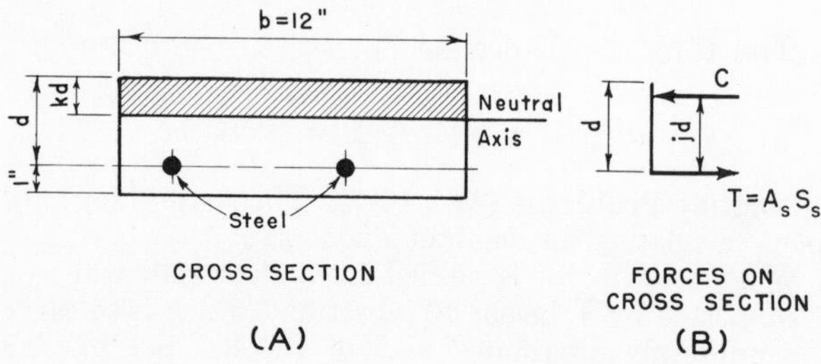

Fig. 9. Cross Section of Rectangular Beam

The neutral axis of the beam is at the distance kd below the top of the beam. The concrete above the neutral axis is in *compression* and the steel is in *tension*. Fig. 9*B* shows the forces on the cross section of the beam. Here C is the total force in the concrete and T is the total force in the steel.

$$T = A_s S_s$$

where A_s is the *area* of the steel rods, and S_s is the *stress* in the steel rods.

You already know how to calculate k and j for the beam or slab. Also, you know how to calculate the bending moments at different points in the slab, and the depth of the slab. The next step is to figure out how much steel to use. To do this, take the formula,

$$M = T\,jd = A_s S_s jd$$

We know how to calculate M, j, and d; and S_s is the working stress for the steel. If we write the equation as (prove that this is correct),

$$A_s = \frac{M}{S_s jd}$$

we can use it to calculate the area of steel required. This area is the area of cross section of the steel rods in the 12″ strip.

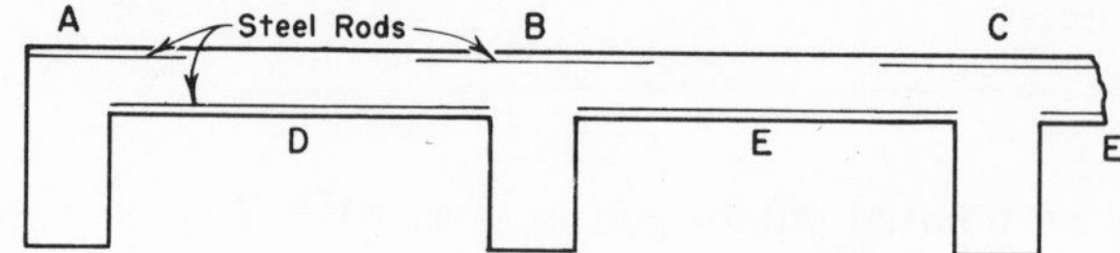

Fig. 10. Section through Floor Slab

Do you remember how we *rounded off* the depth of the slab? You should be able to see that when we increase the total depth to the next half inch, we are increasing the distance d by the same amount, since the center of the steel rods is 1″ above the bottom of the slab. This *rounded-off* value of d should be used when you calculate the steel area.

You must remember that the bending moment is *negative* over a support and *positive* in the center of a span. The steel is placed in the top of the slab, where the bending moment is negative, and in the bottom of the slab, where the bending moment is positive.

The numerical value of the bending moment at an exterior support is taken as $\frac{WL}{16}$. This is at point A in Fig. 10. Then, at the center of an exterior span and at a first interior support (points B and D in Fig. 10), the bending moment is taken as $\frac{WL}{10}$, and at the center of an interior span and at an interior support (points C and E in Fig. 10), we use $\frac{WL}{12}$

Knowing the depth of the slab, we use the formula

$$A_s = \frac{M}{S_s jd}$$

Table I. Area of Steel for a 12″ Strip of Slab

Size of Rod	Spacing												
	4″	4½″	5″	5½″	6″	6½″	7″	7½″	8″	8½″	9″	9½″	10″
1	2	3	4	5	6	7	8	9	10	11	12	13	14
¼″ round	0.147	0.131	0.118	0.107	0.098	0.091	0.084	0.079	0.074	0.070	0.066	0.062	0.059
⅜″ round	0.331	0.294	0.265	0.240	0.220	0.204	0.189	0.176	0.165	0.155	0.147	0.139	0.133
½″ round	0.589	0.523	0.472	0.428	0.393	0.363	0.347	0.314	0.294	0.278	0.262	0.249	0.236
½″ square	0.750	0.667	0.600	0.546	0.500	0.462	0.428	0.400	0.375	0.353	0.333	0.316	0.300
⅝″ round	0.920	0.817	0.736	0.669	0.614	0.566	0.526	0.491	0.460	0.433	0.409	0.387	0.368
¾″ round	1.325	1.177	1.060	0.965	0.885	0.818	0.758	0.708	0.664	0.623	0.588	0.558	0.530

to calculate the steel area needed at the center of each span and at each support. You will probably save time if you calculate $S_s\,jd$ as soon as you know the depth of the slab.

Illustrative Example 1. A concrete floor slab is to carry a uniformly distributed load of 200 lbs. per sq. ft. on spans of 10′. The total depth of the slab is 4.5″ and the working stress in the steel is 20,000 lb. per sq. in. Calculate the area of steel required at each support and at the center of each span. Use $j = 0.875$.

Solution:

1. The first step is to calculate the numbers that will be used throughout the problem.
   a) The total load in one span is

$$W = wL = 200 \times 10 = 2{,}000 \text{ lbs.}$$

   b) The depth d is 1″ less than the total depth of the slab

$$d = 4.5 - 1 = 3.5''$$

   c) $S_s\,jd = 20{,}000 \times 0.875 \times 3.5 = 61{,}300$

2. At an exterior support,

$$a)\ M = \frac{WL}{16} = \frac{2{,}000 \times 10}{16} = 1{,}250 \text{ lb. ft.}$$

$$M = 1{,}250 \times 12 = 15{,}000 \text{ lb. in.}$$

$$b)\ A_s = \frac{M}{S_s jd} = \frac{15{,}000}{61{,}300} = 0.245 \text{ sq. in.}$$

3. At the first interior support and at the center of an exterior span,

$$a)\ M = \frac{WL}{10} = \frac{2{,}000 \times 10}{10} = 2{,}000 \text{ lb. ft.}$$

$$M = 2{,}000 \times 12 \times 24{,}000 \text{ lb. in.}$$

$$b)\ A_s = \frac{M}{S_s jd} = \frac{24{,}000}{61{,}300} = 0.391 \text{ sq. in.}$$

4. At an interior support and at the center of an interior span,

$$a)\ M = \frac{WL}{12} = \frac{2{,}000 \times 10}{12} = 1{,}670 \text{ lb. ft.}$$

$$M = 1{,}670 \times 12 = 20{,}000 \text{ lb. in.}$$

$$b)\ A_s = \frac{M}{S_s jd} = \frac{20{,}000}{61{,}300} = 0.326 \text{ sq. in.}$$

The steel rods are placed in the top of the slab at a support because the bending moment is *negative* there, and the steel rods are placed in the bottom of the slab in the center of a span where the bending moment is *positive*.

Practice Problems (Art. 10-9). Your next job is to calculate a few steel areas. In each of the following problems, we give you the data you need. You are to calculate the steel areas required at: (*a*) An exterior support; (*b*) The center of an exterior span and a first interior support; (*c*) The center of an interior span and an interior support.

Problem	Data				
	w, Lbs. per Sq. Ft.	L Ft.	Total Depth, Inches	S_s, Lbs. per Sq. In.	j
1	185	8	3.5	18,000	0.862
2	260	7	4.0	20,000	0.854
3	320	7.5	4.5	18,000	0.842
4	210	9	4.0	16,000	0.872

10-10. Rod Size and Spacing.

The next step in the design of a concrete floor slab is to determine the size and spacing of the steel rods; that is, to determine the diameter of the steel rods and the distance between them. We will give you a table from which you can select the rod size and spacing when you know the area of steel required for a 12″ strip of the slab.

The most efficient results in reinforcing a slab are secured by using standard-size steel rods. Table I gives you the steel area in a 12″ strip of slab for rods of various sizes at different spacings. Column 1 of this table gives the sizes of the steel rods; column 2 gives the area of steel in a 12″ strip of slab when these rods are spaced 4″ apart. For example, ⅜″

round steel rods provide a steel area of 0.331 square inches when they are spaced 4″ apart. Columns 3 to 10 in the table give the steel areas for other spacings of the rods. Fig. 11 shows a section through the slab, and this section is taken perpendicular to the steel rods. Notice here the distance *s* which is the spacing of the rods. The rods are equally spaced across the entire width of the slab; sometimes this width is as much as 20′.

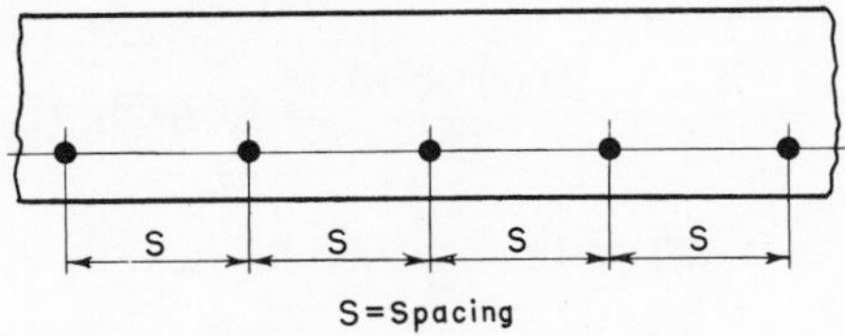

Fig. 11. Section through Floor Slab Perpendicular to Steel Rods

Here is the way to use Table I. You calculate the steel area needed and then look in the table to select the rod size and spacing. Ordinarily, the steel area needed will not be exactly the same as the areas listed in the table in such cases. Take the steel area, which is next larger.

Illustrative Example 1. The steel area required for a 12″ strip of floor slab is 0.286 sq. in. Select a suitable size and spacing of steel rod.

Solution:

1. Look for 0.286 in Table I. You will not find it, but you will find 0.294 in the second line of column 3. This is the next larger area than 0.286.
2. Look across to column 1 to read the size of rod as $\frac{3}{8}$″ round.
3. Look up in column 3 to read the spacing as $4\frac{1}{2}$″.

Alternate Solution:

1. Look in Table I to find 0.294 in the third line of column 10.
2. Look across to column 1 to read the rod size as $\frac{1}{2}$″ round.
3. Look up in column 10 to read the spacing as 8″.

The example just finished is interesting because there are two solutions. This is usually the case in this type of problem, and either solution would be satisfactory, as long as the spacing is not more than about two and one-half times the total depth of the slab. In fact, this is worth stating as a rule.

Rule. *The opening of the rods should not be more than two and one-half times the total depth of the slab.*

For example, if the total depth of the slab is 4″, the rod spacing should not be more than

$$2\frac{1}{2} \times 4 = 10''$$

Illustrative Example 2. Determine a suitable size and spacing of steel rods in a floor slab which requires a steel area of 0.397 sq. in. for a 12″ strip.

Solution:

1. In line 3, column 5 of Table I, you find the number 0.428
2. Look across to column 1 to read the rod size as $\frac{1}{2}$″ round
3. Look up column 5 to read the spacing as $5\frac{1}{2}$″

Alternate Solution:

1. In line 4, column 9 of Table I, you find the number 0.400.
2. Look across to column 1 to read the rod size as $\frac{1}{2}$″ square
3. Look up column 9 to read the spacing as $7\frac{1}{2}$″. Either $\frac{1}{2}$″ round rods, spaced at $5\frac{1}{2}$″, or $\frac{1}{2}$″ square rods, spaced at $7\frac{1}{2}$″, would do in this case.

Practice Problems (Art. 10-10). In each problem, the figure given is the steel area required in a 12″ strip of floor slab. Select a suitable rod size and spacing.

1. 0.248
2. 0.373
3. 0.352
4. 0.274
5. 0.458
6. 0.312

You have learned to make many calculations for concrete floor slabs. You can calculate the depth of the slab, and the area of steel needed at the supports and at the centers of the spans. You have learned, also, how to select the rod size and spacing for a given steel area.

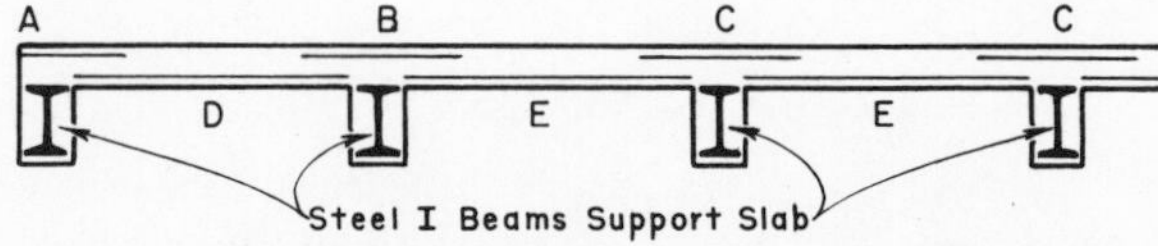

Fig. 12. Section through Floor Slab Supported by Steel I Beams

You remember that we calculated the steel area needed at such points as A, B, C, D, and E in Fig. 12, and that the steel area is not the same at all of these points. The maximum bending moment occurs at B (the first interior support), so the greatest steel area is needed at B.

You will notice, in Fig. 12, that the beams which support the floor slab are steel **I** beams, and that the

I beams are encased in concrete. This is a rather common structural arrangement.

As a practical matter, it is best to have all of the reinforcing rods in the slab of the same size. This leads to economy and simplicity in construction. An easy way to work this out is to select first the size and spacing of rod for the points *B* and *D*. (The steel area is the same at these points.) Then, for the same size of rod, select the spacings that will provide the necessary areas at the other points.

It will help, in this procedure, to remember that the greatest area is needed at points *B* and *D*, where the bending moment on a 12″ strip is taken as $\frac{WL}{10}$; that a smaller area is needed at points *C* and *E*, where the bending moment is $\frac{WL}{12}$; and that the smallest area is needed at *A*, where the bending moment is $\frac{WL}{16}$.

Illustrative Example 3. The following steel areas are needed in a floor slab: (*a*) 0.324 sq. in. at the centers of exterior spans and at the first interior supports; (*b*) 0.270 sq. in. at the centers of interior spans and at the interior supports; and (*c*) 0.202 sq. in. at the exterior supports. Select a suitable size of steel rod and determine the spacings.

Solution:

1. At the centers of exterior spans and at the first interior supports,
   a) Look in Table I for 0.324 and notice 0.331 in the second line of column 2
   b) The size of rod is ⅜″ round
   c) The spacing is 4″
2. At the centers of interior spans and at the interior supports,
   a) The rod size is ⅜″ round
   b) Look in the second line of Table I for 0.270 and take 0.294 in column 3 as the next larger number
   c) The spacing is 4½″
3. At exterior supports,
   a) The rod size is ⅜″ round
   b) Look across the second line of Table I for 0.202 and take 0.204 as the next larger (column 7)
   c) The spacing is 6½″

Practice Problems (Art. 10-10—*Continued*). In each of the following problems, the first number is the steel area required at the centers of exterior spans and at the first interior supports; the second number is the steel area needed at the centers of interior spans and at the interior supports; and the third number is the steel area needed at the exterior supports. You are to determine the rod size and spacings.

1. 0.375; 0.313; 0.234.
2. 0.282; 0.235; 0.176.
3. 0.416; 0.347; 0.260.
4. 0.323; 0.269; 0.202.
5. 0.237; 0.198; 0.148.

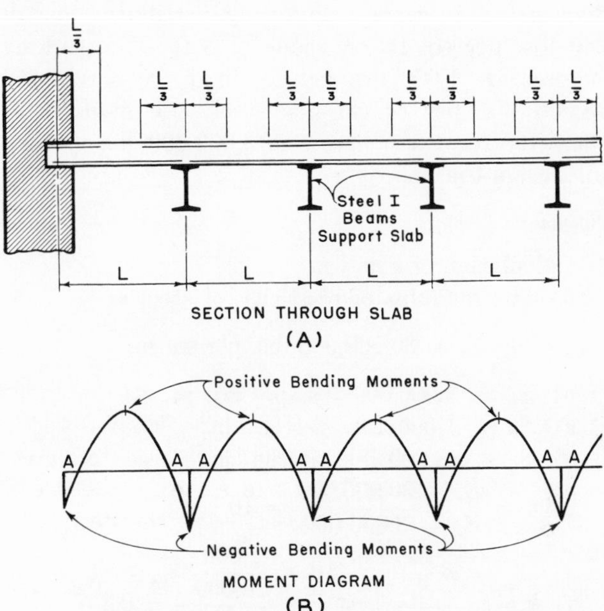

Fig. 13. Section through Floor Slab, and Diagram Showing Positive and Negative Bending Moments

10-11. Lengths of Reinforcing Rods.

There is one more question to settle. That is: *How long should the reinforcing rods be?* Fig. 13*A* shows a reasonable answer to this question. The steel rods in the bottom of the slab extend through the entire span, and the steel rods in the top of the slab extend into each span for one-third of the length of the span.

We could argue for a long time about whether the lengths of the steel rods in Fig. 13*A* represent the best possible arrangement, and we would not settle the question. However, the lengths shown in Fig. 13*A* are reasonable and safe. You can use them with confidence, and you can see how they fit the moment diagram of the slab in Fig. 13*B*. Notice that the bending moment is negative at each support and for some distance away from the support. The distance from the center of the support to the point of *zero* bending moment (points *A*, in Fig. 13*B*) is usually not greater than $L/4$; so if the rods extend for a distance of $L/3$, there will be steel where it is needed. If the steel in the bottom of the slab extends through the entire length of the span, you can be sure of having steel in the right place when the bending moment is positive.

Now we can take an example in which we start at the beginning and go through the entire procedure of designing a reinforced concrete floor slab.

Illustrative Example 1. A reinforced-concrete floor slab is to carry a uniformly distributed load of 240 lbs. per sq. ft. on spans of 8 ft. The working stresses are 1,000 lbs. per sq. in. for concrete and 18,000 lbs. per sq. in. for steel; the modulus of elasticity for the concrete is 3,000,000 lbs. per sq. in. Design the slab.

Solution:

1. Calculation of k and j,
   a) The modulus of elasticity of steel is

$$E_s = 30{,}000{,}000 \text{ lbs. per sq. in.}$$

   b) $E_c = 3{,}000{,}000$ lbs. per sq. in.
   c) $S_c = 1{,}000$ lbs. per sq. in.
   d) $S_s = 18{,}000$ lbs. per sq. in.
   e) $n = \dfrac{E_s}{E_c} = \dfrac{30{,}000{,}000}{3{,}000{,}000} = 10$
   f) $k = \dfrac{n\dfrac{S_c}{S_s}}{1 + n\dfrac{S_c}{S_s}} = \dfrac{10 \times \dfrac{1{,}000}{18{,}000}}{1 + 10 \times \dfrac{1{,}000}{18{,}000}} = 0.357$
   g) $j = 1 - \dfrac{k}{3} = 1 - \dfrac{0.357}{3} = 0.881$
2. Calculation of the bending moments,
   a) $w = 240$ lbs. per sq. ft.
   b) $L = 8'$
   c) The total load on a 12″ strip is

$$W = wL = 240 \times 8 = 1{,}920 \text{ lbs.}$$

   d) The maximum bending moment occurs at the centers of the exterior spans and at the first interior supports

$$M = \frac{WL}{10} = \frac{1{,}920 \times 8}{10} = 1{,}540 \text{ lb. ft.}$$

$$M = 1{,}540 \times 12 = 18{,}400 \text{ lb. in.}$$

   e) The bending moment at the centers of interior spans and at the interior supports is

$$\frac{WL}{12} = \frac{1{,}920 \times 8}{12} \times 12 = 15{,}400 \text{ lb. in.}$$

   f) The bending moment at the exterior supports is

$$\frac{WL}{16} = \frac{1{,}920 \times 8}{16} \times 12 = 11{,}500 \text{ lb. in.}$$

3. Calculation of the depth,
   a) The maximum bending moment on a 12″ strip is 18,400 lb. in.
   b) The distance d from the top of the slab to the center of the steel rods is

$$d = \sqrt{\frac{M}{6kjS_c}}$$

$$= \sqrt{\frac{18{,}400}{6 \times 0.881 \times 0.357 \times 1{,}000}} = 3.13''$$

   c) The total depth needed is 1″ greater than d, or

$$3.31 + 1 = 4.31''$$

   d) We increase this figure to the next larger half inch, so the total depth will be 4.5″
   e) We increase d by the same amount as the total depth, so hereafter we will use d as 3.5″
4. Calculation of the reinforcing rods,
   a) $S_s jd = 18{,}000 \times 0.881 \times 3.5 = 55{,}400$
   b) At the centers of exterior spans and at the first interior supports,

$$A_s = \frac{M}{S_s jd} = \frac{18{,}400}{55{,}400} = 0.333 \text{ sq. in.}$$

   From Table I we select a ½″ round rod with a 7″ spacing.
   c) At the centers of interior spans and at the interior supports,

$$A_s = \frac{M}{S_s jd} = \frac{15{,}400}{55{,}400} = 0.278 \text{ sq. in.}$$

   In Table I, for a ½″ round rod, we see that the spacing should be 8½″
   d) At the exterior supports,

$$A_s = \frac{M}{S_s jd} = \frac{11{,}500}{55{,}400} = 0.208 \text{ sq. in.}$$

   In Table I, for a ⅜″ round rod, we take the spacing as 6″
5. Lengths of the rods,
   a) Over the supports, the rod lengths are

$$2 \times \frac{L}{3} = 2 \times \frac{8}{3} = 5.67' = 5'8'' \left(\frac{L}{3} \text{ into each span}\right)$$

   b) The rods in the bottom of the slab are of the same length as the slab; that is, 8′

Practice Problems (Art. 10-11). Design the following slabs. The data is given in the form of a table.

Problem Number	Uniform Load in Lbs. per Sq. Ft.	Span in Ft.	Working Stresses in Lb. per Sq. In.		Modulus of Elasticity of Concrete in Lb. per Sq. In.
			Concrete	Steel	
1	190	8	1,125	20,000	2,500,000
2	330	6	1,200	18,000	3,000,000
3	220	10	900	16,000	2,000,000
4	170	7	1,350	20,000	3,000,000

SUMMARY OF CHAPTER X

Study the following summary carefully, so you will become familiar with new words and new symbols.

1. Concrete is a mixture of cement, fine aggregate, coarse aggregate, and water.
   a) These materials are mixed in a revolving drum.
   b) The wet concrete is placed in forms of the shape the concrete is to have.
   c) Concrete is fairly strong in compression but is not ordinarily considered to have any strength in tension.
2. A reinforced concrete beam or slab contains steel rods.
   a) The concrete is in compression.
   b) The steel is in tension. The steel rods are placed on the tension side of the beam or slab.
3. A concrete floor slab is a relatively wide reinforced-concrete beam of rectangular shape.
   a) A 12″ strip of the slab is used in designing the slab.
   b) The slab is a continuous beam with negative bending moment over a support and positive bending moment at the center of a span.
   c) The reinforcing rods are placed in the top of the slab at the supports, and in the bottom of the slab at the centers of the spans.
4. The load on a floor slab is usually taken as w pound per square foot.
   a) w is the load per foot of length of the 12″ strip.
   b) The total load on a 12″ strip is $W = wL$.
5. The maximum bending moment in a 12″ strip of slab is taken as $\frac{WL}{10}$. This occurs at the centers of the exterior spans and at the first interior supports.
   a) The bending moment at the center of an interior span and at an interior support is taken as $\frac{WL}{12}$
   b) The bending moment at an exterior support is taken as $\frac{WL}{16}$
6. The properties of concrete and steel are represented by these symbols.
   a) S_c is the working stress in the concrete in compression.
   b) S_s is the working stress in the steel in tension.
   c) E_c is the modulus of elasticity of the concrete in compression.
   d) E_s is the modulus of elasticity of the steel in tension. E_s = 30,000,000 pounds per square inch.
7. The following formulas are used:
   a) $n = \frac{E_s}{E_c}$
   b) $k = \frac{n\frac{S_c}{S_s}}{1 + n\frac{S_c}{S_s}}$
   c) $j = 1 - k/3$
8. The depth of the slab from the top of the slab to the center of the steel rods is given by

$$d = \sqrt{\frac{M}{6kjS_c}}$$

   where M is the maximum bending moment in the slab and is $\frac{WL}{10}$.
   a) We add 1″ to d to get the total depth required for the slab.
   b) The required total depth is *rounded off* to the next larger one-half inch.
9. The steel area needed is given by the formula,

$$A_s = \frac{M}{S_s jd}$$

   We calculate the steel area needed at each point by using the bending moment at that point.
   a) Then we select a standard size of rod and choose a spacing to get the required amount of steel. Table I can be useful in this operation.
   b) The steel rods are placed in the top of the slab at the supports. A safe rule is to let these rods extend one-third of the span length into the span on each side.
   c) The steel rods are placed in the bottom of the slab at the centers of the spans. It is well to let these rods extend through the entire span.

Review Questions

See how much you remember from your study of this chapter.

1. What is *concrete?*
2. What is *fine aggregate?*
3. What is *coarse aggregate?*
4. What is a *form?*
5. In what way is concrete strong?
6. In what way is concrete weak?
7. What is *reinforced concrete?*
8. Why is it necessary to reinforce a concrete beam?
9. What kind of stress do the steel rods in a concrete beam take?
10. What is a *floor slab?*
11. Why do we take a 12″ strip to design a floor slab?
12. Where is the bending moment *positive* in a floor slab?
13. Where is the bending moment *negative* in a floor slab?
14. Where does the maximum bending moment occur in a floor slab?
15. What does M stand for?
16. What does S_c stand for?
17. What does S_s stand for?
18. What does E_c stand for?
19. What does E_s stand for?
20. What is n?
21. What is k?

22. What is j?
23. What is d?
24. What is the formula,

$$d = \sqrt{\frac{M}{6kjS_c}}$$

used for?
25. How do you calculate the total depth of the floor slab?
26. What is A_s?
27. What do you do with the formula,

$$A_s = \frac{M}{S_s jd}$$

28. When are the steel rods placed in the top of the slab?
29. How long should the steel rods be?
30. When are the steel rods placed in the bottom of the slab?

Review Problems

The following are typical problems in designing a concrete floor slab. If you can do them, the objective of this chapter has been accomplished. If you cannot solve these problems, you need to study the chapter again. Design the floor slabs for the following conditions.

Problem Number	Uniform Load in Lbs. per Sq. Ft.	Span in Ft.	Working Stresses in Lbs. per Sq. In.		Modulus of Elasticity of Concrete in Lbs. per Sq. In.
			Concrete	Steel	
1	250	6	1,200	18,000	3,000,000
2	210	8	1,350	20,000	3,000,000
3	130	5	900	16,000	2,000,000
4	370	9	1,000	18,000	2,500,000

CHAPTER XI

BENDING COMBINED WITH TENSION OR COMPRESSION

PURPOSE OF THIS CHAPTER. The purpose of this chapter is the study of *bending combined with tension or compression.* You learned how to calculate tensile and compressive stresses in Chapter V, and you learned how to calculate the bending stress in Chapter VI. Now you must learn how to calculate the maximum stress in a bar or post when it is subjected to bending at the same time that it is in tension or compression.

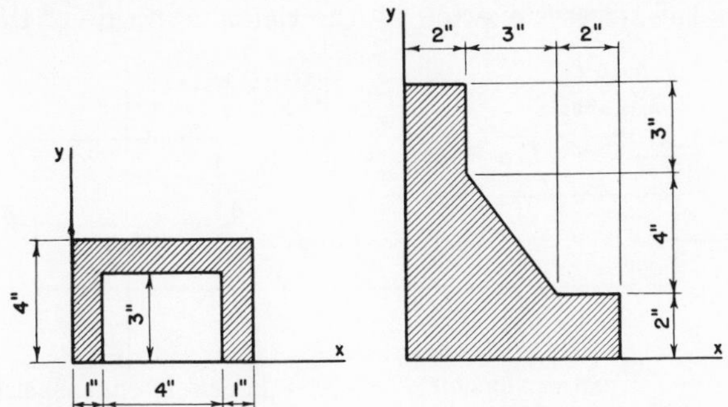

Fig. 1. Area for Problem 11 (Art. 11-1)

Fig. 2. Area for Problem 13 (Art. 11-1)

The combination of bending with tension or compression occurs frequently in structural members. In such cases, the structural designer has to make sure that the maximum stress in the material does not exceed the working stress. Naturally, he has to know how to calculate the maximum stress, in order to be able to do this. We will show you how to calculate the maximum stress in this chapter.

11-1. Review of Centroid of an Area.

You have to know what the *centroid* of an area is and how to locate the centroid of an area if you are going to understand this chapter. You studied centroids in Chapter III and then reviewed the subject in Chapter VI, so we are not going through a long review here. Instead we are giving you a list of questions and problems on centroids. If you can answer the questions and work the problems, you are ready to go on with the chapter. If you cannot, then study Chapter III until you can answer all of the questions, and work all of the problems.

1. What is the *centroid of an area?*
2. Where is the *centroid of a rectangle?*
3. Where is the *centroid of a circle?*
4. Where is the *centroid of a right triangle?*
5. What is the moment of an area with respect to an axis?
6. What do M_x and M_y represent?
7. What is a *composite area?*
8. How do you locate the centroid of a composite area?
9. What do $\bar{x}$ and $\bar{y}$ represent?
10. What is an *axis of symmetry?*
11. Locate the *centroid* of the area in Fig. 1.
12. What is the connection between the *centroid* of an area and an *axis of symmetry?*
13. Locate the *centroid* of the area in Fig. 2.

11-2. Review of Moment of Inertia of an Area.

You need to know how to calculate the *moment of inertia* of an area, also, if you are to understand this chapter. You studied moment of inertia in Chapter IV and reviewed it in Chapter VI, but maybe you have forgotten what you learned. The following questions and problems will help you review the subject. If you cannot answer the questions or solve the problems, turn back to Chapter IV for the answers.

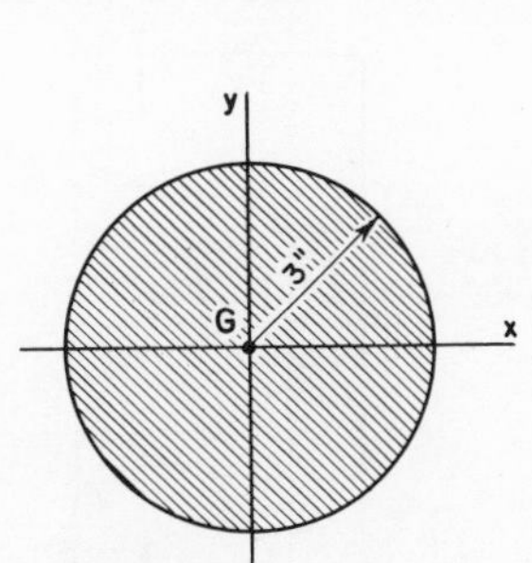

Fig. 3. Circular Area for Problem 7 (Art. 11-2)

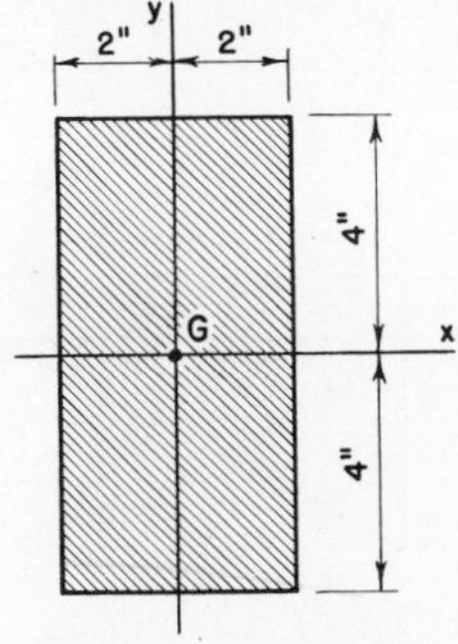

Fig. 4. Rectangular Area for Problem 8 (Art. 11-2)

1. What is *moment of inertia of an area?*
2. What is the *moment of inertia of a circular area* with respect to an axis through the center?
3. What is the *moment of inertia of a rectangular area* with respect to an axis which is through the center and parallel to the base?
4. What is the *moment of inertia of the area of a*

right triangle with respect to an axis which is through the centroid and parallel to a leg of the triangle?

5. In what units is moment of inertia expressed?
6. What do I_x and I_y represent?
7. Calculate I_x and I_y for the area in Fig. 3.
8. Calculate I_x and I_y for the area in Fig. 4.

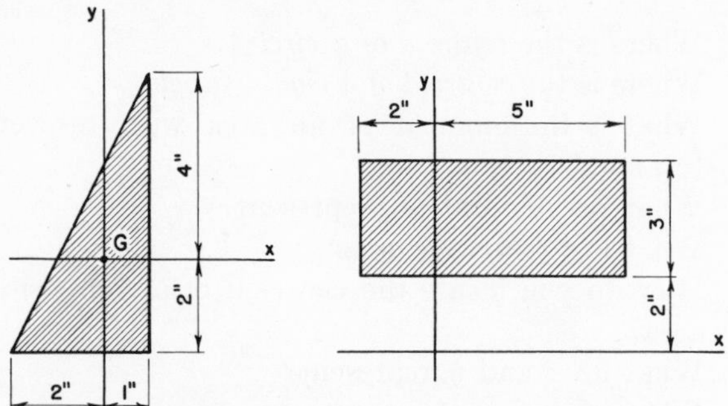

Fig. 5. Triangular Area for Problem 9 (Art. 11-2)

Fig. 6. Area for Problem 11 (Art. 11-2)

9. Calculate I_x and I_y for the area in Fig. 5.
10. What is the *parallel axis theorem?*
11. Use the parallel axis theorem to calculate I_x and I_y for the area in Fig. 6.
12. Use the parallel axis theorem to calculate I_x and I_y for the area in Fig. 7.
13. Calculate I_x and I_y for the area in Fig. 8.
14. Find I_x and I_y for a wide-flange beam, 14 WF 68.
15. Find Z_x and Z_y for an **I** beam, 10 **I** 25.4.
16. Find I_x and I_y for a 6(x)12 rectangular wood beam.

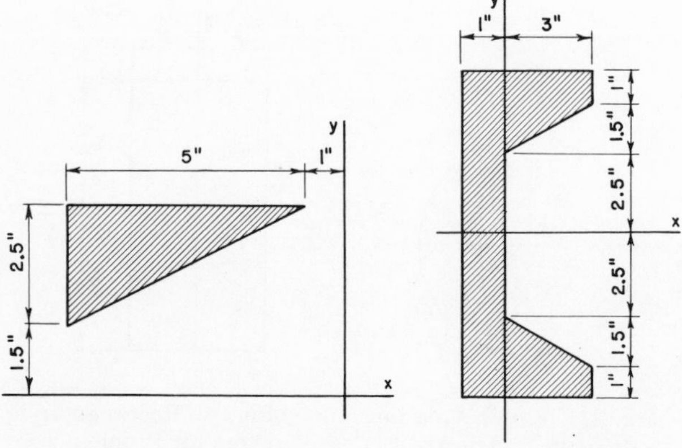

Fig. 7. Area for Problem 12 (Art. 11-2)

Fig. 8. Composite Area for Problem 13 (Art. 11-2)

11-3. Review of Axial Force and Axial Stress.

You should remember our studies of tension and compression in Chapter V. Material is in tension when the forces tend to stretch it, as in Fig. 9*A*, and in compression when the forces tend to shorten it, as in Fig. 9*B*. Notice the dotted line in Fig. 9*A*. The dotted line is parallel to the length of the bar and passes through the centroid of each cross section of the bar. We will call this line the *axis of the bar*. If the forces act along the axis of the bar, the stress is distributed uniformly over the cross section of the bar and is

$$S = \frac{P}{A}$$

as you should remember from Chapter V. Here A is the area of the cross section of the bar. We say that the force P is an axial force and the stress S is an axial stress. Fig. 9*C* shows the uniform distribution of axial stress over the cross section of the bar. These are the stresses exerted by the right-hand side of the

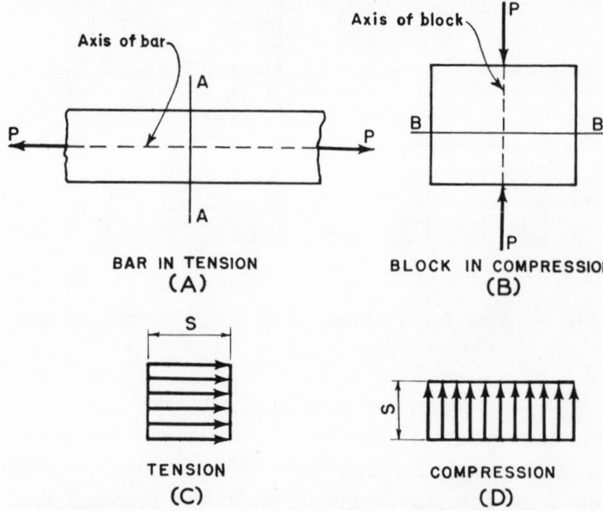

Fig. 9. Bar in Tension and Block in Compression

bar on the left-hand side at such a cross section as *AA* in Fig. 9*A*.

We can take the axis of a structural member to be either horizontal or vertical. For the block in Fig. 9*B*, we would take the axis to be vertical, because the forces are vertical. The axis is parallel to the sides of the block and passes through the centroid of each cross section. When the forces act along the axis of the bar, the stress is distributed uniformly over the cross section of the bar and is

$$S = \frac{P}{A}$$

Fig. 9*D* shows the distribution of stress over such a cross section as *BB*, in Fig. 9*B*. You can think of these as the stresses exerted by the lower part of the bar on the upper part.

Illustrative Example 1. An axial compressive force of 27,600 lbs. is applied to a 6x6 wood post. Calculate the axial stress.

Solution:

1. The force P is 27,600 lbs.
2. The area of cross section of the post is 30.25 sq. in. (From Table V, in Chapter VII)
3. $S = \frac{P}{A} = \frac{27{,}600}{30.25} = 913$ lbs. per sq. in.

Practice Problems (Art. 11-3). This is a review, so you should be able to work through these problems quickly.

1. Calculate the *axial stress in a circular steel rod* 1.5″ in diameter, due to an axial force of 24,800 lbs.
2. An axial force of 17,600 lbs. is applied to a rectangular steel bar, 3″x$\frac{3}{8}$″. Calculate the axial stress.
3. A short wide-flange beam 10 WF 100 is subjected to an axial force of 282,000 lbs. in compression. Calculate the axial stress.
4. Calculate the stress due to an axial force of 73,000 lbs. applied to a post which has the cross section shown in Fig. 10.

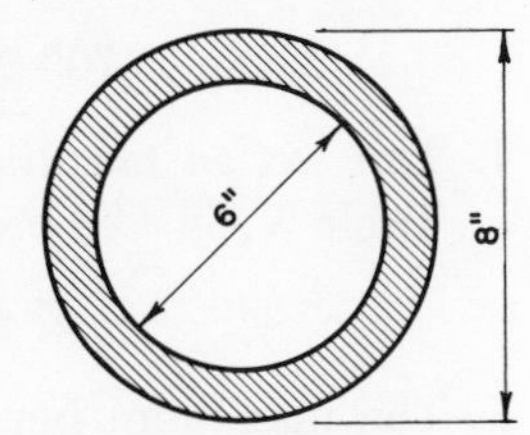

Fig. 10. Hollow Section of Post for Problem 4 (Art. 11-3)

11-4. Review of Bending and Bending Stress.

We studied beams and bending stress in Chapter VI. Fig. 11A shows a beam which is supported at the ends, and carries a concentrated load P. The forces which support the beams at the ends are called *reactions* and we represent them by R_1 and R_2.

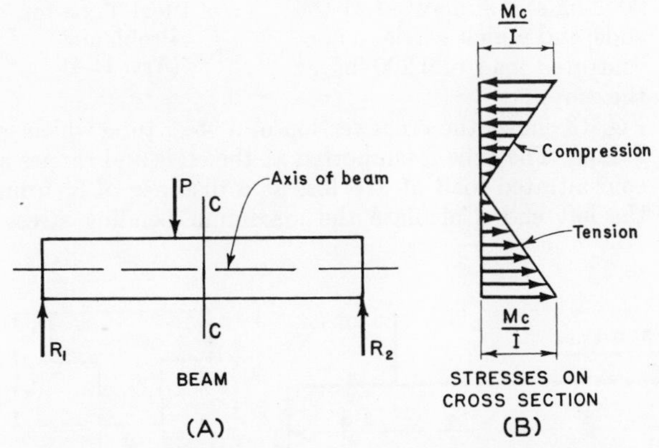

Fig. 11. Bending Stresses in Beam Supported at Ends

Fig. 11B shows the distribution of bending stress on a cross section of the beam. When the *bending moment* is positive, there is compression in the top of the beam and tension in the bottom; the stress is *zero* at the neutral axis. The maximum bending stress is

$$S = \frac{Mc}{I}$$

where M is the *maximum bending moment* in pound inches, I is the *moment of inertia* of the cross section with respect to the neutral axis, and c is the distance from the neutral axis to the farthest point in the cross section.

The first step in finding the maximum bending stress in a beam is to calculate the reactions. This is usually done by means of *moment equations.*

When we know the reactions, we can calculate the shearing force at any point in the beam. *The shearing force at any point is equal to the sum of the forces to the left of the point;* the shear diagram shows the value of the shear at each point along the beam. We draw enough of the shear diagram to locate the point where the shearing force is *zero;* this is the point where the maximum bending moment occurs.

The bending moment at any point in a beam is equal to the moment, with respect to that point, of all of the forces to the left of the point. *We take clockwise moments as positive and counterclockwise moments as negative.*

The neutral axis of the beam passes through the centroid of the cross section, so we must locate the *centroid.* Then we calculate the moment of inertia, I, with respect to the neutral axis.

Finally, the maximum bending stress is

$$S = \frac{Mc}{I}$$

You must be sure to express M in pound inches when you use this formula.

When the beam has a standard section, as has a wide-flange beam or a rectangular wood beam, you do not have to calculate the moment of inertia. You can just look up the section modulus, Z, in the proper table in Chapter VII. The section modulus is

$$Z = \frac{I}{c}$$

so the maximum bending stress is

$$S = \frac{M}{Z}$$

Illustrative Example 1. Fig. 12A shows the free-body diagram of an 8x12 rectangular wood beam. Calculate the maximum bending stress.

Solution:

1. The reactions
   a) We write the moment equation $\Sigma M_a = 0$ to find the reaction R_2. So, taking the forces in order from left to right,

$$\Sigma M_a = 2{,}400 \times 5 + 3{,}000 \times 10 - 16R_2 = 0$$
$$16R_2 = 2{,}400 \times 5 + 3{,}000 \times 10 = 12{,}000 + 30{,}000 = 42{,}000$$
$$R_2 = 2{,}630 \text{ lbs.}$$

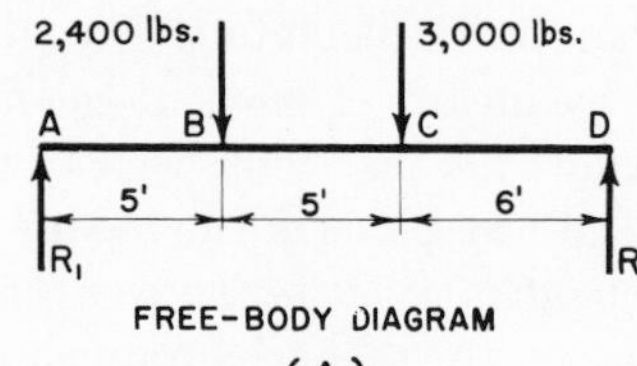

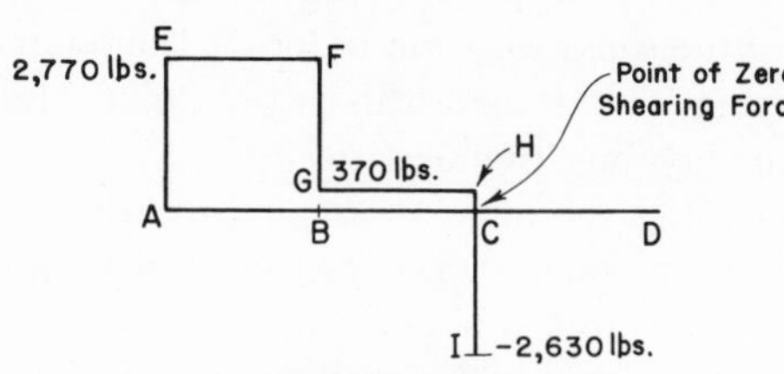

Fig. 12. Free-Body and Shear Diagrams for Rectangular Wood Beam for Example 1 (Art. 11-4)

   b) Next we write the moment equation $\Sigma M_d = 0$ to find the reaction R_1

$$\Sigma M_d = 16R_1 - 2{,}400 \times 11 - 3{,}000 \times 6 = 0$$
$$16R_1 = 2{,}400 \times 11 + 3{,}000 \times 6 = 26{,}400 + 18{,}000 = 44{,}400$$
$$R_1 = 2{,}770 \text{ lbs.}$$

   c) Then we check the reactions by writing the equation

$$\Sigma F_y = 0$$
$$\Sigma F_y = 2{,}770 - 2{,}400 - 3{,}000 + 2{,}630 = 0$$
$$5{,}400 - 5{,}400 = 0$$
$$0 = 0$$

2. The shear diagram Fig. 12*B* shows part of the shear diagram. Look at the diagram while you study this example.
   a) We start by drawing the base line *ABCD*
   b) We plot the reaction R_1 (2,770 lbs.) upward from *A* to locate *E*. The shear at *E* is 2,770 lbs.
   c) We draw the horizontal line *EF*
   d) We plot the 2,400-lb. load downward from *F* to locate *G*. The shear at *G* is

$$2{,}770 - 2{,}400 = 370 \text{ lbs.}$$

   e) We draw the horizontal line *GH*
   f) We plot the 3,000-lb. load downward from *H* to locate point *I*. The shear at *I* is

$$370 - 3{,}000 = -2{,}630 \text{ lbs.}$$

   g) The shearing force is *zero* at point *C*

3. The maximum bending moment occurs at *C*

$$M = 2{,}770 \times 10 - 2{,}400 \times 5 = 27{,}700 - 12{,}000 = 15{,}700 \text{ lb. ft.}$$
$$M = 15{,}700 \times 12 = 188{,}000 \text{ lb. in.}$$

4. The *section modulus* is found from column 5 of Table V, in Chapter VII, as

$$Z = 165.3 \text{ in.}^3$$

5. The maximum bending stress is

$$S = \frac{M}{Z} = \frac{188{,}000}{165.3} = 1{,}140 \text{ lbs. per sq. in.}$$

Practice Problems (Art. 11-4). Review bending stress by solving the following problems.

1. A wide-flange beam, 8 WF 27, is 12′ long and is supported at the ends. The beam carries a uniformly distributed load of 1,460 lbs. per ft. of length. Calculate the *maximum bending stress.*
2. Find the maximum bending stress in an American standard beam, 10 I 35, which is 20′ long and supported at the ends, and which carries a concentrated load of 9,200 lbs. at the center.

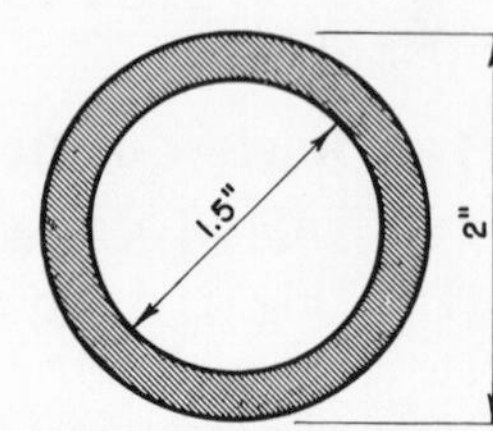

Fig. 13. Cross Section of Steel Tube for Problem 3 (Art. 11-4)

3. Fig. 13 shows the cross section of a steel tube which is 7′ long. The tube is supported at the ends and carries a concentrated load of 470 lbs. at a distance of 3′ from the left end. Calculate the maximum bending stress.

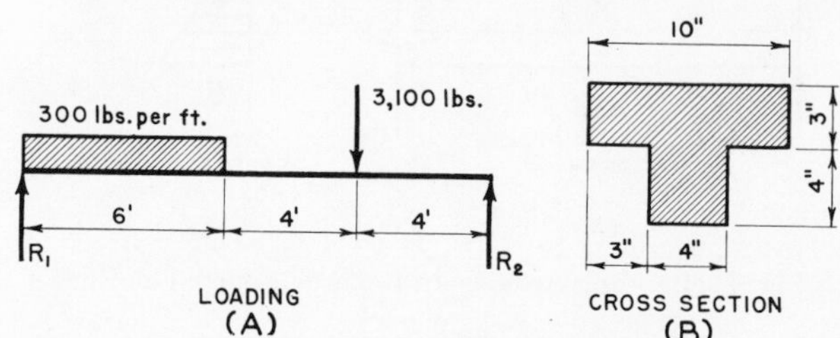

Fig. 14. Beam for Problem 4 (Art. 11-4)

4. Fig. 14 shows the loading and cross section for a beam. Calculate the maximum bending stress.

11-5. Beams with Axial Loads.

We are ready now to study the stresses in a beam which is subjected to axial forces in addition to forces perpendicular to the beam. Fig. 15*A* shows such a beam. The beam carries the loads P_1 and P_2 which causes bending stress, and also the axial forces P. We can now calculate maximum stress.

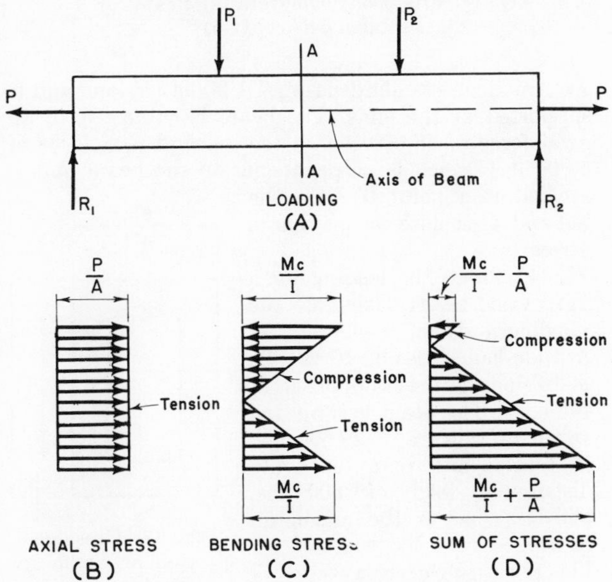

Fig. 15. Bending Stress Combined with Axial Force

If the axial forces P were the only forces acting on the beam, the only stress would be an *axial stress*. Its value would be, $S = \frac{P}{A}$. Fig. 15*B* shows the axial stresses as they act on such a cross section as AA in Fig. 15*A*. These are the stresses which are exerted by the right-hand part of the beam on the left-hand part. The force P is a tensile force, so the axial stress is a tensile stress.

The forces P_1 and P_2 in Fig. 15*A* cause bending stresses. If P_1 and P_2 were the only loads applied to the beam, there would only be bending stress in the beam. The maximum bending stress would be $S = \frac{Mc}{I}$. Fig. 15*C* shows the bending stress on such a cross section as AA in Fig. 15*A*. When the bending moment is positive, there is compression in the top of the beam and tension in the bottom.

The beam in Fig. 15*A* is subjected to both axial forces and bending forces, so both the axial stress in Fig. 15*B* and the bending stress in Fig. 15*C* act on the cross section AA. The total stress at any point in the cross section is equal to the axial stress in Fig. 15*B* plus the bending stress in Fig. 15*C*. Fig. 15*D* shows the final distribution of stress on the cross section due to the combination of axial stress and bending stress.

At the bottom of the beam the axial stress is tension and so is the bending stress. The final stress is the sum of the two tensile stresses, so the final stress at the bottom of the beam is

$$S = \frac{Mc}{I} + \frac{P}{A}$$

and it is tension.

At the top of the beam, the axial stress is tension but the bending stress is compression. A compressive stress is the opposite of a tensile stress, so the two stresses tend to cancel each other. If the bending stress is greater than the axial stress, the final stress at the top of the beam is

$$S = \frac{Mc}{I} - \frac{P}{A}$$

and it is compression. However, if the axial stress is greater than the bending stress, the final stress at the top of the beam is

$$S = \frac{P}{A} - \frac{Mc}{I}$$

and it is tension.

The axial stress is usually the same at all cross sections of the beam, but the bending stress is not, because the bending moment varies along the beam. The maximum bending stress occurs where the bending moment is maximum. To get the maximum stress in the beam, then, we must use the maximum bending moment to calculate $\frac{Mc}{I}$, and then add $\frac{P}{A}$.

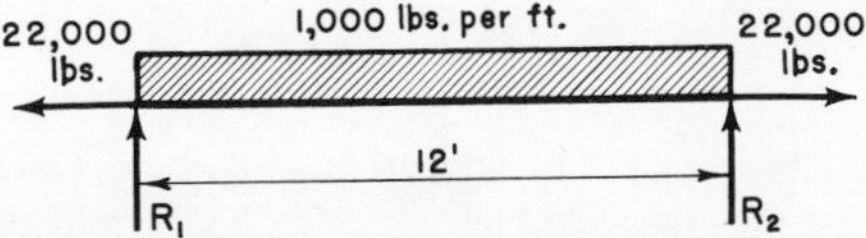

Fig. 16. Wide-Flange Beam for Example 1 (Art. 11-5)

Illustrative Example 1. Fig. 16 shows the free-body diagram of a wide-flange beam, 6 WF 20. Calculate the maximum stress in the beam.

Solution:

1. You should be able to see that each reaction is equal to half of the total load because the loading on the beam is symmetrical. The total load is

$$W = wL = 1{,}000 \times 12 = 12{,}000 \text{ lbs.}$$

Then,

$$R_1 = R_2 = \frac{W}{2} = \frac{12{,}000}{2} = 6{,}000 \text{ lbs.}$$

2. The maximum bending moment occurs at the center of the beam (can you prove this?) and is

$$M = 6{,}000 \times 6 - 1{,}000 \times 6 \times 3 = 36{,}000 - 18{,}000 = 18{,}000 \text{ lb. ft.}$$

$$M = 18{,}000 \times 12 = 216{,}000 \text{ lb. in.}$$

3. You can look up the section modulus, Z, in column 9 of Table I, in Chapter VII

$$Z = 13.4 \text{ in.}^3$$

4. The maximum bending stress is

$$S = \frac{M}{Z} = \frac{216{,}000}{13.4} = 16{,}100 \text{ lbs. per sq. in.}$$

This is compression at the top of the beam and tension at the bottom because the bending moment is positive.

5. The axial force is

$$P = 22{,}000 \text{ lbs.}$$

and it is tension.

6. The area of the cross section can be read in column 3 of Table I, in Chapter VII, as

$$A = 5.90 \text{ sq. in.}$$

7. The axial stress is

$$S = \frac{P}{A} = \frac{22{,}000}{5.90} = 3{,}730 \text{ lbs, per sq. in. tension}$$

8. The maximum stress occurs at the bottom of the beam where both the bending stress and the axial stress are tension. It is

$$S = \frac{Mc}{I} + \frac{P}{A} = 16{,}100 + 3{,}730 = 19{,}830 \text{ lbs. per sq. in. tension}$$

The axial stress is the same at all points in the cross section, and may be either tension or compression. The bending stress is tension at the bottom of the section and compression at the top when the bending moment is positive; it is compression at the bottom of the section and tension at the top when the bending moment is negative. You know how to calculate bending stress and axial stress; you have to add them in problems of the type we are doing now.

You can always tell where the bending stress is tension and where it is compression; also, you can always tell whether the axial stress is tension or compression. Then you can combine the bending stress and the axial stress to get the maximum stress.

Practice Problems (Art. 11-5). The more you practice the more you learn.

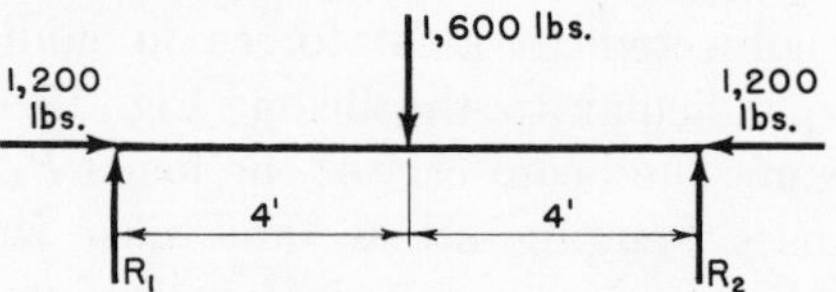

Fig. 17. Free-Body Diagram for Beam for Problem 2 (Art. 11-5)

1. An American standard beam, 7 I 20, is 15′ long and is supported at the ends. The beam is subjected to an axial force of 18,000 lbs. in tension and to a force of 5,000 lbs. which is perpendicular to the beam and is applied at a point 6′ from the left end. Calculate the maximum stress.
2. Fig. 17 shows the loading for a 2x12 wood beam. Calculate the maximum stress.
3. A wide-flange beam, 10 WF 23, is 16′ long and is supported at the ends. The beam is subjected to an axial force of 29,600 lbs. in tension and to a uniformly distributed load of 600 lbs. per ft. What is the maximum stress?
4. Fig. 18 shows the cross section of a beam which is 10′ long and which is supported at the ends. The beam is subjected to an axial force of 6,200 lbs. compression. Also, it carries a concentrated load of 3,400 lbs., 3′ from the left end, and a concentrated load of 4,700 lbs., 7′ from the left end. Find the maximum stress.

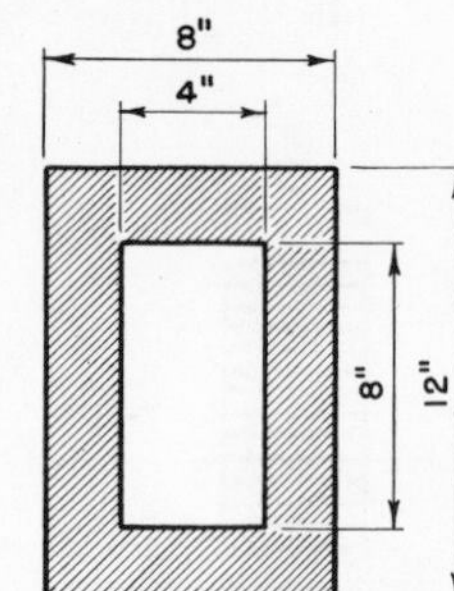

Fig. 18. Cross Section of Beam for Problem 4 (Art. (11-5)

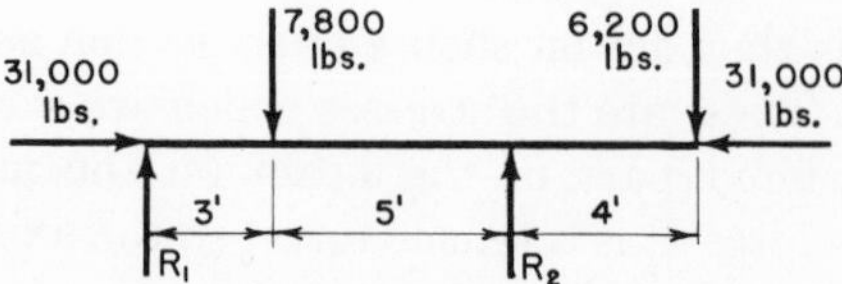

Fig. 19. Free-Body Diagram for Wide-Flange Beam for Problem 5 (Art. 11-5)

5. Fig. 19 shows the loading for a wide-flange beam, 8 WF 27. Calculate the maximum stress.
6. Fig. 20*A* shows the cross section of a beam and Fig. 20*B* shows the loading. Calculate the maximum stress.

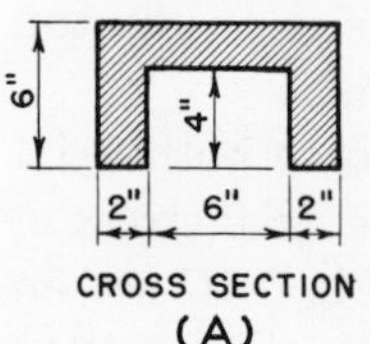

CROSS SECTION
(A)

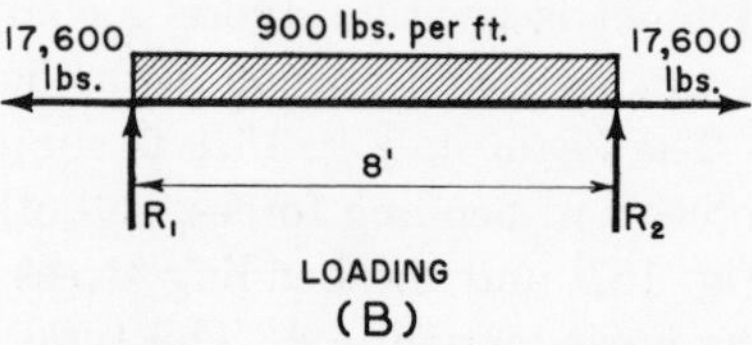

LOADING
(B)

Fig. 20. Cross Section and Loading on Beam for Problem 6 (Art. 11-5)

11-6. Eccentric Loads.

An *eccentric load* is a load which is off center. The load may be parallel to the axis of a bar or post but not on the axis. For example, Fig. 21 shows a bar which is subjected to the forces P. Notice the line

Fig. 21. Bar with Eccentric Load

AA which passes through the centroid of each cross section and is the axis of the bar. The forces P are parallel to the axis but are not on the axis, so we do not call them axial forces. We say they are *eccentric forces* and call the distance e the *eccentricity*.

Fig. 22A shows another example of an eccentric load. The end of the beam is supported by the post, but the beam does not extend over all of the top of the post. We can represent the length of contact of the beam on the post as b; then the force exerted by the beam on the post will be at the center of this length b, or at a distance of $\frac{b}{2}$ from the right side of the post. The line AA is the axis of the post; the axis is a line which passes through the centroid of each cross section of the post. The force P is at a distance e from the axis of the post; we say the force is

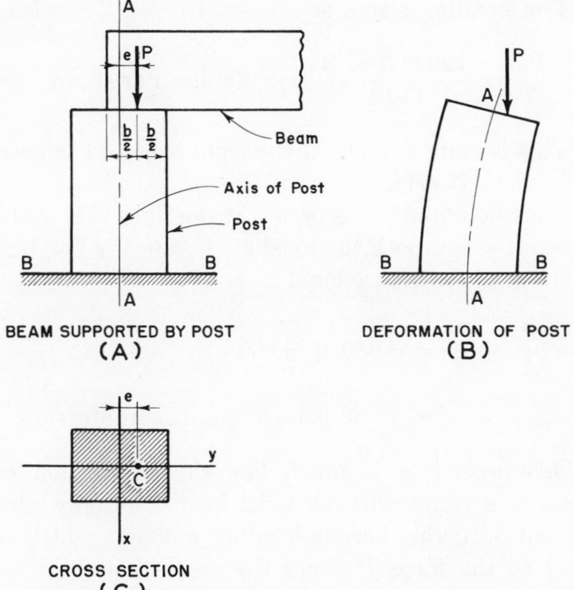

Fig. 22. Eccentric Load and Deformation of Post

eccentric and call e the *eccentricity*. Our problem here is to calculate the maximum stress on such a cross section as BB.

The eccentric load in Fig. 22A is a compressive force, so it causes the post to shorten. Also, because it is off center, it bends the post. Fig. 22B shows how the post deforms. The bending causes compressive stresses on the right side of the post and tensile stresses on the left side.

We calculate the kinds of stress for an eccentric load just as we did for a beam with an axial load. One kind of stress is *axial stress* and we calculate this

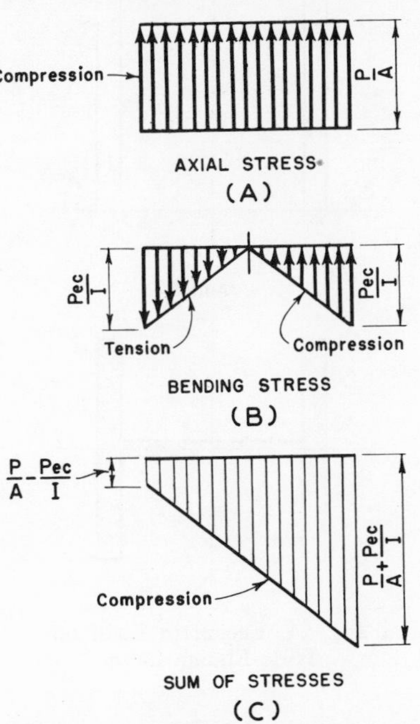

Fig. 23. Stresses on Cross Section of Post

as if the force P were applied at the center of the post. This is

$$S = \frac{P}{A}$$

and you can see it is compression in this case.

Fig. 22C shows the cross section of the post. Notice how we have placed the x and y axes here. Point C is where the load is applied to the section. Now there is a bending moment at such a cross section as BB, in Fig. 22A, and this bending moment is

$$M = Pe$$

where e is the eccentricity of the load. Then the bending stress is

$$S = \frac{Mc}{I} = \frac{Pec}{I}$$

Here we take the moment of inertia, I, with respect to the x axis.

The axial stress is distributed uniformly over the cross section of the post. Fig. 23*A* shows this and you can think of these stresses as exerted by the support upon the section *BB* in Fig. 22*A*.

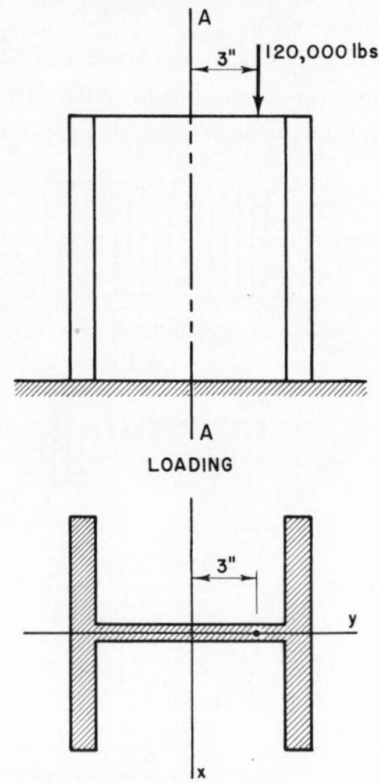

Fig. 24. Eccentric Load on Wide-Flange Beam

Fig. 23*B* shows the bending stresses on the cross section of the post. The bending stress is *zero* at the centroid of the cross section and maximum at the sides. There is compression at the right side of the post and tension at the left side.

We can add the two sets of stresses just as we did in studying beams with axial loads. Fig. 23*C* shows the result. The maximum stress occurs at the right side of the post where we add the compressive stress $\frac{P}{A}$ to the compressive stress $\frac{Pec}{I}$ to get

$$S = \frac{P}{A} + \frac{Pec}{I}$$

The smallest stress occurs at the left side of the post, where we have the difference between the compressive stress $\frac{P}{A}$ and the tensile stress $\frac{Pec}{I}$. This difference is

$$S = \frac{P}{A} - \frac{Pec}{I}$$

Now you know how to calculate the maximum stress due to an eccentric load. It is

$$S = \frac{P}{A} + \frac{Pec}{I}$$

If the bar or post has a standard section, you can look up the section modulus Z in Chapter VII. Then the bending stress is

$$\frac{Pec}{Z} = \frac{Pe}{Z}$$

Illustrative Example 1. Fig. 24*A* shows a short length of wide-flange beam, 10 WF 100, with an eccentric load. Calculate the maximum stress.

Solution:

1. The load P is 120,000 lbs.
2. The area of the cross section (do you know where to find it?) is

$$A = 29.43 \text{ sq. in.}$$

3. The axial stress is

$$\frac{P}{A} = \frac{120{,}000}{29.43} = 4{,}080 \text{ lbs. per sq. in. compression}$$

4. The eccentricity e is 3″
5. The section modulus Z is 112.4 in.^{3}
6. The bending stress is

$$\frac{Pe}{Z} = \frac{120{,}000 \times 3}{112.4} = 3{,}200 \text{ lbs. per sq. in.}$$

This is compression on the right side and tension on the left side.

7. The maximum stress occurs at the right side of the beam where both the axial stress and the bending stress are compression.

$$S = \frac{P}{A} + \frac{Pe}{Z} = 4{,}080 + 3{,}200$$

$$= 7{,}280 \text{ lbs. per sq. in. compression}$$

This procedure is much like the calculation of stress in a beam with an axial load. The only new element occurring here is bending moment which is equal to the force P times the eccentricity e.

Practice Problems (Art. 11-6). You can learn more by working problems than you can by reading the text. For additional practice, solve the following problems.

1. Fig. 25 shows the cross section of a steel bar. Calculate the maximum stress due to a tensile force of 17,900 lbs. which is applied to the cross section at *A*.

2. Fig. 26 shows the cross section of an American standard beam, 8 I 23. A compressive force of 36,400 lbs. is applied to the section at A. Calculate the maximum stress.

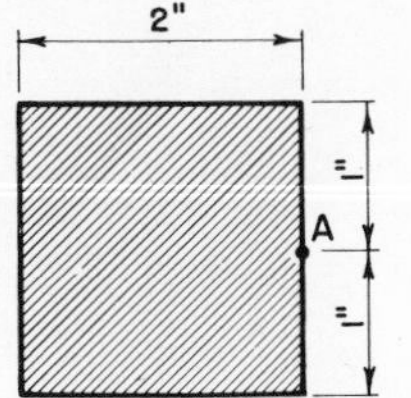

Fig. 25. Cross Section of a Square Steel Bar for Problem 1 (Art. 11-6)

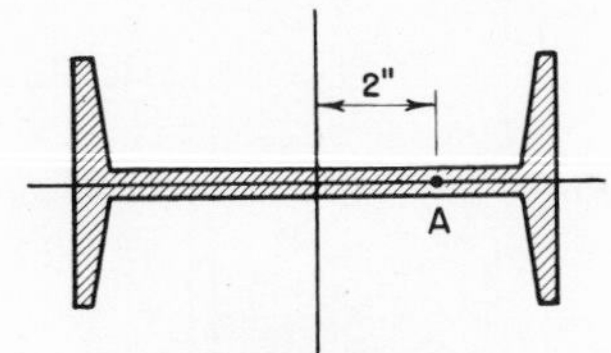

Fig. 26. Cross Section of American Standard Beam for Problem 2 (Art. 11-6)

3. A 2x12 wood beam carries a compressive force of 14,100 lbs. at a point A, as shown in Fig. 27. Calculate the maximum stress.
4. A steel tube has the cross section shown in Fig. 28. Calculate the maximum stress due to a tensile force of 21,000 lbs. which is applied to the cross section at A.

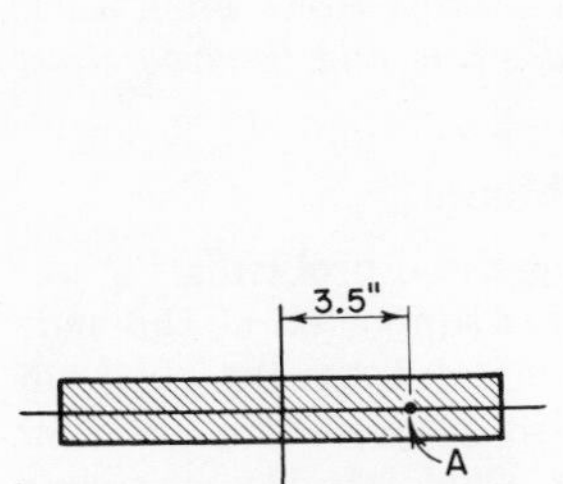

Fig. 27. Cross Section of Wood Beam for Problem 3 (Art. 11-6)

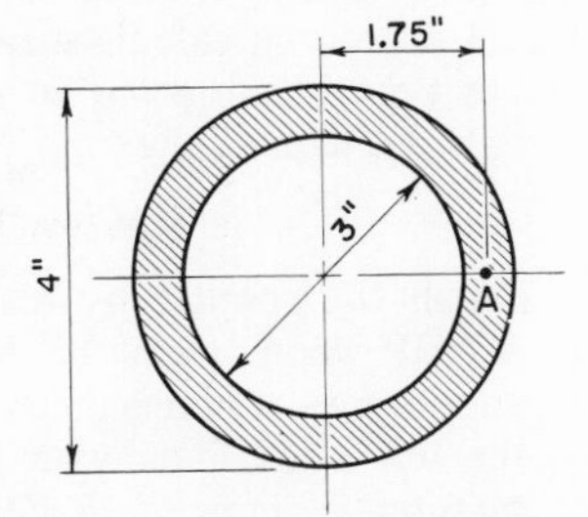

Fig. 28. Cross Section of Steel Tube for Problem 4 (Art. 11-6)

5. A steel angle is riveted to a short length of wide-flange beam, 14 WF 68, as shown in Fig. 29. A force of 92,000 lbs. is applied to the angle. Calculate the maximum stress in the beam.

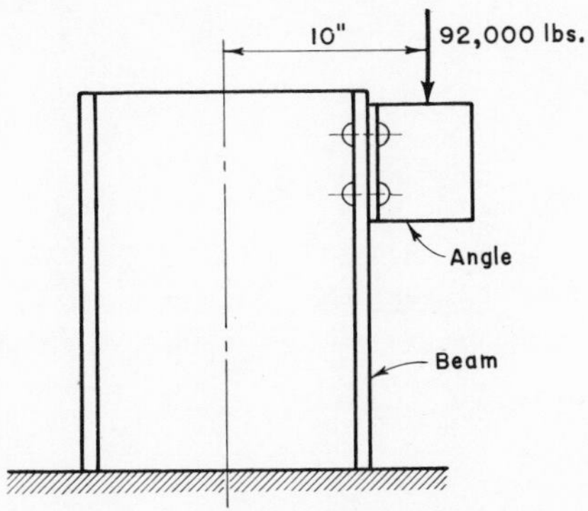

Fig. 29. Eccentric Load on Steel Angle for Problem 5 (Art. 11-6)

SUMMARY OF CHAPTER XI

We will summarize only the new material in this chapter.

1. Axial stress is caused by a force which is parallel to the axis of a beam or post.
   a) The axis of a beam or post is a line which passes through the centroid of each cross section.
   b) The axial stress is distributed uniformly over the cross section and is

$$S = \frac{P}{A}$$

   where P is the force and A is the area of the cross section.
   c) The axial stress is compression when the forces tend to shorten the beam or post.
   d) The axial stress is tension when the forces tend to stretch the beam or post.
2. Bending stress in a beam is caused by forces which are perpendicular to the axis of the beam.
   a) The bending moment at any point in the beam is equal to the moment, with respect to that point, of all forces to the left of the point. *Clockwise moments are positive and counterclockwise moments are negative.*
   b) The bending stress is *zero* at the centroid of the cross section and is maximum at the edge. The maximum stress is

$$S = \frac{Mc}{I}$$

   where M is the bending moment, I is the moment of inertia of the cross section and c is the distance from the neutral axis to the farthest point in the cross section.
   c) A positive bending moment causes compression in the top of the beam and tension in the bottom.
   d) A negative bending moment causes tension in the top of the beam and compression in the bottom.
3. Bending stress in a post or bar is due to the eccentricity of forces that are parallel to the axis of the bar. We represent the eccentricity by e.
   a) The bending moment is Pe.
   b) The maximum bending stress is

$$S = \frac{Mc}{I} = \frac{Pec}{I}$$

4. The final stress at any point in a beam or post is equal to the sum of the axial stress and the bending stress. The maximum stress is

$$S = \frac{Mc}{I} + \frac{P}{A}$$

Review Questions

Check your knowledge of this chapter by answering these questions.

1. What is the *axis of a beam* or *post?*
2. What is *axial stress?*
3. What causes *axial stress?*
4. What is the difference between *tension* and *compression?*

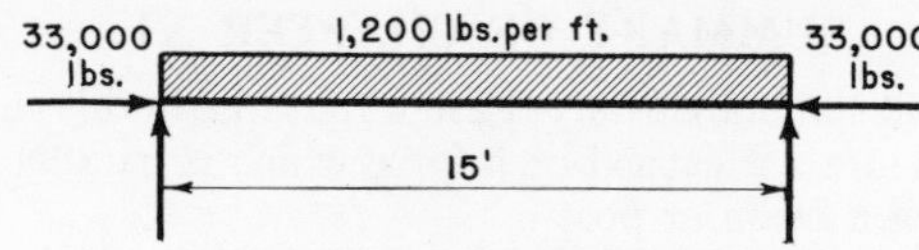

Fig. 30. Loading on Wide-Flange Beam for Problem 2 (Review Problems)

5. How is axial stress distributed over the cross section of a beam?
6. How is the *bending moment* calculated in a beam?

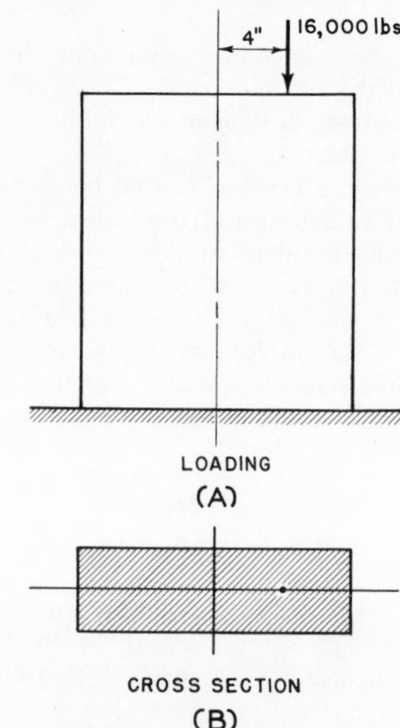

Fig. 31. Cross Section of Wood Post for Problem 3 (Review Problems)

7. What is a *positive bending moment?*
8. What is a *negative bending moment?*
9. How is *bending stress* distributed over the cross section of the beam?
10. What is the *maximum bending stress* equal to?
11. Where do tensile and compressive stresses occur when the bending moment is positive?
12. Where do tensile and compressive stresses occur when the bending moment is negative?

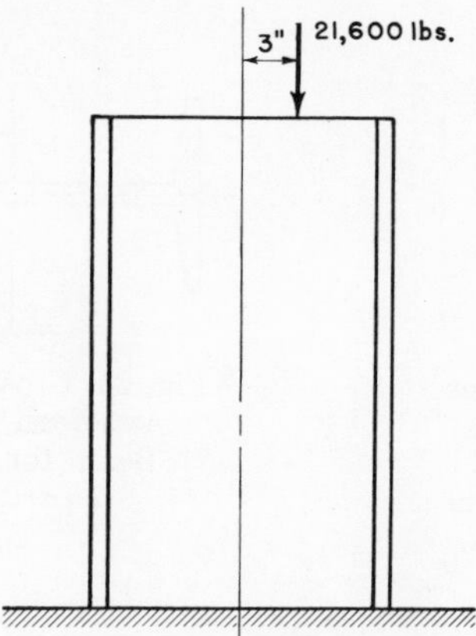

Fig. 32. Loading on Post for Problem 4 (Review Problems)

13. What is an *eccentric load?*
14. What is the *bending moment due to an eccentric load?*
15. How do you calculate the *maximum stress* when a bar or post is subjected to *axial stress* and *bending stress* at the same time?

Review Problems

Finish the chapter by working these problems.

1. A 6x10 wood beam, 10′ long, is supported at the ends and carries a concentrated load of 4,300 lbs., 6′ from the left end. The beam is also subjected to an *axial compressive force* of 15,200 lbs. Calculate the *maximum stress.*
2. A wide-flange beam, 12 WF 45, is subjected to the loading shown in Fig. 30. Calculate the *maximum stress.*
3. Fig. 31 shows the load on a 4x12 wood post. What is the *maximum stress?*
4. An American standard beam, 8 I 23, is used as a post to carry the load shown in Fig. 32. Calculate the *maximum stress.*

CHAPTER XII

COMPRESSION MEMBERS

PURPOSE OF THIS CHAPTER. The purpose of this chapter is to study compression members; to learn how different types of compression members behave under load, and to learn how to calculate the strength of a compression member. You remember that a member is in compression when the forces tend to shorten it.

A common example of a compression member is a column such as you see in Fig. 1. Fig. 1*A* shows the column supporting a beam; in turn the column is supported by the floor below. Fig. 1*B* shows the forces exerted on the column by the beam and floor. Here the force P is the load on the column.

A brick or a concrete block in a wall is also a compression member. Fig. 2 shows the forces exerted on a brick in a wall. A force P is exerted by the bricks above and another force P by the bricks below.

12-1. Radius of Gyration.

Radius of gyration (prounounced jī-rā′shun) is a property of area that we have passed over until now, because there was no need to use it before. However, we will study it now, in connection with compression members.

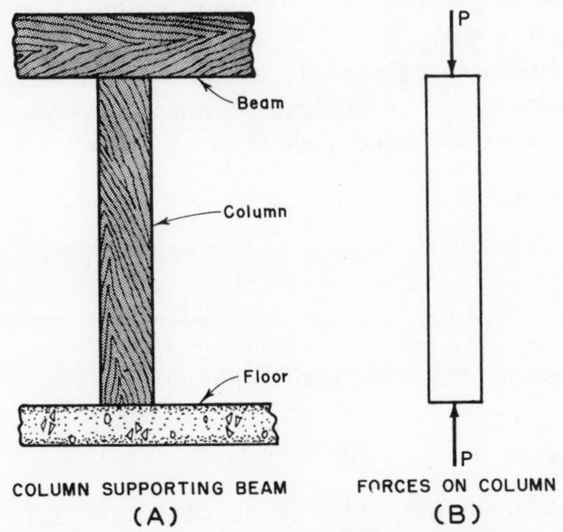

Fig. 1. Example of Column Supporting Beam

First, examine the rectangular area in Fig. 3. You already know that the area of a rectangle is

$$A = bh$$

and that the area is expressed in square inches. Also, you know what the *moment of inertia of a rectangle* is. The moment of inertia of the rectangle in Fig. 3, with respect to the x axis is

$$I_x = \frac{1}{12} bh^3$$

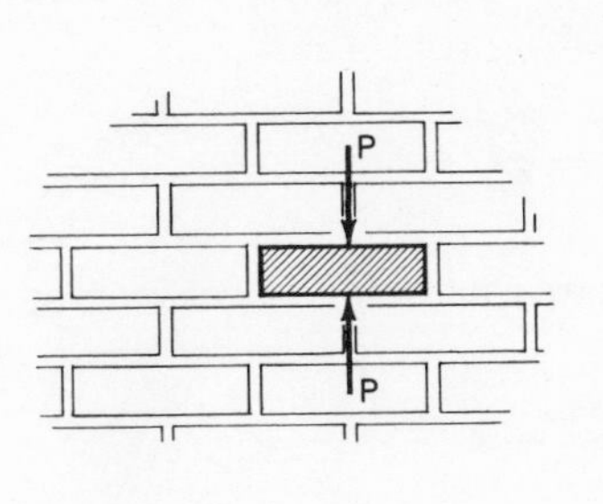

Fig. 2. Structural Brick in Compression

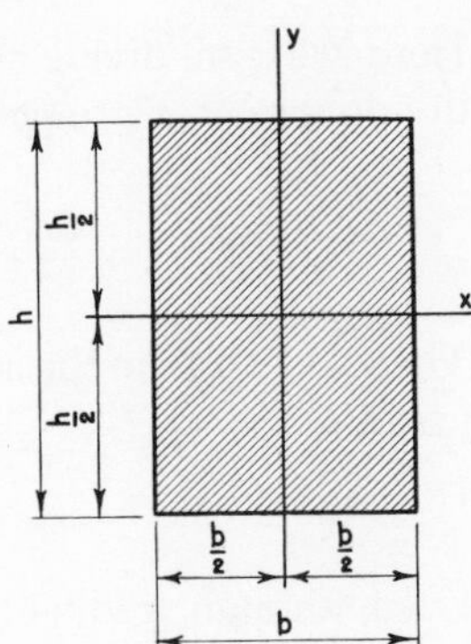

Fig. 3. Rectangular Area for Study of Radius of Gyration

and the moment of inertia with respect to the y axis is

$$I_y = \frac{1}{12} hb^3$$

Moment of inertia is expressed in in.[4] (inches to the fourth power).

The radius of gyration of an area is the square root of the moment of inertia of the area divided by the area; we will represent the radius of gyration by r so it is

$$r = \sqrt{\frac{I}{A}}$$

We can calculate the moment of inertia of an area with respect to any axis, and for each different moment of inertia we have a different radius of gyration. For instance, we can calculate the moment of inertia of an area with respect to the x axis (see Fig. 3). Then, the radius of gyration, with respect to the x axis, is

$$r_x = \sqrt{\frac{I_x}{A}}$$

and the radius of gyration with respect to the y axis is

$$r_y = \sqrt{\frac{I_y}{A}}$$

As a practical matter (which we will not take time here to justify) we usually calculate moments of inertia with respect to centroidal axes and so we only calculate radii (*radii* is the plural of *radius*) of gyration with respect to centroidal axes.

Radius of gyration is expressed in inches. We calculate moment of inertia, I, in in.^{4} and area A, in in.^{2} (sq. in.). Then, in terms of dimensions

$$r = \sqrt{\frac{\text{in.}^4}{\text{in.}^2}} = \sqrt{\text{in.}^2} = \text{in.}$$

Here we can divide in.^{4} by in.^{2}, just as we would divide x^4 by x^2 to get x^2.

$$\frac{x^4}{x^2} = x^2$$

Then we can take the square root of in.^{2} to get inches, just as

$$\sqrt{x^2} = x$$

Even though radius of gyration is expressed in inches, it does not represent any special length in the area. Think of it as a property of the area, and be sure that you learn how to calculate it.

Illustrative Example 1. Fig. 4 shows a rectangular area. Calculate the radii of gyration with respect to the x and y axes.

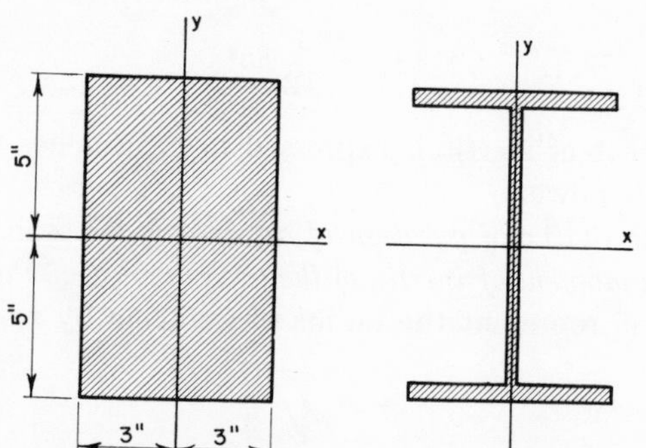

Fig. 4. Rectangular Area for Example 1 (Art 12-1)

Fig. 5. Cross Section of Wide-Flange Beam

Solution:

1. The moment of inertia with respect to the x axis is

$$I_x = \tfrac{1}{12}\,bh^3 = \tfrac{1}{12} \times 6\,(10)^3 = 500 \text{ in.}^4$$

2. The moment of inertia with respect to the y axis is

$$I_y = \tfrac{1}{12}\,hb^3 = \tfrac{1}{12} \times 10\,(6)^3 = 180 \text{ in.}^4$$

3. The area of the rectangle is

$$A = 6 \times 10 = 60 \text{ in.}^2$$

4. The radius of gyration with respect to the x axis is

$$r_x = \sqrt{\frac{I_x}{A}} = \sqrt{\frac{500}{60}} = \sqrt{8.33} = 2.89''$$

5. The radius of gyration with respect to the y axis is

$$r_y = \sqrt{\frac{I_y}{A}} = \sqrt{\frac{180}{60}} = \sqrt{3} = 1.73''$$

Do you remember how we studied standard sections in Chapter VII? Fig. 5 shows the cross section

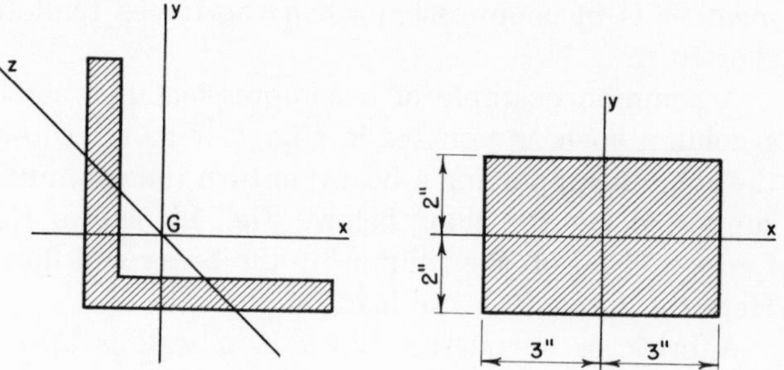

Fig. 6. Cross Section of Structural Steel Angle

Fig. 7. Rectangular Area for Problem 1 (Art. 12-1)

of a wide-flange beam. The properties of a few sample wide-flange beams are given in Table I, of Chapter VII. This table gives the dimensions of the cross section, the area and the moments of inertia. Also, it gives the radii of gyration with respect to the x and y axes. You do not have to calculate a radius of gyration of a standard section. You look it up in a table.

Illustrative Example 2. What are the radii of gyration for a wide-flange beam, 12 WF 58, with respect to the x and y axes?

Solution:

1. Column 10 of Table I, in Chapter VII, gives

$$r_x = 5.28''$$

2. Column 13 of the same table gives

$$r_y = 2.51''$$

The structural angle is an important type of member because structural angles are often used as compression members. Fig. 6 shows the cross section of an angle, and Tables III and IV, in Chapter VII, give the properties of sample structural angles. Table III gives the properties of equal angles and Table IV gives the properties of unequal angles. Notice the axes, x, y, and z, in Fig. 6. These axes intersect at the centroid of the area.

We are especially interested in the radius of gyration of an angle section with respect to the z axis, because this is the smallest radius of gyration of the area. The smallest radius of gyration is an important figure for a compression member.

Illustrative Example 3. Find the least radius of gyration for a structural angle, ∠6x6x½.

Solution:

From column 9, of Table III, in Chapter VII,

$$r = 1.18''$$

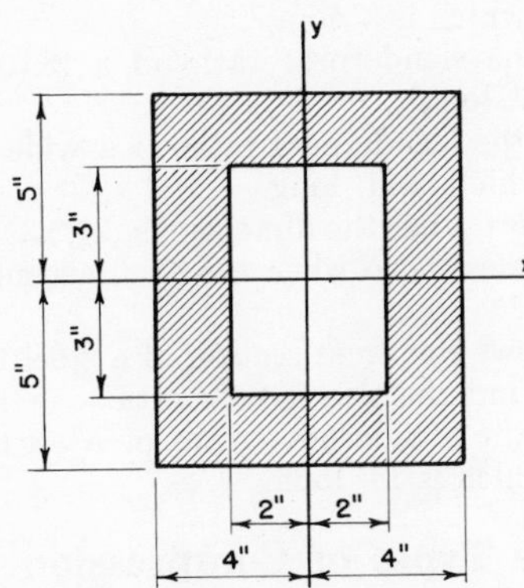

Fig. 8. Area for Problem 3 (Art. 12-1)

Illustrative Example 4. Find the least radius of gyration of a structural angle, ∠5x3x$\frac{5}{16}$.

Solution:

From column 13, of Table IV, in Chapter VII,

$$r = 0.66''$$

Practice Problems (Art. 12-1). You can learn how to find radius of gyration if you work these problems.

1. Calculate r_x and r_y for the area in Fig. 7.
2. Find r_x and r_y for a 4x10 wood beam.
3. Calculate r_x and r_y for the area in Fig. 8.
4. Find r_x and r_y for a wide-flange beam, 10 WF 100.
5. Find the least radius of gyration of a structural angle, ∠4x4x⅜.
6. Find the least radius of gyration of a structural angle, ∠8x4x⅞.

12-2. Slenderness Ratio.

The slenderness ratio of a compression member is the ratio of the length of the member to the least radius of gyration of the cross section. For example, Fig. 9*A* shows a compression member which is subjected to the load *P;* the length of the member is *L*. Fig. 9*B* shows the cross section of the compression member. You know how to calculate the radius of gyration of the cross section with respect to each of the x and y axes; the smaller of the two radii of gyration is the least radius of gyration of the cross section; call it r. Then the slenderness ratio of the compression member is

$$\frac{L}{r}$$

We leave it as a ratio, since there is no special symbol for slenderness ratio. Both L and r must be expressed in inches.

You can always find the *radius of gyration* of a standard section in a table. For any other section, you must calculate the radius of gyration.

Illustrative Example 1. What is the slenderness ratio for a wide-flange beam, 14 WF 68, which is 15′ long?

Solution:

1. The length L is 15′. In inches,

$$L = 15 \times 12 = 180''$$

2. Look up r in Table I of Chapter VII. Notice that r_x is 6.02″ and r_y is 2.46″. Here r_y is the smaller, so it is the least radius of gyration.

$$r = 2.46''$$

3. The slenderness ratio is

$$\frac{L}{r} = \frac{180}{2.46} = 73.2$$

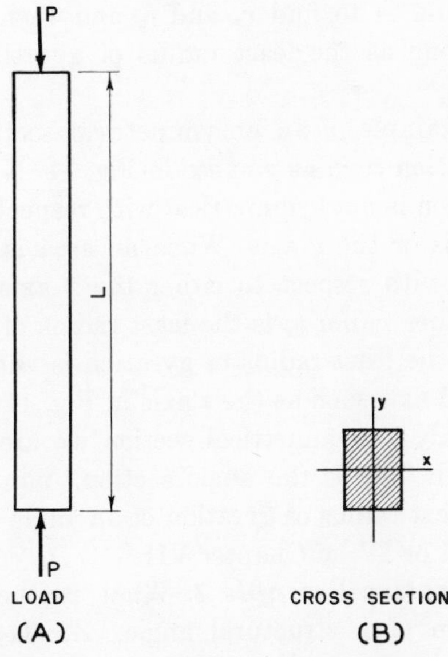

Fig. 9. Compression Member Subjected to Load

Back in Chapter III we said that an area was symmetrical with respect to an axis when the part of the area on one side of the axis was the same as the part on the other side of the axis. For example, the wide-flange section in Fig. 10*A* is symmetrical with respect to the x axis and also with respect to the y axis; so is the rectangular area in Fig. 10*B*. The **T** section in Fig. 10*C* is symmetrical with respect to the y axis but is not symmetrical with respect to the x axis.

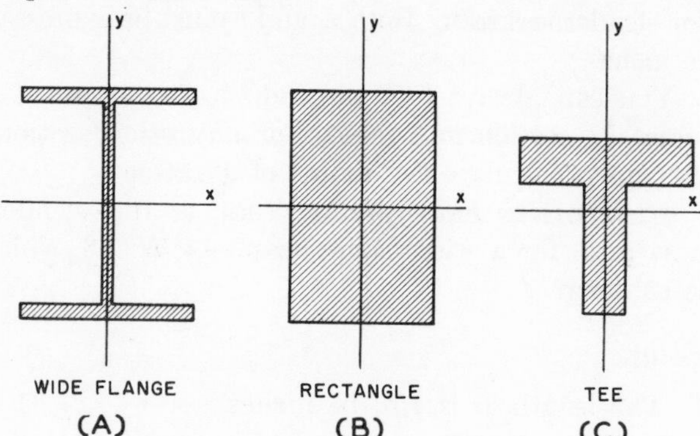

Fig. 10. Three Types of Symmetrical Sections

We are going to give you a few facts about axes of symmetry and least radius of gyration. We will not prove our statements, because we would have to use calculus to do so.

When an area is symmetrical with respect to either or both the x and y axes, the least radius of gyration is with respect to one of these axes. This means that the least radius of gyration of a symmetrical section is the smaller of r_x and r_y. All you have to do is to find r_x and r_y and then take the smaller one as the least radius of gyration of the section.

One example of an unsymmetrical section is the angle section such as you see in Fig. 11. Notice that this section is not symmetrical with respect to either the x axis or the y axis. When an area is not symmetrical with respect to either the x axis or the y axis, neither r_x nor r_y is the least radius of gyration. Instead, the least radius of gyration is with respect to a third axis such as the z axis in Fig. 11.

The only unsymmetrical section we are going to work with here is the angle section. You can look up the least radius of gyration of an angle section in Table III or IV, of Chapter VII.

Illustrative Example 2. What is the slenderness ratio of a structural angle, $\angle 3\text{x}3\text{x}\frac{5}{16}$, which is 7.5′ long?

Solution:

1. The length L is 7.5′, or

$$L = 7.5 \times 12 = 90''$$

2. Read the least radius of gyration in column 9 of Table III, of Chapter VII, as

$$r = 0.59''$$

3. The slenderness ratio is

$$\frac{L}{r} = \frac{90}{0.59} = 153$$

Practice Problems (Art. 12-2). Better learn to calculate slenderness ratio now. You will need the knowledge soon.

1. What is the slenderness ratio of a structural angle, $\angle 6\text{x}3\frac{1}{2}\text{x}\frac{1}{2}$, which is 8′ long?
2. What is the slenderness ratio of a 2x10 wood beam which is 6′ long?
3. Calculate the slenderness ratio of a wide-flange beam, 8 WF 27, which is 11′ long.
4. A *common brick* has the dimensions, $2\frac{1}{4}''\text{x}3\frac{3}{4}''\text{x}8''$. What is the slenderness ratio when the 8″ dimension is taken as the length?
5. Fig. 12 shows the cross section of a steel tube which is 10′ long. Find the slenderness ratio.
6. Calculate the slenderness ratio of a structural angle, $\angle 8\text{x}8\text{x}1$, which is 14′ long.

12-3. Three Types of Compression Members.

Compression members are such important parts of bridge and building structures that a great many experiments have been performed to study their behavior under load. Also, a lot of theoretical work has been done on this subject. As a result of all of this work and study, compression members can be classified into three types: (1) Short compression members; (2) Intermediate columns; (3) Long columns. The main difference between the three types of compression members is in the behavior under load and the manner of failure. We will study each type and see what the load does to each.

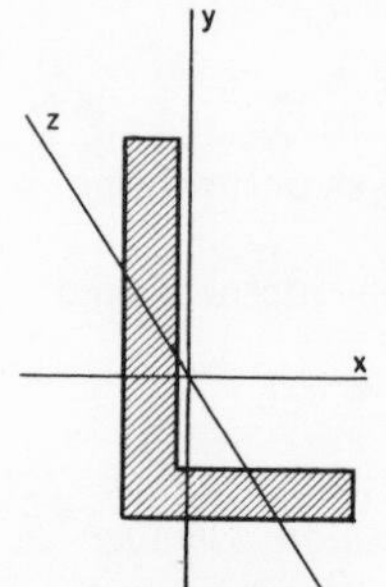

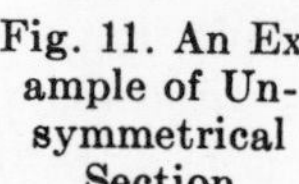
Fig. 11. An Example of Unsymmetrical Section

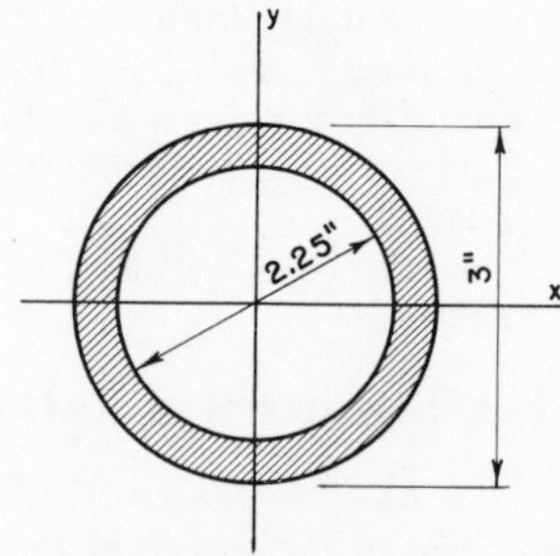

Fig. 12. Cross Section of Steel Tube

Short compression members fail by crushing. A steel member *barrels out* as shown in Fig. 13*A* and a wood member fails by sliding as shown in Fig.

13*B*. You may wonder how to tell whether a compression member is a short compression member. The answer is that *a steel compression member which has a slenderness ratio of less than about 50 is a short compression member; a wood compression member is a short compression member if the length is less than 10 times the smallest lateral dimension.*

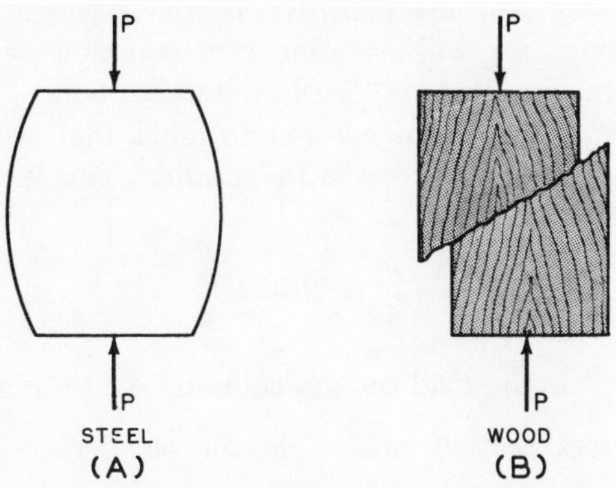

Fig. 13. Failure of Short Compression Steel or Wood Members

Intermediate columns fail by a combination of crushing and bending. The compressive stress is high enough so that crushing is an important factor and, also, the column bends. The result is that the column fails by bending sharply at one point.

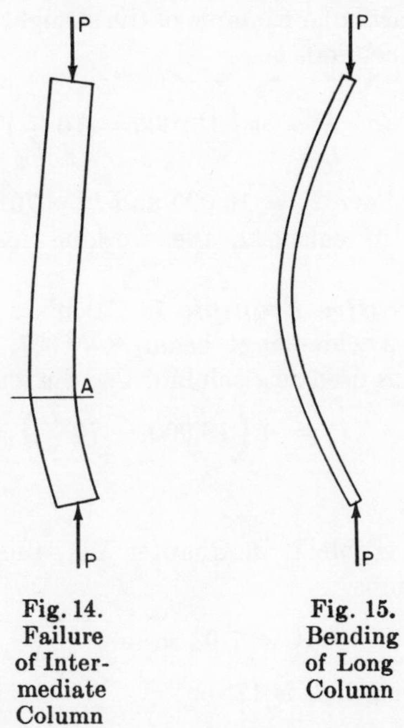

Fig. 14. Failure of Intermediate Column

Fig. 15. Bending of Long Column

Fig. 14 shows an intermediate steel column as it looks after failure. Notice the sharp kink at *A*. A steel compression member is considered to be an intermediate column if the slenderness ratio is between about 50 and 150. A wood compression member is considered to be an *intermediate column* if the ratio of the length to the least lateral dimension is between about 10 and 25.

A *long column* bends into a smooth curve, see Fig. 15, when the load reaches the capacity of the column. This is a remarkable type of bending in that the long column will straighten out when the load is removed. A *steel compression member* is classified as a *long column* when the slenderness ratio is greater than about 150. A *wood compression member* is classified as a *long column* when the ratio of the length to the smallest lateral dimension of the cross section is greater than about 25.

You know now what the three types of compression members are. Next, we will study short compression members and intermediate columns in detail so you can learn how to calculate the strengths of such members.

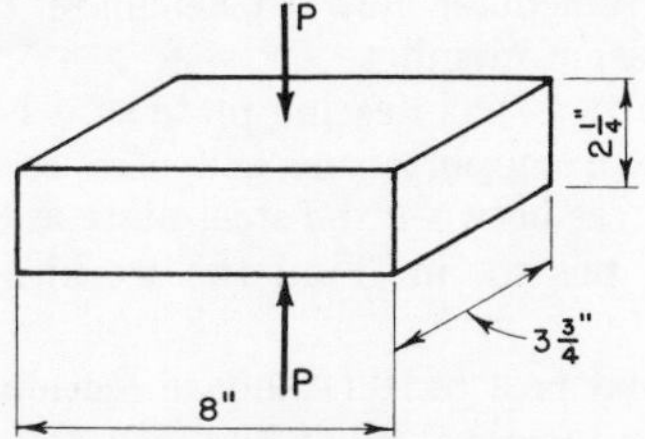

Fig. 16. Compressive Forces of Load on Brick

12-4. Short Compression Members.

Short compression members fail by crushing as we showed you in Fig. 13. Here the compressive stress is distributed uniformly over the cross section of the member and the load is

$$P = AS$$

where P is the *load* in pounds, A is the *area* of the cross section in square inches and S is the *stress* in pounds per square inch. If you take S as the working stress for the material, the force P is the working load for the member; that is, the load which is to be applied to the member in service.

You have worked a number of problems with the formula

$$P = AS$$

so it should not give you any trouble here.

Illustrative Example 1. Fig. 16 shows compressive forces on a brick. The working stress in compression is 125 lbs. per sq. in. Find the working load.

Solution:

1. The area of cross section is

$$A = 3\tfrac{3}{4} \times 8 = 30 \text{ sq. in.}$$

2. The stress S is 125 lbs. per sq. in.
3. The working load is

$$P = AS = 30 \times 125 = 3{,}750 \text{ lbs.}$$

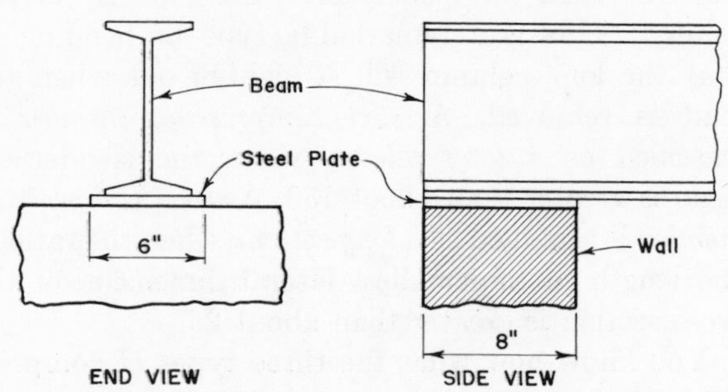

Fig. 17. End and Side Views of Beam Support for Problem 1 (Art. 12-4)

Practice Problems (Art. 12-4). A few problems will help you to remember how to calculate the load on a short compression member.

1. Fig. 17 shows a steel bearing plate as it is used where a concrete wall supports one end of a steel beam. The working stress between the steel plate and the concrete is 600 lbs. per sq. in. Find the working load on the plate.
2. A short wood post 8x10 (standard section) is used as a compression member. What load will develop the working stress of 1,200 lbs. per sq. in.?
3. The working stress in compression for the concrete block in Fig. 18 is 800 lbs. per sq. in. Calculate the working load.
4. A short length of wide-flange beam, 12 WF 45, is used as a compression member. The working stress is 16,000 lbs. per sq. in. What is the working load?

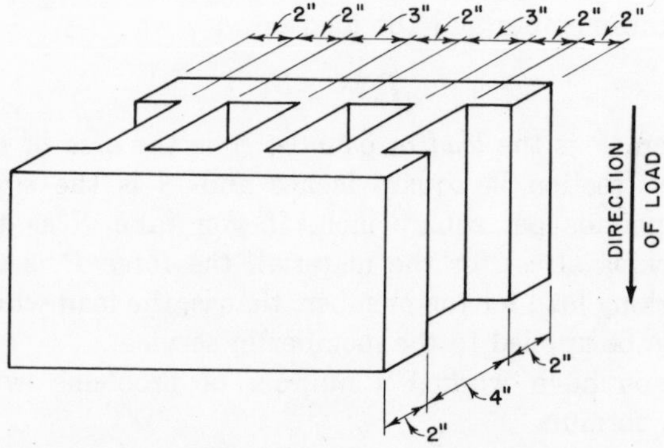

Fig. 18. Concrete Block in Compression for Problem 3 (Art. 12-4)

12-5. Straight-Line Formulas for Steel Columns.

Intermediate columns are important structural members because they are used so widely; you can see them in nearly any building.

The failure of an intermediate column is so complicated that there is no one formula which is accepted as being the correct formula and the best one. Instead, there are several types of formulas in common use. One type of formula may be *best* in the opinion of one group of engineers and another type may be considered *best* by a second group. We will not enter into any controversy about which is *best.* However, we will examine two common types of column formulas and see how to use them.

The first type of column formula that we want to examine is the *straight-line formula.* This is usually written as

$$\frac{P}{A} = S - k\frac{L}{r}$$

Here P is the load on the column, A is the area of the cross section and $\frac{L}{r}$ is the slenderness ratio; S and k are numbers that depend upon the type of column and the way in which it is used. We will find it better to write the straight-line formula as

$$P = A\left(S - k\frac{L}{r}\right)$$

and you should be able to see that the algebra used in making this change is correct.

One particular example of the straight-line formula for steel columns is

$$P = A\left(16{,}000 - 70\frac{L}{r}\right)$$

Here we have $S = 16{,}000$ and $k = 70$. We use this formula to calculate the working load P for a column.

Illustrative Example 1. Calculate the working load for a wide-flange beam, 8 WF 27, which is 12′ long and is used as a column. Use the formula,

$$P = A\left(16{,}000 - 70\frac{L}{r}\right).$$

Solution:

1. From Table I, in Chapter VII, the area of the column is

$$A = 7.93 \text{ sq. in.}$$

2. The length L is 12′ or

$$L = 12 \times 12 = 144''$$

3. The least radius of gyration is found in column 13 of Table I, in Chapter VII, as

$$r = 1.62''$$

4. The slenderness ratio is

$$\frac{L}{r} = \frac{144}{1.62} = 88.8$$

5. The working load is

$$P = A\left(16{,}000 - 70\,\frac{L}{r}\right)$$
$$= 7.93\,(16{,}000 - 70 \times 88.8)$$
$$= 77{,}600 \text{ lbs.}$$

Another example of a straight-line formula for steel columns is

$$P = A\left(15{,}000 - 50\,\frac{L}{r}\right)$$

This is used in the same way as the one we have already studied.

There are other straitht-line formulas for steel columns but all are used in the same way. A good general rule to remember is that straight-line formulas should be used only when the slenderness ratio is between about 50 and 150.

You may wonder which formula to use. This usually depends upon where you are working. For instance, if you design a building to be erected in a city, the *Building Code* of that city will specify which formula to use. You will be given the formula to use in the following practice problems.

Practice Problems (Art. 12-5). The best way to learn the processes involved in the study of *Elementary Structural Design* is by working problems.

1. Calculate the working load for an American standard beam, 10 I 35, which is 10′ long and used as a column. Use

$$P = A\left(15{,}000 - 50\,\frac{L}{r}\right)$$

2. What is the working load for a structural angle, ∠6x6x½, 11′ long, as a column? Use

$$P = A\left(16{,}000 - 70\,\frac{L}{r}\right)$$

3. A wide-flange beam, 14 WF 95, is 18′ long and is used as a column. Calculate the working load. Use

$$P = A\left((15{,}000 - 50\,\frac{L}{r}\right)$$

4. A structural angle, ∠5x3x$\frac{5}{16}$, is 8′ long, and is used as a column. What is the working load? Use

$$P = A\left(15{,}000 - 50\,\frac{L}{r}\right)$$

5. Fig. 19 shows the cross section of a steel column which is made by welding plates together. The column is 24′ long and the plate is ½″ thick. Find the working load. Use

$$P = A\left(16{,}000 - 70\,\frac{L}{r}\right)$$

6. Fig. 20 shows the cross section of a tube which is 9′ long, and which is used as a column. Calculate the working load. Use

$$P = A\left(15{,}000 - 50\,\frac{L}{r}\right)$$

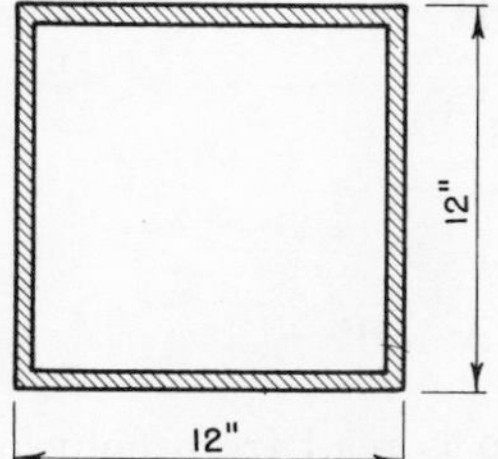

Fig. 19. Cross Section of Steel Column for Problem 5 (Art. 12-5)

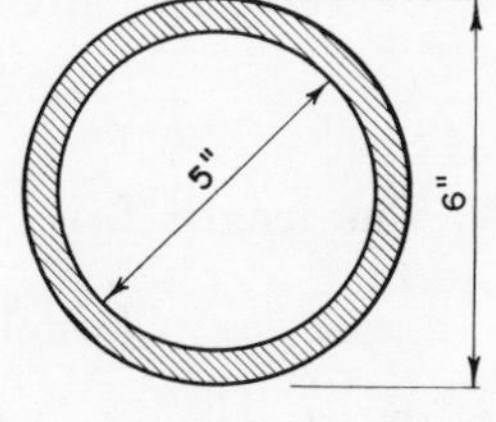

Fig. 20. Cross Section of Steel Tube for Problem 6 (Art. 12-5)

12-6. Gordon-Rankine Formulas for Steel Columns.

Another type of formula for intermediate steel columns is the Gordon-Rankine formula, named after the men who worked it out. The formula is usually written as

$$\frac{P}{A} = \frac{S}{1 + k\left(\frac{L}{r}\right)^2}$$

but we will find it easier to use if we write it as

$$P = A\left[\frac{S}{1 + k\left(\frac{L}{r}\right)^2}\right]$$

Here, P is the working load on the column, A is the area of the cross section and $\frac{L}{r}$ is the slenderness ratio; S and k are numbers that depend upon the circumstances under which the formula is to be used.

One example of the Gordon-Rankine formula is

$$P = A\left[\frac{18{,}000}{1 + \frac{1}{18{,}000}\left(\frac{L}{r}\right)^2}\right]$$

In this formula,

$$S = 18{,}000; \quad \text{and } k = \frac{1}{18{,}000}$$

Illustrative Example 1. A structural angle, ∠8x6x½, is 10′ long and is used as a column. Find the working load. Use

$$P = A\left[\frac{18{,}000}{1 + \frac{1}{18{,}000}\left(\frac{L}{r}\right)^2}\right]$$

Solution:

1. The area of cross section is read from column 4 of Table IV, in Chapter VII

$$A = 6.75 \text{ sq. in.}$$

2. The length L is

$$L = 10 \times 12 = 120''$$

3. The least radius of gyration is read from column 13 of Table IV, in Chapter VII

$$r = 1.30''$$

4. The slenderness ratio is

$$\frac{L}{r} = \frac{120}{1.30} = 92.4$$

5. The working load for the column is

$$P = A\left[\frac{18{,}000}{1 + \frac{1}{18{,}000}\left(\frac{L}{r}\right)^2}\right]$$

$$= 6.75\left[\frac{18{,}000}{1 + \frac{1}{18{,}000}(92.4)^2}\right]$$

$$= 6.75\left[\frac{18{,}000}{1 + 0.474}\right]$$

$$= 6.75 \times 12{,}200 = 82{,}500 \text{ lbs.}$$

Another example of the Gordon-Rankine type of formula is

$$P = A\left[\frac{16{,}250}{1 + \frac{1}{11{,}000}\left(\frac{L}{r}\right)^2}\right]$$

We could mention others, too, but two are enough for you to see what this type of formula is like. The formulas are just as easy to use with other values of S and k.

A designer must use the particular formula which the *Building Code* or *Specification* requires, so you should learn to use each type of formula now.

Practice Problems (Art. 12-6). Practice now on the Gordon-Rankine formula.

1. A wide-flange section, 12 WF 58, is 16′ long, and is used as a column. Calculate the working load from the formula.

$$P = A\left[\frac{16{,}250}{1 + \frac{1}{11{,}000}\left(\frac{L}{r}\right)^2}\right]$$

2. A structural angle, ∠7x4x⅜, is to be used as a column on a length of 10′6″. What is the working load? Use

$$P = A\left[\frac{18{,}000}{1 + \frac{1}{18{,}000}\left(\frac{L}{r}\right)^2}\right]$$

3. What is the working load for an American standard beam 8 **I** 23 when used as a column 9′ long? Use

$$P = A\left[\frac{18{,}000}{1 + \frac{1}{18{,}000}\left(\frac{L}{r}\right)^2}\right]$$

4. A structural angle, ∠5x5x$\frac{7}{16}$, is 7′ long, and is used as a column. Calculate the working load. Use

$$P = A\left[\frac{16{,}250}{1 + \frac{1}{11{,}000}\left(\frac{L}{r}\right)^2}\right]$$

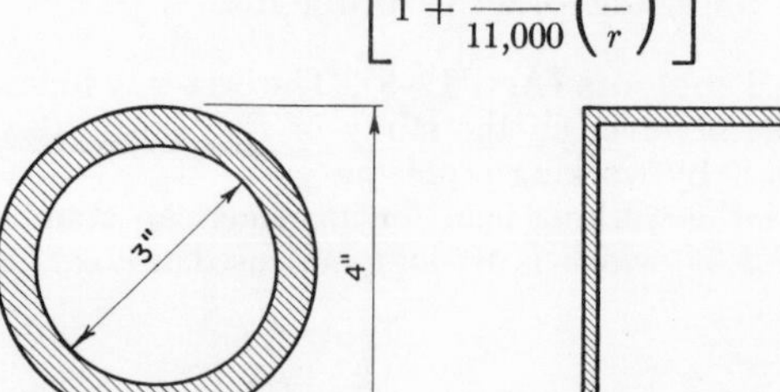

Fig. 21. Cross Section of Steel Tube for for Problem 5 (Art. 12-6)

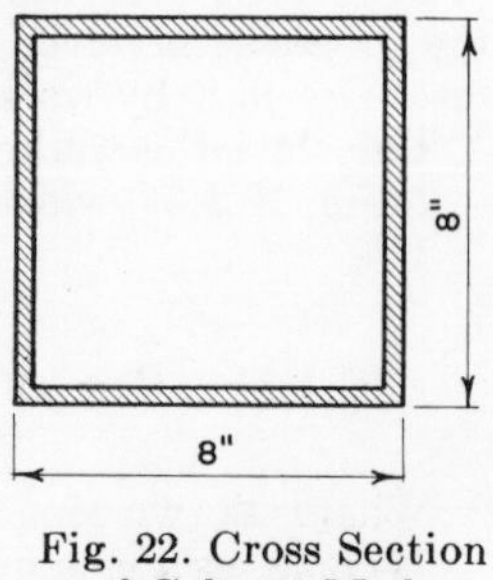

Fig. 22. Cross Section of Column Made of Steel Plates for Problem 6 (Art. 12-6)

5. Fig. 21 shows the cross section of a steel tube which is 7′ long and which is used as a column. Use the formula,

$$P = A\left[\frac{18{,}000}{1 + \frac{1}{18{,}000}\left(\frac{L}{r}\right)^2}\right]$$

to calculate the working load.

6. Fig. 22 shows the cross section of a column which is made by welding quarter-inch steel plate together. The

column is 15′ long. Find the working load from the formula,

$$P = A\left[\frac{18{,}000}{1 + \frac{1}{18{,}000}\left(\frac{L}{r}\right)^2}\right]$$

12-7. Straight-Line Formulas for Wood Columns.

One simple type of formula for intermediate wood columns is the straight-line formula, also known as *Winslow's formula.* This is

$$\frac{P}{A} = S\left(1 - \frac{L}{80d}\right)$$

as it is usually written. However, it is easier to use if we write it as

$$P = AS\left(1 - \frac{L}{80d}\right)$$

Here P is the working load on the column, A is the area of cross section, L is the length and d is the smaller lateral dimension of the column; S is a stress and the value depends on the strength of the wood. We will give you S in our problems.

We are only interested in *rectangular wood columns* because that is the only kind of wood columns used to any great extent. You can look up the area A and the smaller lateral dimension d in Table V of Chapter VII.

Illustrative Example 1. An 8x12 wood column is 14′ long. Calculate the working load. Use

$$S = 1{,}000.$$

Solution:

1. From column 3 of Table V, in Chapter VII, we find the area of the cross section is

$$A = 86.25 \text{ sq. in.}$$

2. The stress S is 1,000 lbs. per sq. in.
3. The length is

$$L = 14 \times 12 = 168''$$

4. The actual dimensions of the cross section are $7\frac{1}{2}''$ and $11\frac{1}{2}''$, from column 2 of Table V, in Chapter VII. The smaller lateral dimension is

$$d = 7\tfrac{1}{2}'' = 7.5''$$

5. The ratio L is

$$\frac{L}{d} = \frac{168}{7.5} = 22.4$$

6. The working load for the column is

$$P = AS\left(1 - \frac{L}{80d}\right)$$

$$= 86.25 \times 1{,}000\left(1 - \frac{22.4}{80}\right) = 62{,}100 \text{ lbs.}$$

It is easy to use a straight-line formula for a wood column. However, you should keep in mind that the formula only applies when the ratio $\frac{L}{d}$ is between about 10 and 25.

Practice Problems (Art. 12-7).

1. Calculate the working load for a 6x6 wood column 9′ long. Use $S = 1{,}200$.
2. What is the working load for a 10x10 wood column 11′ long? Use $S = 1{,}300$.
3. Find the working load for a 6x10 wood column 8′ long. Use $S = 900$.
4. An 8x10 wood column is 12′ long. Use $S = 1{,}000$ to calculate the working load.
5. Find the working load for a 2x4 which is 30″ long and which is used as a column. Use $S = 1{,}200$.

12-8. Forest-Products Laboratory Formula for Wood Columns.

A useful formula for intermediate wood columns was developed at the Forest Products Laboratory[1]. This formula is

$$\frac{P}{A} = S\left[1 - \frac{1}{3}\left(\frac{1}{K}\frac{L}{d}\right)^4\right]$$

but it will be easier to use if we write it as

$$P = AS\left[1 - \frac{1}{3}\left(\frac{1}{K}\frac{L}{d}\right)^4\right]$$

Here P is the working load on the column, A is the area of the cross section, L is the length of the column and d is the smaller lateral dimension; S is a stress and K is

$$K = \frac{\pi}{2}\sqrt{\frac{E}{6S}}$$

where E is the modulus of elasticity of the wood and $\pi = 3.14$.

The Forest-Products Laboratory formula is used to calculate the working load on a wood column. You can always look up the area and the smaller lateral dimension of the column in Table V of Chapter VII; we will give you S and E. Do not worry about raising $\left(\frac{1}{K}\frac{L}{d}\right)$ to the fourth power; you can

[1] Forest Products Laboratory, United States Department of Agriculture, Madison, Wis.

do it by squaring and then squaring again. Thus,

$$\left(\frac{1}{K}\frac{L}{d}\right)^2\left(\frac{1}{K}\frac{L}{d}\right)^2 = \left(\frac{1}{K}\frac{L}{d}\right)^4$$

as you learned in algebra.

Illustrative Example 1. A 10 x 12 wood column is 15′ long. Use the Forest-Products Laboratory formula to calculate the working load. Let

$$E = 1{,}600{,}000$$

and

$$S = 1{,}400.$$

Solution:

1. From Table V, in Chapter VII, the area is

$$A = 109.25 \text{ sq. in.}$$

2. $S = 1{,}400$
3. $L = 15 \times 12 = 180''$
4. The actual dimensions of the cross section are $9\frac{1}{2}''$ and $11\frac{1}{2}''$. The smaller is

$$d = 9\tfrac{1}{2}'' = 9.5''$$

5. $\dfrac{L}{d} = \dfrac{180}{9.5} = 18.95$
6. The modulus of elasticity is

$$E = 1{,}600{,}000$$

7. $K = \dfrac{\pi}{2}\sqrt{\dfrac{E}{6S}} = \dfrac{3.14}{2}\sqrt{\dfrac{1{,}600{,}000}{6 \times 1{,}400}} = 21.7$
8. The working load is

$$P = AS\left[1 - \frac{1}{3}\left(\frac{1}{K}\frac{L}{d}\right)^4\right]$$

$$= 109.25 \times 1{,}400\left[1 - \frac{1}{3}\left(\frac{18.95}{21.7}\right)^4\right]$$

$$= 153{,}000\left[1 - \frac{0.58}{3}\right] = 123{,}000 \text{ lbs.}$$

Practice Problems (Art. 12-8). Use the Forest-Products Laboratory formula in each of the following problems.

1. Calculate the working load for a 4x4 post 4′ long. Let $E = 1{,}200{,}000$ and $S = 1{,}000$.
2. A 6x8 wood column is 8′ long. Calculate the working load using $E = 1{,}400{,}000$ and $S = 1{,}200$.
3. What is the working load for a 10x14 wood column which is 10′ long? Take $E = 1{,}600{,}000$ and $S = 1{,}200$.
4. Take $E = 1{,}400{,}000$ and $S = 1{,}000$ and calculate the working load on an 8x12 wood column which is 14′ long.

SUMMARY OF CHAPTER XII

Here are the main points on compression members.

1. Material is in compression when the forces tend to shorten it.
2. The radius of gyration of an area is

$$r = \sqrt{\frac{I}{A}}$$

3. The slenderness ratio of a column is equal to the length divided by the least radius of gyration of the cross section; that is, $\dfrac{L}{r}$.
4. Compression members may be divided into three classes:
   a) Short compression members
   b) Intermediate columns
   c) Long columns
5. Short compression members fail by crushing.
   a) A steel compression member is a short compression member if the slenderness ratio is less than about 50.
   b) A wood compression member is a short compression member if the ratio of the length to the smaller lateral dimension is less than about 10.
   c) The formula

$$P = AS$$

   gives the working load for a short compression member.
6. Intermediate columns fail by a combination of crushing and bending.
   a) A steel compression member is an intermediate column if the slenderness ratio is between about 50 and 150.
   b) A wood compression member is an intermediate column if the ratio of the length to the smaller lateral dimension is between about 10 and 25.
7. There are many formulas available for calculating the working load on an intermediate column. The usual procedure is to use the formula given by a *Building Code* or by a set of builder's *Specifications*.
8. Two formulas for calculating the working load on an intermediate steel column are:
   a) The straight-line formula,

$$P = A\left(S - k\frac{L}{r}\right)$$

   b) The Gordon-Rankine formula,

$$P = A\left[\frac{S}{1 + k}\right]\left(\frac{L}{r}\right)^2$$

9. Two formulas for calculating the working load on an intermediate wood column are:
   a) The straight-line formula,

$$P = AS\left(1 - \frac{L}{80d}\right)$$

b) The Forest-Products Laboratory formula,

$$P = AS\left[1 - \frac{1}{3}\left(\frac{1}{K}\frac{L}{d}\right)^4\right]$$

where

$$K = \frac{\pi}{2}\sqrt{\frac{E}{6S}}$$

Review Questions

Check your knowledge of this chapter by answering these questions.

1. What is *compression?*
2. What is a *compression member?*
3. What is *moment of inertia?*
4. What is *radius of gyration?*
5. What is the *slenderness ratio of a compression member?*
6. How does a short compression member fail?
7. When is a steel compression member a short compression member?
8. When is a wood compression member a short compression member?
9. How is the working load calculated for a short compression member?
10. How does an intermediate compression member fail?
11. What does the slenderness ratio have to do with an intermediate column?
12. When is a steel compression member an intermediate column?
13. When is a wood compression member an intermediate column?
14. Give the straight-line formula for intermediate steel columns.
15. State the Gordon-Rankine formula for intermediate steel columns.
16. State the straight-line formula for intermediate wood columns.
17. Give the Forest-Products Laboratory formula for intermediate wood columns.
18. What does a formula for an intermediate column give?

Review Problems

1. Calculate the working load on a wide-flange section, 10 WF 100, which is 16′ long, and which is used as a column. Use

$$P = A\left(15{,}000 - 50\frac{L}{r}\right)$$

2. A structural angle, ∠4x4x⅜, is used as a column 8′ long. Use

$$P = A\left[\frac{18{,}000}{1 + \frac{1}{18{,}000}\left(\frac{L}{r}\right)^2}\right]$$

and calculate the working load.

3. Use the straight-line formula to calculate the working load on an 8x10 wood column which is 11′ long. Let $S = 1{,}200$.
4. A 10x10 wood column is 15′ long. Use the Forest-Products Laboratory formula to calculate the working load. Take $E = 1{,}400{,}000$ and $S = 1{,}200$.

Chapter XIII

STRUCTURAL CONNECTIONS

Purpose of This Chapter. The purpose of this chapter is the study of *structural connections:* that is, the methods and devices which are used to fasten beams and columns together. You have studied *beams* in Chapters VI and VII, and *columns* in Chapter XII. By this time you should know how to calculate the strength of a beam or column. Now it is time to learn how they are fastened together and how to calculate the *strength of a fastening.*

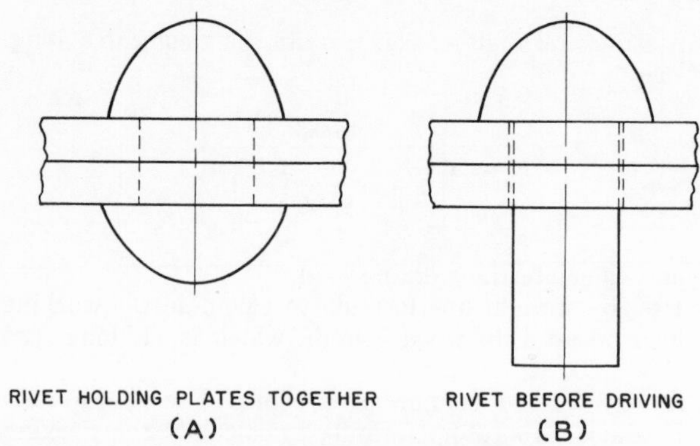

Fig. 1. Steel Plates and Rivets

The usual procedure in designing a structure is to design the members (the beams and columns) first, and then to design the connections between these members. Steel beams and columns are usually riveted or welded together. Wood members in residences are nailed together, and in heavier structures, special connectors are often used. We will study the common types of connections in detail, so you can become familiar with them.

13-1. Rivets.

A rivet is a round rod designed for holding two pieces of metal together. Fig. 1*A* shows a rivet which holds two steel plates together. The rivet is manufactured with a head on one end, as shown in Fig. 1*B*. The rivet is heated to a temperature sufficient to make the metal malleable under pressure, and then it is inserted in holes in the two plates. (The holes are a little larger than the rivet.) Fig. 1*B* shows the rivet at this stage. Next, the unfinished head of the rivet is struck with a hammer or squeezed in a press to form the second head and make the complete rivet such as you see in Fig. 1*A*. In this process, the metal flows laterally and makes a tight fit in the hole.

We showed you rivets with full heads in Fig. 1, but there are other types of heads, too. Fig. 2 shows some of them. The rivet in Fig. 2*A* has full heads as before and the rivet in Fig. 2*B* has countersunk

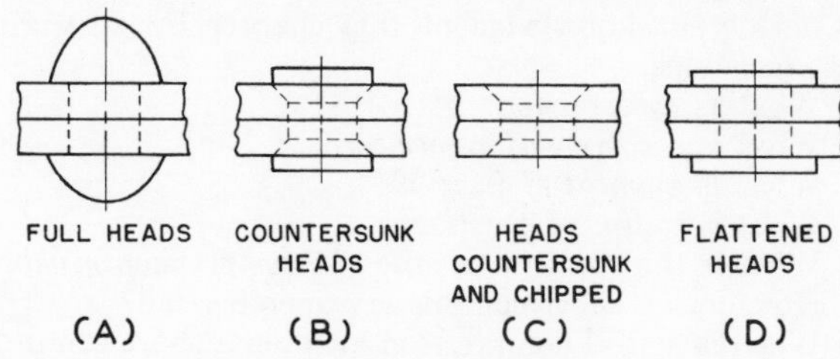

Fig. 2. Four Types of Rivet Heads

heads. Fig. 2*C* shows a rivet with heads countersunk and chipped, and Fig. 2*D* shows a rivet with flattened heads. One advantage of a rivet with heads countersunk and chipped is that the rivet heads do not extend beyond the surface of the plate; this is a help when space is at a premium.

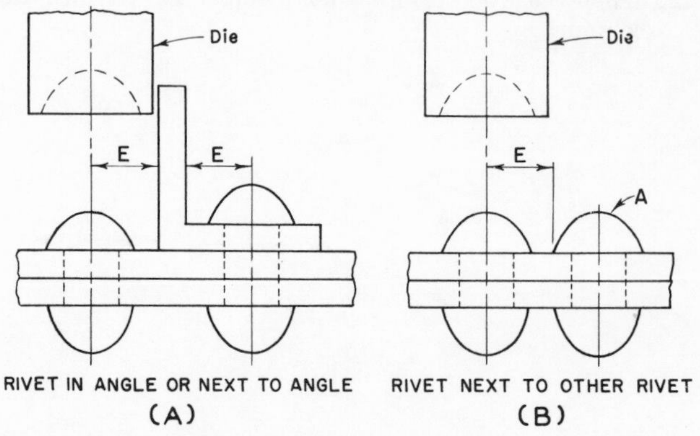

Fig. 3. Driving Clearance

Most structural rivets are made of steel and come in standard sizes. Table I gives the diameters of the standard sizes and also the driving clearances. The *driving clearance* is the distance which must be maintained between the center of the rivet and any other part of the structure such as the angle in

Table I. Diameters, Driving Clearance, and Minimum Pitch for Standard Rivets

Diameter in inches	1/2	5/8	3/4	7/8	1	1 1/8	1 1/4	1 3/8	1 1/2
Driving clearance	3/4	7/8	1	1 1/8	1 1/4	1 3/8	1 1/2	1 5/8	1 3/4
Minimum pitch	1 1/2	1 7/8	2 1/4	2 5/8	3	3 3/8	3 3/4	4 1/8	4 1/2

Fig. 3*A* or the rivet *A* in Fig. 3*B*. Here the distance *E* is the driving clearance.

The driving clearance must be maintained to provide room for the die which forms the head of the rivet. The driving clearances in Table I are minimum distances, which means that it is permissible to make the clearances greater, but they cannot be made smaller.

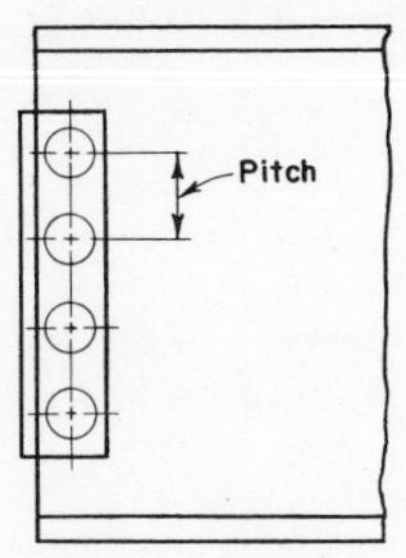

Fig. 4. Rivet Pitch

It is often necessary to place several rivets in a row as you see them in Fig. 4. The distance from the center of one rivet to the center of the next rivet is called the *pitch*. There is a minimum value for the pitch in order to maintain driving clearance. The *minimum pitch* is usually equal to three times the diameter of the rivet. Table I gives the minimum pitch for each standard rivet diameter.

13-2. Shearing Stress in Rivets.

Shear is *sliding*, as you learned in Chapter V. We will review it briefly here, because of the importance of shearing stress in rivets, in structural connections.

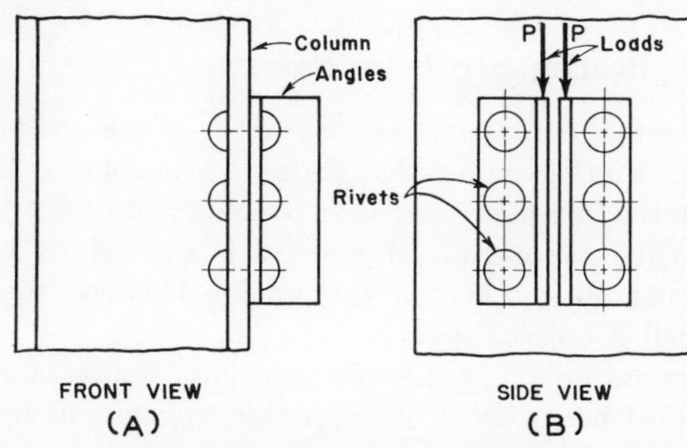

Fig. 5. Angles Riveted to Column

Figure 5 shows a pair of structural angles which are riveted to a steel column. Each angle is fastened to the column by three rivets and a load *P* is applied to each angle. The load tends to make the angle slide down along the face of the column and causes shearing stress in the rivets. Each rivet is in shear on just one plane and this is the plane of contact between the angles and the column; we call this *single shear*, as you should remember.

The area in shear, for one rivet, is the area of the cross section of the rivet; that is

$$\frac{\pi d^2}{4}$$

where *d* is the diameter of the rivet. Since there are three rivets in each angle, the area in shear for each load *P* is three times the area of one rivet, or

$$\frac{3\pi d^2}{4}$$

The shearing stress in a rivet or in a group of rivets is

$$S_s = \frac{P}{A_s}$$

where S_s is the *stress*, *P* is the load, and A_s is the *area in shear*.

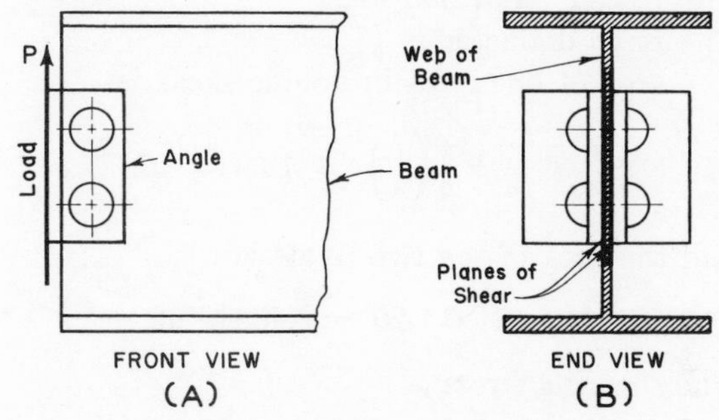

Fig. 6. Angles Riveted to Beam

Illustrative Example 1. The rivets in Fig. 5 are $\frac{3}{4}''$ in diameter and each load *P* is 16,400 lbs. Calculate the shearing stress in the rivets.

Solution:

1. The load *P* is 16,400 lbs.
2. The rivet diameter is $\frac{3}{4}''$
3. There are three rivets for each load, so the area in shear is

$$A_s = \frac{3\pi d^2}{4} = 3\frac{\pi}{4}\left(\frac{3}{4}\right)^2 = 1.33 \text{ sq. in.}$$

4. The shearing stress is

$$S_s = \frac{P}{A_s} = \frac{16{,}400}{1.33} = 12{,}300 \text{ lbs. per sq. in.}$$

A rivet is in double shear when there is shearing stress on two cross sections of the rivet. For example, Fig. 6 shows two views of a steel beam which is riveted to a pair of structural angles. Here, a force *P* is applied to the angles and tends to slide the angles along the web of the beam. Each rivet is in shear on two planes so the area in shear for each rivet is

$$2\frac{\pi}{4}d^2$$

For two rivets, then, the area in shear is two times the area in shear for one rivet and this is

$$2 \times 2\frac{\pi}{4}d^2 = 4\frac{\pi}{4}d^2 = \pi d^2$$

The shearing stress is

$$S_s = \frac{P}{A_s}$$

Illustrative Example 2. The rivets in Fig. 6 are $\frac{7}{8}''$ in diameter and the load P is 37,600 lbs. Calculate the shearing stress in the rivets.

Solution:

1. The load P is 37,600 lbs.
2. The rivet diameter is $\frac{7}{8}''$
3. The area of one rivet in double shear is

$$2\frac{\pi}{4}d^2 = 2\frac{\pi}{4}\left(\frac{7}{8}\right)^2 = 1.20 \text{ sq. in.}$$

and the area of the two rivets is

$$A_s = 2 \times 1.20 = 2.40 \text{ sq. in.}$$

4. The shearing stress is

$$S_s = \frac{P}{A_s} = \frac{37{,}600}{2.40} = 15{,}700 \text{ lbs. per sq. in.}$$

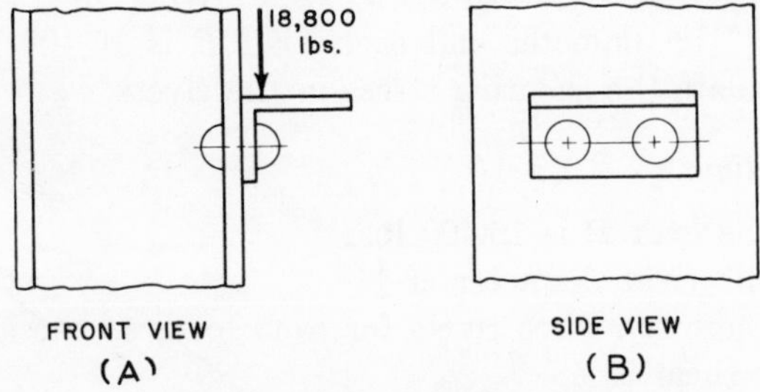

Fig. 7. Angle Riveted to Column for Problem 1 (Art. 13-2)

Practice Problems (Art. 13-2).

1. Fig. 7 shows two views of a structural angle which is riveted to a steel column. The rivets are 1″ in diameter. Calculate the shearing stress in the rivets.

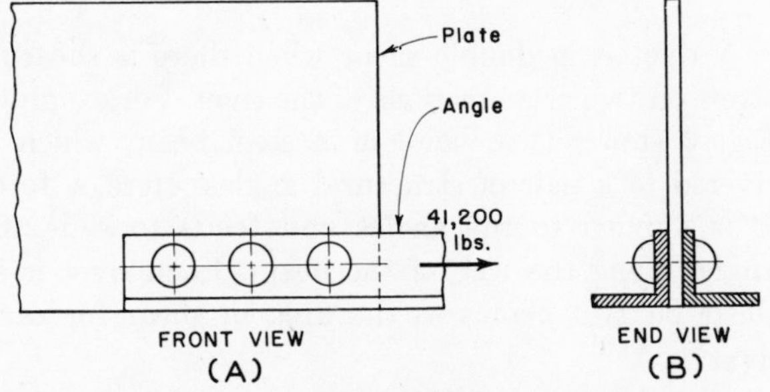

Fig. 8. Angle Riveted to Plate for Problem 4 (Art. 13-2)

2. Four rivets, each $\frac{5}{8}''$ in diameter, are subjected to a load of 31,500 lbs. and the rivets are in double shear. Calculate the shearing stress.
3. Three rivets, each $1\frac{1}{8}''$ in diameter, are subjected to a load of 27,300 lbs. in single shear. Find the shearing stress.
4. Fig. 8 shows a pair of structural angles which are riveted to a steel plate. The rivets are $\frac{3}{4}''$ in diameter. What is the shearing stress in the rivets?

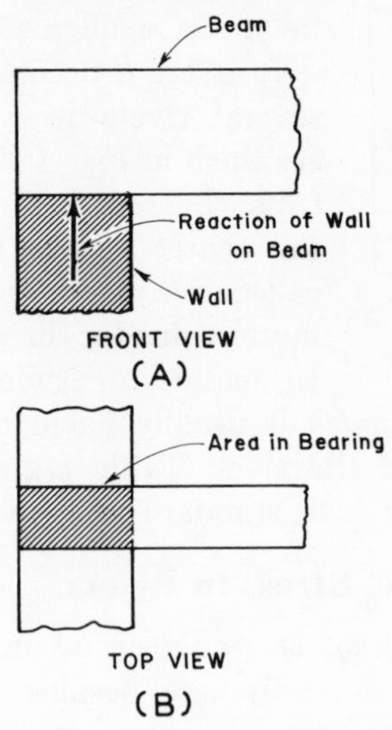

Fig. 9. A Beam Supported by Wall

13-3. Bearing Stress in Rivets.

Bearing stress is a special kind of compressive stress. You remember that material is in compression when the forces on it act so as to squeeze it or shorten it. When the compressive stress is exerted by one member on another, at the surface between them, we call it *bearing stress.*

For example, Fig. 9 shows two views of a rectangular steel beam which is supported at one end by a wall. The wall exerts a reaction on the end of the beam to hold it up; this reaction causes compressive stress on the shaded area in Fig. 9B and, since the compressive stress is exerted by the wall on the beam at the surface between them, we call it *bearing stress.*

There is always bearing stress in a riveted connection between the rivets and the members which are fastened together. Fig. 10A shows two views of a structural angle which is fastened to a steel column by means of two rivets. Notice here the thickness t of the angle. The force P tends to push the angle down and is resisted by forces exerted on the angle by the rivets. Fig. 10B shows the free-body diagram of the angle; here you see the forces $\frac{P}{2}$ exerted on the angle by the rivets. The rivets push against the angle and cause compressive stress between the rivets and the angle; we call it *bearing stress* because it is at the surface between the rivets and the angle.

The actual area in bearing, for one rivet, is the upper half of the surface between the rivet and the angle, and is shown in Fig. 10*C*. However, this actual

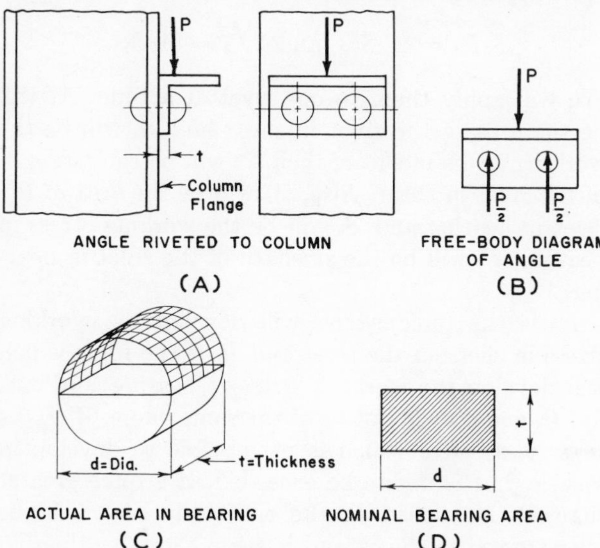

Fig. 10. Bearing Stress in Rivets

area is not used in stress calculations. Instead, the nominal area in Fig. 10*D* is used. This nominal area is a rectangle with one dimension equal to the diameter of the rivet and the other dimension equal to the thickness of the angle. Thus the area in bearing for one rivet is *dt*, and, for two rivets, the area is 2*dt*.

The bearing stress is

$$S_b = \frac{P}{A_b}$$

where S_b is the *bearing stress*, *P* is the *load*, and A_b is the *area in bearing*.

Whether a rivet bears against an angle, a plate, a beam, or a column, the bearing area is equal to the rivet diameter times the thickness of the member: always, *dt*. There is bearing stress between the rivet and each member it connects.

Illustrative Example 1. In Fig. 10*A* the rivets are $\frac{7}{8}''$ in diameter and the load *P* is 28,700 lbs. The column flange is 0.606″ thick. Calculate the bearing stress between the rivets and the column flange.

Solution:

1. The load *P* is 28,700 lbs.
2. The rivet diameter is $\frac{7}{8}''$
3. The thickness *t* is 0.606″
4. The area in bearing (remember there are two rivets) is

$$A_b = 2dt = 2 \times \tfrac{7}{8} \times 0.606 = 1.06 \text{ sq. in.}$$

5. The bearing stress is

$$S_b = \frac{P}{A_b} = \frac{28{,}700}{1.06} = 27{,}100 \text{ lbs. per sq. in.}$$

Fig. 11 shows a more complicated case of bearing stress. The two angles are riveted to the beam and the load *P* acts upward on the angles. The angles push against the rivets so there is bearing stress between the angles and the rivets, but each rivet bears against *both* angles so there are two bearing areas for each rivet. Hence, the area in bearing for one rivet against the angles is 2*dt* where *d* is the *rivet diameter* and *t* is the thickness of the angle. For the three rivets, the area in bearing is

$$3 \times 2dt = 6dt$$

Illustrative Example 2. The rivets in Fig. 11 are $\frac{3}{4}''$ in diameter and the thickness of the angles is $\frac{3}{8}''$. The load *P* is 34,700 lbs. Calculate the bearing stress between the rivets and the angles.

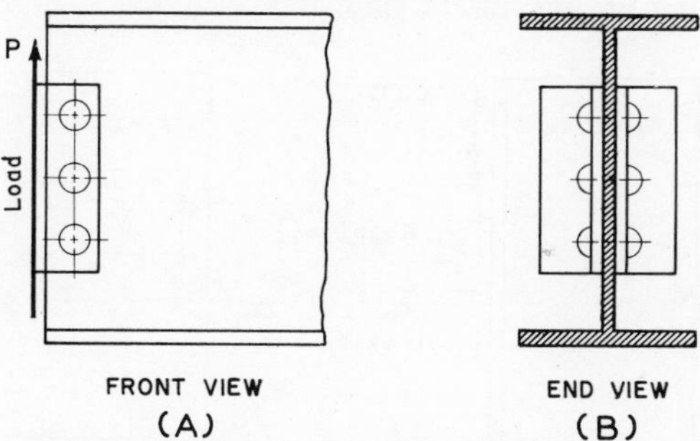

Fig. 11. Two Angles Riveted to Beam

Solution:

1. The load *P* is 34,700 lbs.
2. The rivet diameter is $\frac{3}{4}''$
3. The thickness *t* is $\frac{3}{8}''$
4. The area of one rivet in bearing against the angles is

$$2dt = 2 \times \tfrac{3}{4} \times \tfrac{3}{8} = 0.563 \text{ sq. in.}$$

and the area of the three rivets in bearing is

$$A_b = 3 \times 0.563 = 1.69 \text{ sq. in.}$$

5. The bearing stress is

$$S_b = \frac{P}{A_b} = \frac{34{,}700}{1.69} = 20{,}500 \text{ lbs. per sq. in.}$$

Practice Problems (Art. 13-3).

1. Calculate the bearing stress between the rivets and angles in Fig. 12.
2. What is the bearing stress between the rivets and the column in Fig. 12?

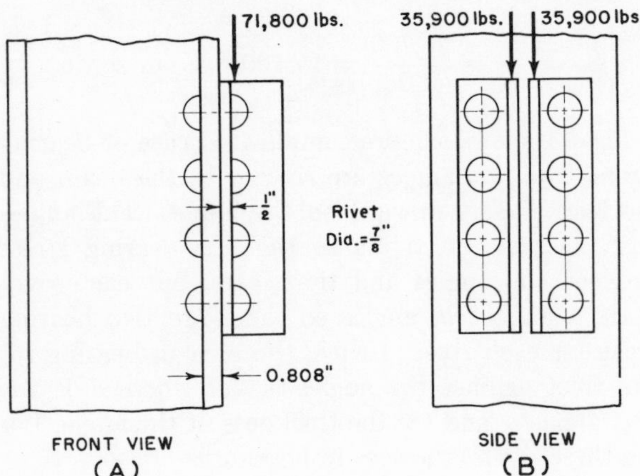

Fig. 12. Angles Riveted to Column for Problems 1 and 2 (Art. 13-3)

3. Find the bearing stress between the rivets and the angle in Fig. 13.
4. Calculate the bearing stress between the rivets and the column in Fig. 13.

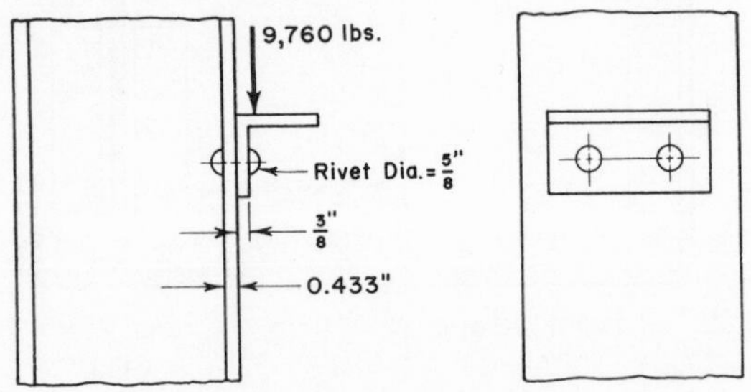

Fig. 13. Angle Riveted to Column for Problems 3 and 4 (Art. 13-3)

5. Determine the bearing stress between the rivets and the angles in Fig. 14.
6. What is the bearing stress between the rivets and the plate in Fig. 14?

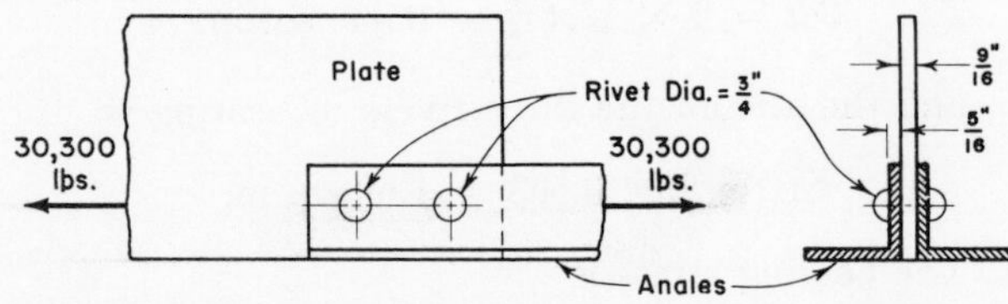

Fig. 14. Angles Riveted to Plate for Problems 5 and 6 (Art. 13-3)

13-4. Strength of a Rivet.

We have been using the formulas,

$$S_s = \frac{P}{A_s}; \quad \text{and} \quad S_b = \frac{P}{A_b}$$

to find shearing stress and bearing stress in rivets. Now write the formulas as

$$P_s = A_s S_s, \quad \text{and} \quad P_b = A_b S_b$$

We will apply them to one rivet at a time. A_s will be the area of the rivet in shear and S_s will be the working stress in shear; then P_s will be the strength of the rivet in shear. Also, A_b will be the area of the rivet in bearing and S_b will be the working stress in bearing; P_b will be the strength of the rivet in bearing.

P_s is the force which will develop the working stress in shear in the rivet and P_b is the force which will develop the working stress in bearing; ordinarily, P_s and P_b will not be of the same value. *Working stress* is a stress which is permissible to develop in service, but is not to be exceeded. If a force greater than P_s is applied to the rivet, the rivet will be overstressed in shear; and if a force greater than P_b is applied, the rivet will be overstressed in bearing.

The greatest force that can be applied safely, then, is the smaller of P_s and P_b. We will call this smaller force the *strength of the rivet*, and use it in designing beam connections.

The best way to calculate the strength of a rivet is to calculate both P_s and P_b, and take the smaller value. Where pieces of different thicknesses are fastened together, we must calculate a bearing strength for the rivet against each.

Illustrative Example 1. Fig. 15 shows two views of a riveted connection between a pair of structural angles and a wide-flange beam. The working stresses are 12,000 lbs. per sq. in. in shear, and 30,000 lbs. per sq. in. in bearing. Calculate the strength of one rivet.

Solution:

1. Strength in shear
   a) The rivet is in double shear so there are two shear areas. Notice in Fig. 15 that the rivet diameter is $\frac{7}{8}''$

$$A_s = 2\frac{\pi}{4}d^2 = 2\frac{\pi}{4}\left(\frac{7}{8}\right)^2 = 1.20 \text{ sq. in.}$$

   b) The working stress in shear is 12,000 lbs. per sq. in.

c) The strength of one rivet in shear is

$$P_s = A_s S_s = 1.20 \times 12{,}000 = 14{,}400 \text{ lbs.}$$

2. Strength in bearing against the web of the beam
 a) The diameter d is $\frac{7}{8}''$
 b) The web thickness is 0.465″
 c) The area in bearing is

$$A_b = dt = \tfrac{7}{8} \times 0.465 = 0.407 \text{ sq. in.}$$

 d) The working stress in bearing is 30,000 lbs. per sq. in.
 e) The strength of one rivet in bearing against the web of the beam is

$$P_b = A_b S_b = 0.407 \times 30{,}000 = 12{,}200 \text{ lbs.}$$

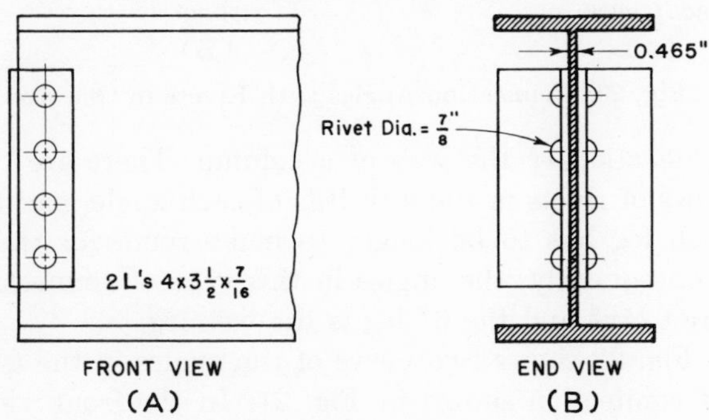

Fig. 15. Angles Riveted to Beam for Example 1 (Art. 13-4)

3. Strength in bearing against the angles
 a) The diameter d is $\frac{7}{8}''$
 b) The combined thickness of the two angles (the rivet bears against both of them) is

$$t = 2 \times \tfrac{7}{16} = \tfrac{7}{8}''$$

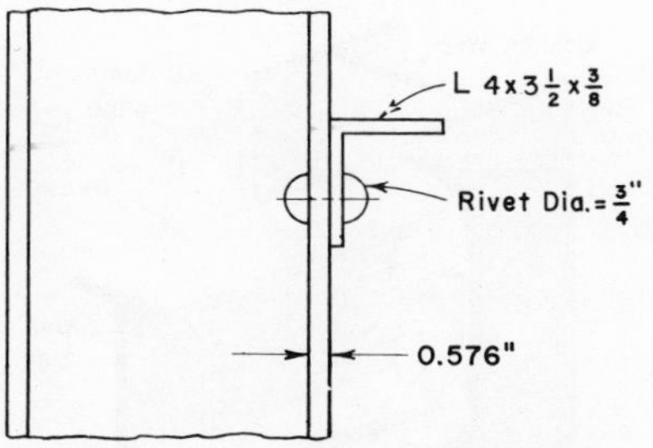

Fig. 16. Angle Riveted to Steel Column for Problem 2 (Art. 13-4)

 c) The area in bearing is

$$A_b = dt = \tfrac{7}{8} \times \tfrac{7}{8} = 0.767 \text{ sq. in.}$$

 d) The working stress in bearing is 30,000 lbs. per sq. in.
 e) The strength of one rivet in bearing against the angles is

$$P_b = A_b S_b = 0.767 \times 30{,}000 = 23{,}000 \text{ lbs.}$$

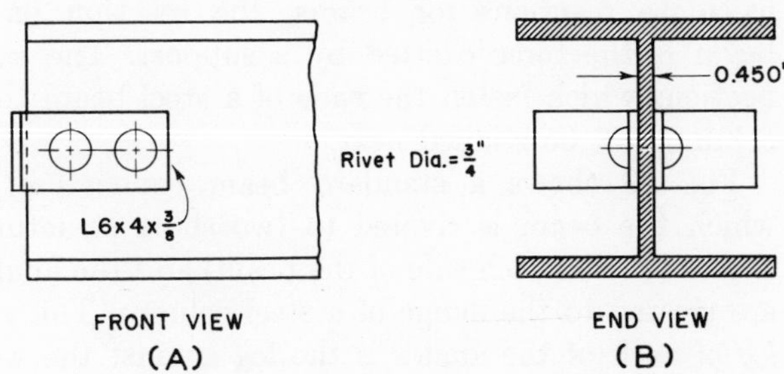

Fig. 17. Angles Riveted to Beam for Problem 3 (Art. 13-4)

4. The strength of the rivet is the smallest of the three forces we have calculated. It is the strength in bearing against the web of the beam

$$P = 12{,}200 \text{ lbs.}$$

Practice Problems (Art. 13-4).

1. A pair of structural angles, 4x3½x⅜, is riveted to a wide-flanged beam which has a web thickness of 0.554″. The working stresses are 15,000 lbs. per sq. in. in shear and 40,000 lbs. per sq. in. in bearing. The rivet diameter is ⅞″. What is the strength of one rivet?
2. Fig. 16 shows an angle riveted to a steel column. The working stresses are 15,000 lbs. per sq. in. in shear and 32,000 lbs. per sq. in. in bearing. Calculate the strength of one rivet.
3. Fig. 17 shows two views of a pair of angles riveted to a beam. Working stresses are 13,500 lbs. per sq. in. in shear and 32,000 lbs. per sq. in. in bearing. Find the strength of one rivet.
4. Fig. 18 shows two views of a pair of angles riveted to a column. Working stresses are 15,000 lbs. per sq. in. in shear and 32,000 lbs. per sq. in. in bearing. Calculate the strength of one rivet.

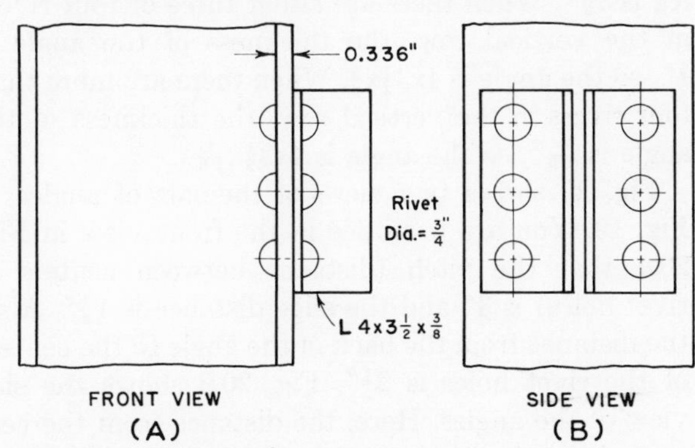

Fig. 18. Angles Riveted to Column for Problem 4 (Art. 13-4)

13-5. Standard Riveted Beam and Column Connections.

You learned to design beams of standard section in Chapter VII, and, before that, you learned to calculate reactions for beams; the reaction on a beam is the force exerted by a support. The connections which fasten the ends of a steel beam to a column will be studied next.

Fig. 19 shows a standard beam connection in which the beam is riveted to two short structural angles (one on each side of the beam) and the angles are riveted to the flange of a steel column. The *web leg* of each of the angles is the leg against the web of the beam; the rivets in the web leg fasten the angle to the beam. The *outstanding leg* of each angle is the leg against the flange of the column; rivets through the outstanding leg fasten the angle to the column.

Certain dimensions are standard for this type of connection, which means that they are always the same.

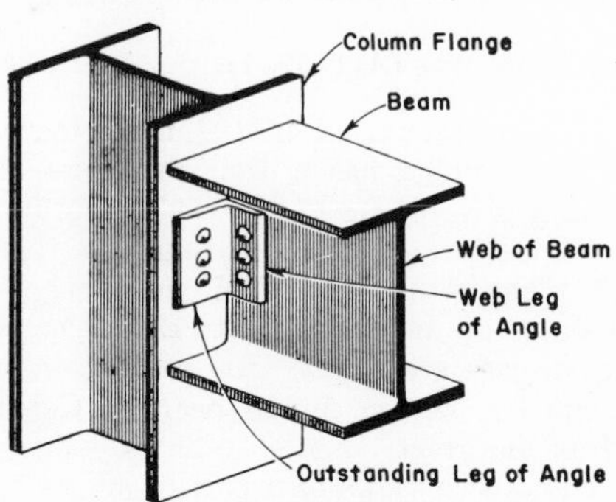

Fig. 19. Standard Beam Connection with Rivets in One Row

Notice in Fig. 19 that the rivets in each leg of the angle are in one vertical row. When this is the case, the outstanding leg of the angle is 4″ and the web leg is $3\frac{1}{2}$″. When there are either three or four rivets in the vertical row, the thickness of the angle is $\frac{3}{8}$″, so the angle is $4x3\frac{1}{2}x\frac{3}{8}$. When there are more than four rivets in the vertical row, the thickness of the angle is $\frac{7}{16}$″, so the angle is $4x3\frac{1}{2}x\frac{7}{16}$.

Fig. 20 shows two views of the pair of angles of Fig. 19. You are to notice in the front view in Fig. 20*A* that the pitch (distance between centers of rivet holes) is 3″ and the edge distance is $1\frac{1}{4}$″. Also, the distance from the back of the angle to the centers of the rivet holes is $2\frac{1}{4}$″. Fig. 20*B* shows the side view of the angles. Here, the distance from the centers of the rivet holes in one angle to the centers of the rivet holes in the other angle is $5\frac{1}{2}$″. The web of the beam is fitted between the angles, so they are separated by the web thickness *t*.

Fig. 21 shows the type of angle connection used when there is only one or two rivets in each vertical row in the angles. Here, for variety, we show the

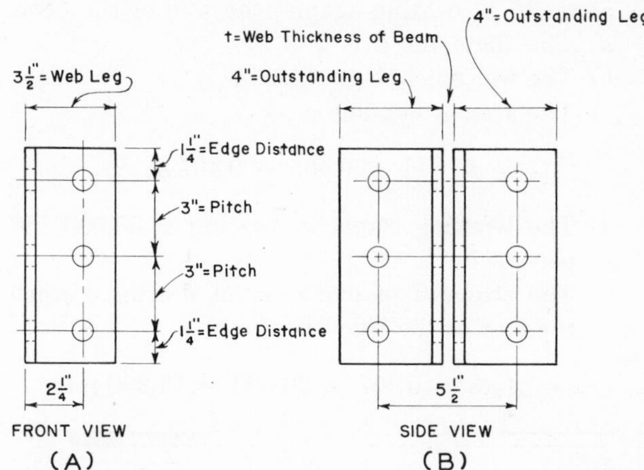

Fig. 20. Connection Angles with Rivets in One Row

connection to the web of a column. There are two rows of rivets in the web legs of each angle, and the web leg has to be longer to make room for them. Consequently, the angles in this type of connection are $6x4x\frac{3}{8}$ and the 6″ leg is the web leg.

Fig. 22 shows two views of the angles in the type of connection shown in Fig. 21. In the front view, in Fig. 22*A*, you can see the dimensions of $2\frac{1}{4}$″ and $2\frac{1}{2}$″ which locate the centers of the rivet holes. Also, you are to notice that the edge distances are $1\frac{1}{2}$″. Fig. 22*B* shows the side view of the angles and this is about the same as you saw in Fig. 20*B*.

The rivets in these connections may be either $\frac{7}{8}$″ or $\frac{3}{4}$″ in diameter. Of course, all rivets in any particular connection are of the same diameter; that is, all are $\frac{7}{8}$″ or all are $\frac{3}{4}$″. When $\frac{7}{8}$″ rivets are used, the

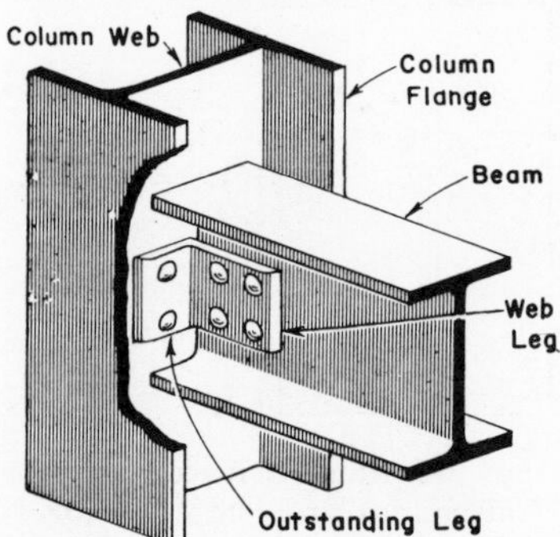

Fig. 21. Standard Beam Connection with Rivets in Two Rows

connections are classified as the *A*[1] series; when $\frac{3}{4}$″ rivets are used, the connections are classified as the *B*[1] series.

[1] *A* series and *B* series are terms used by the American Institute of Steel Construction.

13-6. Design of Standard Riveted-Beam Connections.

It is not hard to design standard-beam connections, because all we have to calculate is the number of rivets.

You would calculate the reactions and design the beam before designing the connection. The reaction is the force which the connection has to withstand, and you can get the web thickness of the beam from one of the tables in Chapter VII. Then you are ready to go to work on designing the connection.

The stresses in the rivets in a beam connection have to be considered. Each rivet in the web legs of the angles is in double shear (2 planes of shear for each rivet) and each rivet in the outstanding legs is in single shear (1 plane of shear for each rivet). However, in Fig. 20 there are twice as many rivets in the outstanding legs as in the web legs, so the rivets in the outstanding legs have the same area in shear as the rivets in the web legs. Because the shear areas are the same, the strengths are the same and you only have to figure one of them.

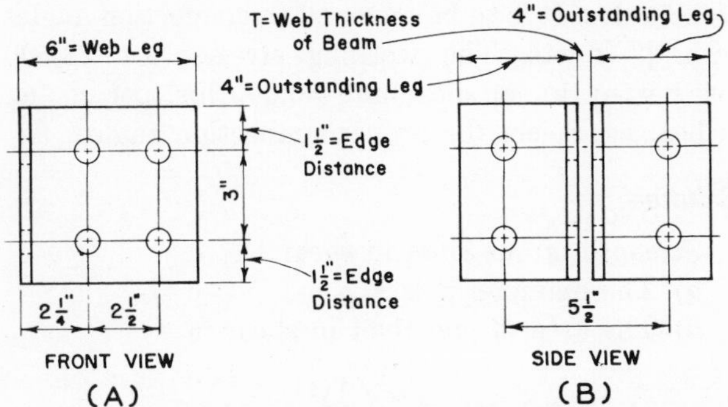

Fig. 22. Connection Angles with Rivets in Two Rows

The rivets are in bearing against the angles, but with a thickness of $\frac{3}{8}''$ or $\frac{7}{16}''$ for the angles, the rivets are stronger in bearing against the angles than they are in shear. Consequently, you can forget about the rivets in bearing against the angles.

The rivets are, also, in bearing against the web of the beam. The web thickness t may be small enough so that the rivet is weaker in bearing against the web than in shear; this must be checked.

You remember how we calculated the strength of a rivet. We used the formula,

$$P_s = A_s S_s$$

to calculate the strength of the rivet in shear, and the formula,

$$P_b = A_b S_b$$

to calculate the strength of the rivet in bearing. The smaller of the two forces is the strength of the rivet.

We will calculate the strength of a rivet in the web legs in shear (double shear) and the strength of a rivet in bearing against the web of the beam. The smaller force is the strength of the rivet and we will divide it into the reaction (R_1 and R_2 designate reactions) to get the number of rivets. We will probably get something like 2.83 or 4.57 for the number of rivets. We will have to increase it to the next whole number. Thus, if the calculations come out as 2.83 for the number of rivets use 3 rivets; if it comes out 4.57, use 5 rivets.

We will give you the rivet diameter and the working stresses in our problems.

Illustrative Example 1. The reaction at one end of a wide-flange beam, 14 WF 30, is 19,800 lbs. How many $\frac{3}{4}''$ rivets are needed to fasten it to a column by means of a standard connection? Use S_s = 15,000 lbs. per sq. in. and S_b = 40,000 lbs. per sq. in. for working stresses.

Solution:

1. Strength of one rivet in shear
   a) The diameter is $\frac{3}{4}''$
   b) The area in shear is

$$A_s = 2\frac{\pi}{4}d^2 = 2\frac{\pi}{4}\left(\frac{3}{4}\right)^2 = 0.884 \text{ sq. in.}$$

   c) The working stress in shear is 15,000 lbs. per sq. in.
   d) The strength of one rivet in shear is

$$P_s = A_s S_s = 0.884 \times 15{,}000 = 13{,}300 \text{ lbs.}$$

2. Strength of one rivet in bearing against the web of the beam
   a) The diameter is $\frac{3}{4}''$
   b) The web thickness of a 14 WF 30 beam is (from Table I of Chapter VII), 0.270″
   c) The area in bearing is

$$A_b = dt = \tfrac{3}{4} \times 0.270 = 0.202 \text{ sq. in.}$$

   d) The working stress in bearing is 40,000 lbs. per sq. in.
   e) The strength of one rivet in bearing is

$$P_b = A_b S_b = 0.202 \times 40{,}000 = 8{,}080 \text{ lbs.}$$

3. Number of rivets
   a) The reaction is 19,800 lbs.
   b) The strength of one rivet is 8,080 lbs. (The smaller of the two values calculated.)

c) The number of rivets needed is

$$\frac{19{,}800}{8{,}080} = 2.45$$

d) We increase this to the next whole number. The answer is 3 rivets

Fig. 23 shows the connection. With three rivets in each vertical row, the angles are the size designated as $4\text{x}3\frac{1}{2}\text{x}\frac{3}{8}$.

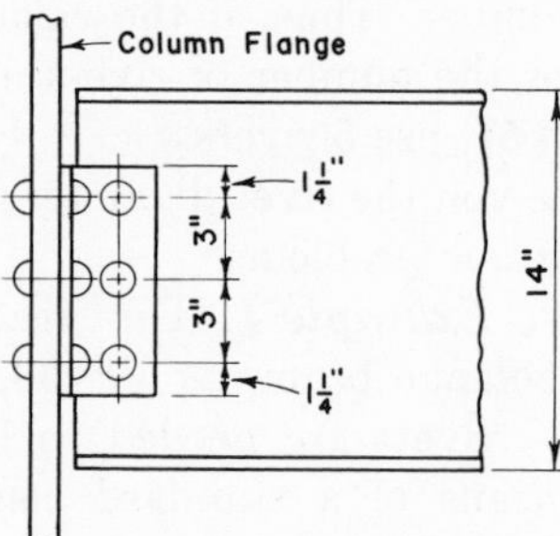

Fig. 23. Connection with Three Rivets in Each Row for Example 1 (Art. 13-6)

Examine Fig. 23 again. Notice there are three rivets in each vertical row and you can see that the angles are $8\frac{1}{2}''$ long. A beam would have to be at least 12″ deep in order to have room for an angle of this length. However, there are cases in which the beam is only 8″ deep but the end reaction is so great that three or four rivets are necessary in the web of the beam. Then, angles which have room for two rows of rivets must be used; the angles are $6\text{x}4\text{x}\frac{3}{8}$ and the 6″ leg is riveted to the web of the beam; Fig. 24*A* shows such an angle.

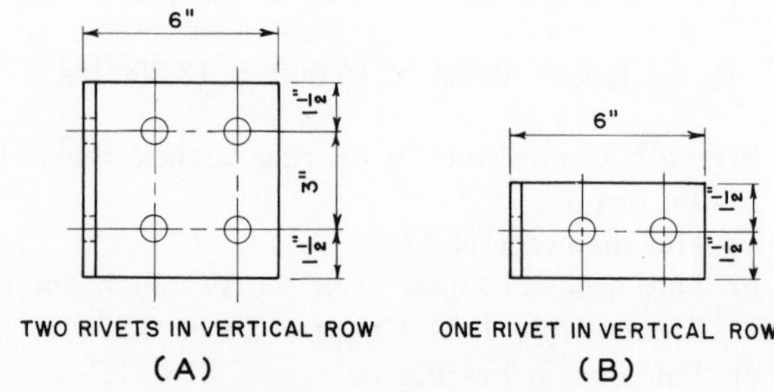

Fig. 24. Two Methods of Riveting Connection Angles

The outstanding leg of the angle in Fig. 24*A* is 4″ in length and contains only one row of rivets. (The outstanding leg is the leg which is riveted to the support.) More rivets are needed in the web leg because the web of an 8″ beam is usually so thin (about $\frac{1}{4}''$ thick) that the web rivets are weak in bearing. The column flange (or whatever) to which the outstanding leg is riveted is so much thicker than the web of the beam that two rivets in the outstanding leg are as strong in bearing as four rivets in the web leg.

Fig. 24*B* shows a $6\text{x}4\text{x}\frac{3}{8}$ angle drilled for two rivets in the web leg and one rivet in the outstanding leg. This angle would be used to fasten a beam of 5″ or 6″ or 7″ depth.

Bearing against the web of the beam is usually the weak point for shallow beams. If no more than two rivets are needed, you would select the connection angle in Fig. 24*B*. If more than two rivets are needed and the beam is less than 12″ deep, you would choose the connection angle in Fig. 24*A*. If more than two rivets are needed and the beam is of 12″ depth or more, you would take a connection angle of the type shown in Fig. 20 or Fig. 23.

Illustrative Example 2. An American standard beam, 6 **I** 12.5, is subjected to an end reaction of 3,800 lbs. It is to be fastened to connection angles with $\frac{3}{4}''$ rivets. The working stresses are 13,500 lbs. per sq. in. in shear and 36,000 lbs. per sq. in. in bearing. Select the proper connection angle.

Solution:

1. Strength of one rivet in shear
   a) The diameter d is $\frac{3}{4}''$
   b) The area of one rivet in shear is

$$A_s = 2\frac{\pi}{4}d^2 = 2\frac{\pi}{4}\left(\frac{3}{4}\right)^2 = 0.883 \text{ sq. in.}$$

   c) The working stress in shear is 13,500 lbs. per sq. in.
   d) The strength of one rivet in shear is

$$P_s = A_sS_s = 0.884 \times 13{,}500 = 11{,}900 \text{ lbs.}$$

2. Strength of one rivet in bearing against the web of the beam
   a) The diameter d is $\frac{3}{4}''$
   b) The web thickness of the beam (6 **I** 12.5) is 0.230″ (from Table II, in Chapter VII)
   c) The area of one rivet in bearing is

$$A_b = dt = \tfrac{3}{4} \times 0.230 = 0.173 \text{ sq. in.}$$

   d) The working stress in bearing is

$$S_b = 36{,}000 \text{ lbs. per sq. in.}$$

   e) The strength of one rivet in bearing against the web of the beam is

$$P_b = A_bS_b = 0.173 \times 36{,}000 = 6{,}230 \text{ lbs.}$$

   This is the strength of the rivet since it is less than P_s.

3. Number of rivets
   a) The reaction is 3,800 lbs.
   b) The strength of one rivet is 6,230 lbs.
   c) The number of rivets needed is

$$\frac{3{,}800}{6{,}230} = 0.61$$

   d) We make this 2 rivets and use the angle shown in Fig. 24*B*

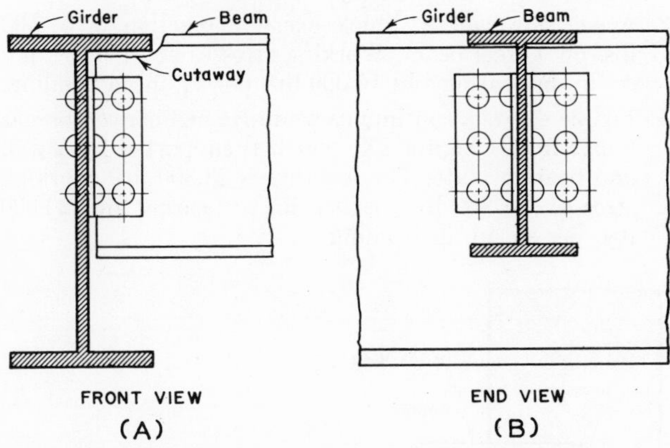

Fig. 25. Connection of Beam to Girder with Angles

Fig. 25 shows another use for angle connections. Here the beam is supported by a girder. (A *girder* is a large *beam.*) The web legs of each angle are riveted to the web of the beam and the outstanding legs are riveted to the web of the girder. There is nothing different about designing a connection to a girder. It is the same as if the beam were supported by a column.

Practice Problems (Art. 13-6). We will give you the data in table form and you are to determine the number of rivets in each row and select the connection angles.

PROBLEM	SIZE OF BEAM	REACTION IN LBS.	RIVET DIA.	WORKING STRESSES	
				Shear	Bearing
1	16 WF 40	33,700	$\frac{3}{4}$	15,000	40,000
2	12 I 35	11,600	$\frac{3}{4}$	12,000	32,000
3	12 WF 36	28,900	$\frac{3}{4}$	13,500	36,000
4	8 WF 17	21,300	$\frac{3}{4}$	12,000	32,000
5	10 I 35	18,900	$\frac{7}{8}$	15,000	40,000
6	15 I 50	45,200	$\frac{7}{8}$	13,500	36,000

13-7. Beam Bearing Plates.

There are many cases in which one end of a steel beam is supported by a concrete wall. Then it is usually necessary to place a steel, bearing plate between the beam and the wall; Fig. 26 shows two views of a bearing plate between a steel beam and a wall.

You can see the reaction, R, of the wall on the beam in Fig. 26*A*. (You learned to calculate beam reactions in Chapter II, and worked beam problems later.) The force R causes bearing stress between the wall and the beam. If no bearing plate were used, the bearing stress on the wall would be too high for the concrete. The bearing plate provides more bearing area against the wall and reduces the bearing stress on the concrete to a reasonable value.

Notice the dimensions of the bearing plate in Fig. 26. The dimension C is the length of the bearing and this is often the same as the thickness of the wall. In any event, C is known when you start to design the bearing plate.

The dimension B is the width of the bearing plate. We can derive a formula for B. The area of bearing between the plate and the wall is the product of the dimensions C and B. Thus,

$$A_b = CB$$

Then, the working stress in bearing against the wall

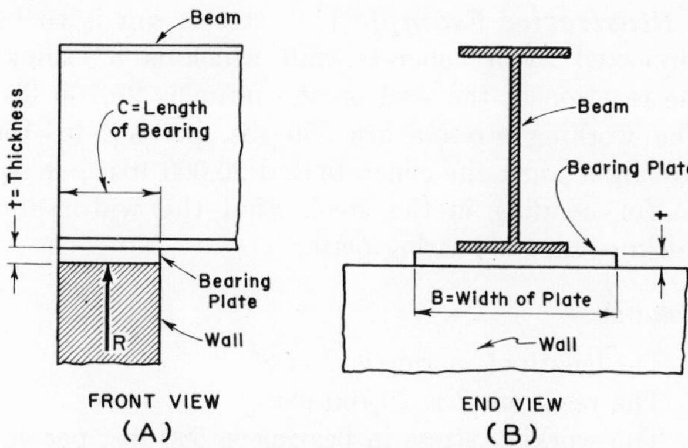

Fig. 26. Steel Bearing Plate for Beam

is S_b and the load is R. The bearing stress is equal to the load divided by the area; that is

$$S_b = \frac{R}{A_b} = \frac{R}{CB}$$

and we can use a little algebra to change this to

$$B = \frac{R}{CS_b}$$

We can solve this formula for the width B when we know the reaction R, the length of bearing C and the bearing stress S_b.

With B known, the only unknown left to find is the thickness t. We could go through the derivation of a formula for t, but we will give it to you to save time. It is

$$t = \sqrt{\frac{3}{4} \frac{RB}{CS}}$$

where R is the reaction, B and C are dimensions of the steel plate and S is the working stress for the steel in bending. (The steel plate does bend.) You know that the symbol $\sqrt{}$ stands for square root.

You need to use two working stresses to design a steel bearing plate: the working stress S_b for the concrete in bearing, and the working stress S for the steel plate in bending. We will give you the working stresses in our problems and, in practical work, you will find them in the building codes.

The dimension B will usually come out as a number, such as 9.73″ or 7.57″, which we will round off to the next larger inch. Thus, if we calculate B as 9.73″, we will increase it to 10″. If we calculate B as 7.57″, we will increase it to 8″. Then we will use the whole number for B when we calculate t. The dimension t will probably come out as something like 0.692″, but we will increase it to the next larger eighth of an inch. Thus, 0.692″ would be increased to 0.75″, which is $\frac{3}{4}$″.

Illustrative Example 1. A steel beam is to be supported by a concrete wall which is 8″ thick; the reaction of the wall on the beam is 29,700 lbs. The working stresses are 500 lbs. per sq. in. for bearing against the concrete and 20,000 lbs. per sq. in. for bending in the steel. Find the width and thickness of the bearing plate.

Solution:

1. The length of bearing is $C = 8''$
2. The reaction R is 29,700 lbs.
3. The working stress in bearing is 500 lbs. per sq. in.
4. The required width of the plate is

$$B = \frac{R}{CS_b} = \frac{29{,}700}{8 \times 500} = 7.43''$$

   and we increase this to the next larger inch, which is 8″
5. The working stress in bending is 20,000 lbs. per sq. in.
6. The thickness needed is

$$t = \sqrt{\frac{3}{4} \frac{RB}{CS}} = \sqrt{\frac{3}{4} \frac{29{,}700 \times 8}{8 \times 20{,}000}} = 1.06''$$

   and we increase this to the next larger eighth of an inch, which is 1.125″ or $1\frac{1}{8}$″
7. Then $B = 8''$; and $t = 1\frac{1}{8}''$

Practice Problems (Art. 13-7). You can learn how to design bearing plates by working problems. In each of the following problems find the width and thickness of the bearing plate.

1. A concrete wall 6″ thick supports a steel beam and exerts a reaction of 16,400 lbs. on the beam. The working stress in bearing is 650 lbs. per sq. in. and the working stress in bending is 18,000 lbs. per sq. in.
2. Fig. 27 shows an arrangement in which the length of bearing is only 4″. The reaction is 14,900 lbs. Working stresses are 600 lbs. per sq. in. in bearing and 20,000 lbs. per sq. in. in bending.
3. A concrete wall 9″ thick exerts a reaction of 41,500 lbs. on a steel beam. Working stresses are 450 lbs. per sq. in. in bearing and 16,000 lbs. per sq. in. in bending.
4. Fig. 28 shows a continuous beam (remember *continuous beams* from Chapter IX) which is supported by a wall and bearing plate. The reaction is 23,300 lbs., working stresses are 800 lbs. per sq. in. in bearing and 20,000 lbs. per sq. in. in bending.

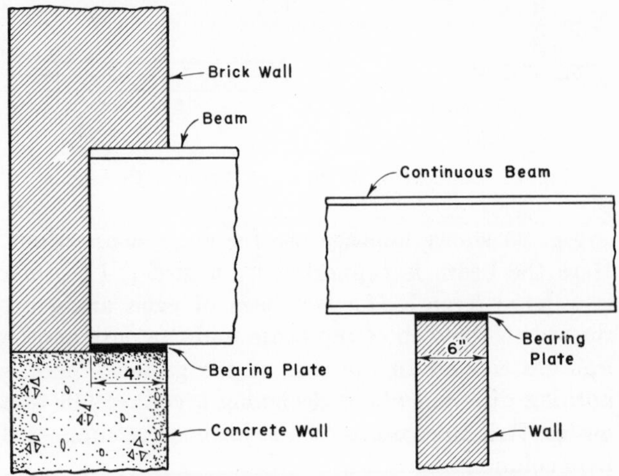

Fig. 27. Short Bearing Plate for Problem 2 (Art. 13-7)

Fig. 28. Wall Support for Continuous Beam for Problem 4 (Art. 13-7)

13-8. Fusion Welding.

Fusion welding is the process of joining pieces of metal by means of heat. It has become a common method for fastening steel structural members together.

Nearly all structural welding is arc welding, so we will study arc welding. Fig. 29 will help you to understand the process. Here two pieces of steel are being welded together.

An electric current flows from the weld rod to the pieces being welded through the arc which you can see in Fig. 29. The current causes a high temperature (as high as 6,000°F., sometimes). As a result, the weld rod melts and so does part of the pieces being welded, so there is a pool of molten metal while the weld is being made. The weld rod is moved along the seam in the direction from A to B. The molten metal solidifies behind the weld rod to form the finished weld.

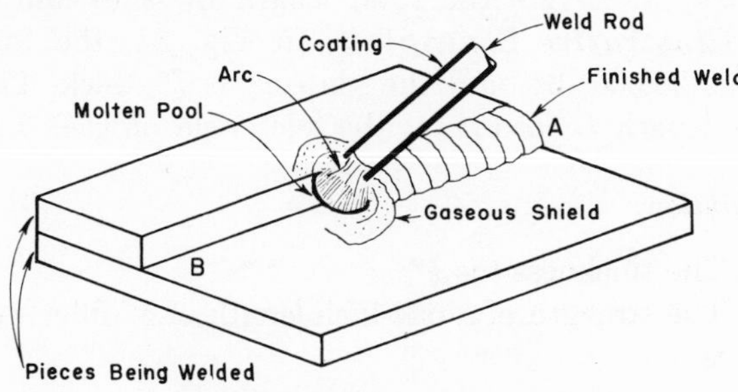

Fig. 29. Arc Weldıng Process

Two other items to notice, in Fig. 29, are the *coating on the weld rod* and the *gaseous shield*. The coating melts and forms the shield of inert gases. These gases shield the metal from the air while it is molten and while it is solidifying. This is an important point because the hot metal would combine with oxygen and nitrogen from the air if it were exposed, and the result would be a poor weld.

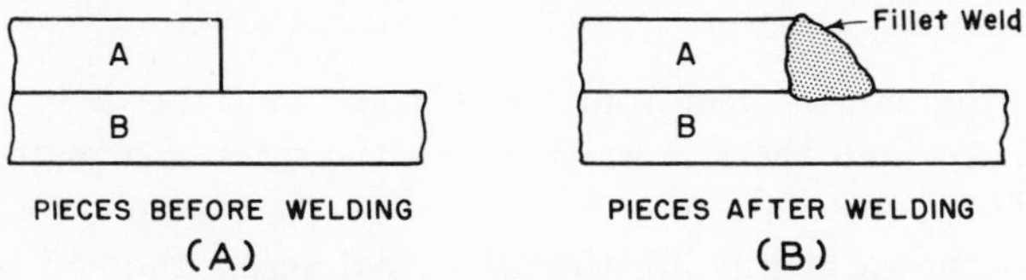

Fig. 30. End View Showing Fillet Weld

13-9. Fillet Welds.

Fillet welds are the most common type of welds in structural work. Fig. 30A shows an end view of two steel plates, A and B, which are to be welded together. Fig. 30B shows the same plates after the weld has been made. The weld in Fig. 30B is called

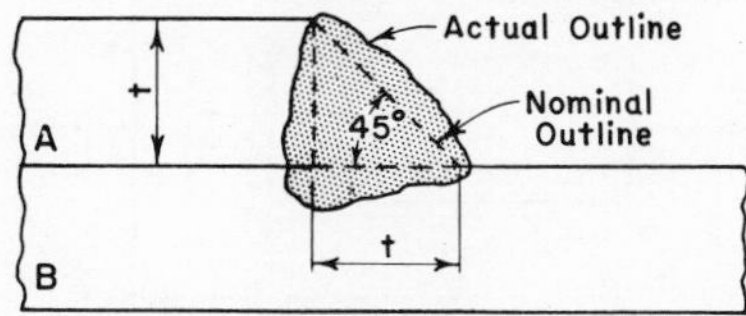

Fig. 31. Cross Section of Fillet Weld

a *fillet weld;* a *fillet* is anything that is used to fill in a corner.

Fig. 31 shows the cross section of a fillet weld. The actual outline is rather irregular, so a nominal outline is used for calculating the strength of the weld. This nominal outline is a 45° right triangle, usually with each leg of the triangle equal to the thickness of the top plate A. The dimension t is given as the size of the fillet weld. Thus, if t is $\frac{1}{2}''$, the fillet weld is a $\frac{1}{2}''$ fillet weld.

Fillet welds are used ordinarily to hold one member from sliding over another. For example, Fig. 32

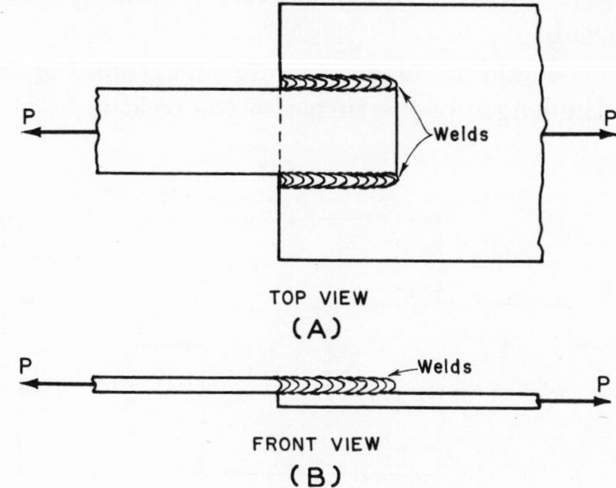

Fig. 32. Side Fillet Welds

shows two views of a pair of steel plates which are fastened together by fillet welds on the sides of the narrower plate. The forces P tend to pull the plates apart and the welds hold the plates together. These welds are called *side fillet welds* because they are on the sides of the narrower plate.

The forces P in Fig. 32 tend to make the upper plate slide to the left, over the lower plate. This tends

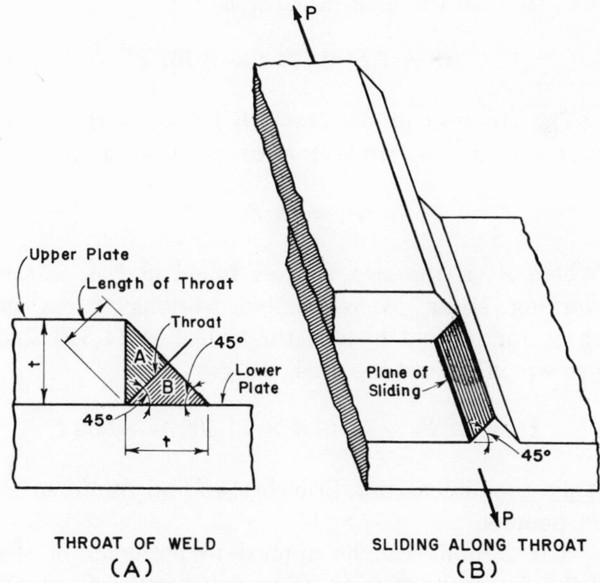

Fig. 33. Failure of Fillet Weld

to shear (*shear* is *sliding*) the weld at the throat, so that half of the weld goes with the upper plate and half with the lower plate. Fig. 33A shows a cross section of a fillet weld; here the *throat* is the 45° line through the weld.

If the weld sheared at the throat, part A of the weld would go with the upper plate and part B would remain with the lower plate. Fig. 33B shows how the plates would look after a shear failure of the weld.

You should be able to figure out from Fig. 33A that the length of the throat of the weld is

$$t \cos 45°$$

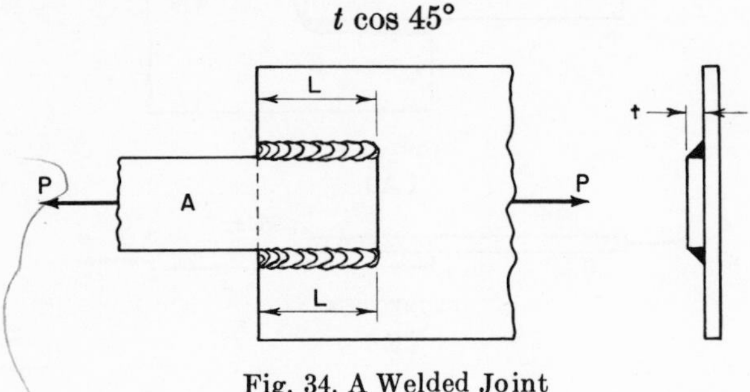

Fig. 34. A Welded Joint

and since the cosine of 45° is 0.707, the length of the throat is

$$0.707\ t$$

where t is the length of one leg of the weld. We can calculate the strength of a one-inch length of a fillet weld. We will have a rectangular area in shear at the throat of the weld in the one-inch length of weld; the length of the rectangle is 1″ and the width is 0.707 t, so the area in shear is

$$A_s = 1 \times 0.707\ t = 0.707\ t$$

The strength of the one-inch length is the force that will develop working stress in shear, it is

$$P_1 = A_s S_s$$

Where A_s is the area we just found and S_s is the working stress. A reasonable working stress in shear for a weld in structural steel is 11,300 lbs. per sq. in.; if we use this, we get

$$P_1 = A_s S_s = 0.707\ t \times 11{,}300 = 8{,}000\ t$$

Take the dimension t, in inches, to find the force P, in pounds.

The formula can be applied to problems of the following type. A force P tends to pull two plates apart, as you see in Fig. 34. The thickness of the plate A is known; this thickness is the same as t in the formula, $P_1 = 8{,}000\ t$. Our problem will be to find the length L of the fillet weld needed on each side of the plate.

We can use t to calculate P_1. This is the force for a one-inch length of weld, so by dividing the force P by P_1 we get the total length of weld needed. Then, we divide the total length by 2 to find L.

Illustrative Example 1. In Fig. 34, the force P is 26,000 lbs. and the plate A is $\frac{1}{2}$″ thick. Find the length L needed for the fillet weld on each side.

Solution:

1. The thickness t is $\frac{1}{2}$″
2. The strength of a one-inch length of $\frac{1}{2}$″ fillet weld is

$$P_1 = 8{,}000\ t = 8{,}000 \times \tfrac{1}{2} = 4{,}000 \text{ lbs.}$$

3. The total force P is 26,000 lbs.
4. The total length of fillet weld needed is

$$\frac{P}{P_1} = \frac{26{,}000}{4{,}000} = 6.5''$$

5. Half of this goes on each side, so

$$L = \frac{6.5}{2} = 3.25''$$

Sometimes the total length of weld needed is more than there is room for on the sides of a plate. Then, the plate may be welded across the end, too, as shown in Fig. 35; the fillet weld across the end is called an *end fillet weld.*

An *end fillet weld* is taken to have the same strength per inch as a side fillet weld, so we calculate the total length of weld needed (as before) and take the total length as the sum of the three lengths in Fig. 35. Thus, the total length is

$$L + L + L_e$$

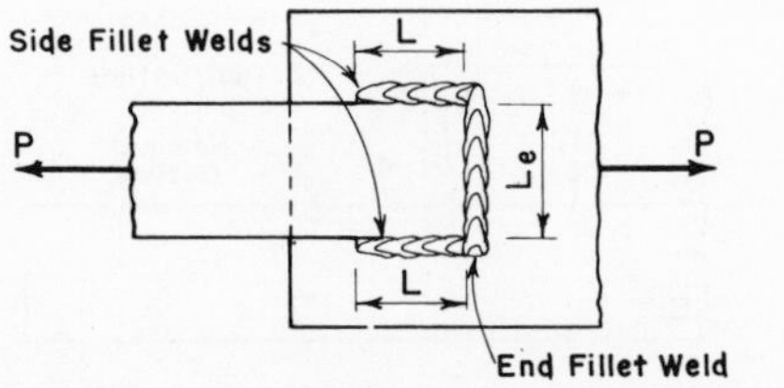

Fig. 35. A Welded Joint Showing Side and End Welds

Illustrative Example 2. In Fig. 35, the force P is 23,000 lbs. The upper plate is $\frac{3}{8}$″ thick and the length L_e is 3″. Find the length L needed.

Solution:

1. The thickness t is $\frac{3}{8}$″

2. The strength of a one-inch length of $\frac{3}{8}''$ fillet weld is

$$P_1 = 8{,}000\ t = 8{,}000 \times \tfrac{3}{8} = 3{,}000 \text{ lbs.}$$

3. The total force P is 23,000 lbs.
4. The total length of fillet weld needed is

$$\frac{P}{P_1} = \frac{23{,}000}{3{,}000} = 7.67''$$

5. There is a 3″ length of weld on the end, so the length left for the sides is

$$7.67 - 3 = 4.67''$$

6. Half of this goes on each side, so

$$L = \frac{4.67}{2} = 2.34''$$

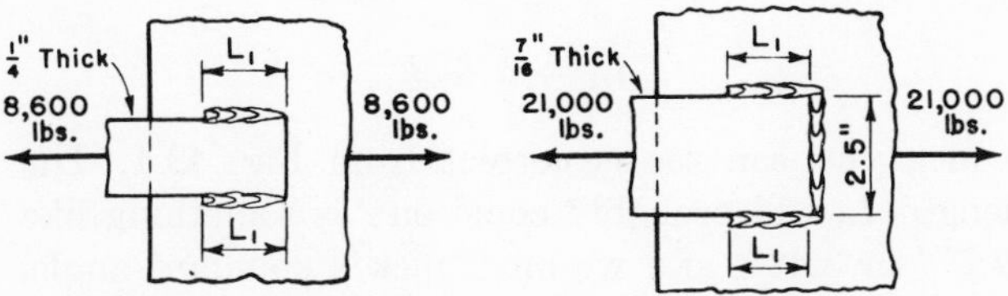

Fig. 36. Welded Joint for Problem 1 (Art. 13-9)

Fig. 37. Welded Joint for Problem 2 (Art. 13-9)

Practice Problems (Art. 13-9). Calculate the length of each weld in the following problems, the figures will be given.

1. Fig. 36. Calculate L_1.
2. Fig 37. Calculate L_1.
3. Fig. 38. Calculate L_1.
4. Fig. 39. Calculate L_e.

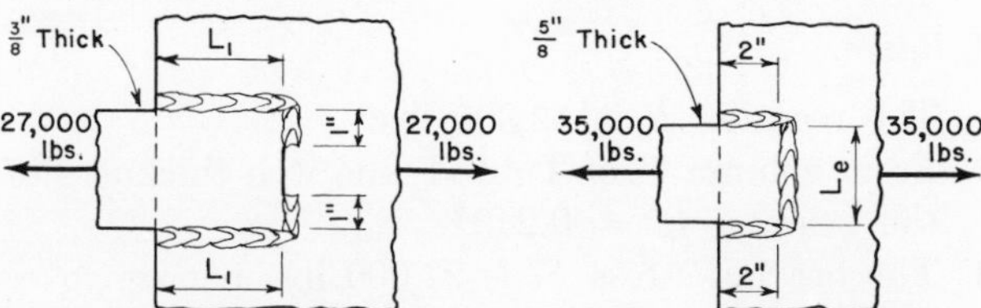

Fig. 38. Welded Joint for Problem 3 (Art. 13-9)

Fig. 39. Welded Joint for Problem 4 (Art. 13-9)

13-10. Welded Beam and Column Connections.

Fillet welds are used to fasten a steel beam to a steel column so the column supports one end of the beam. There are several ways in which the fastening can be made; we are going to study one of the simplest methods.

Fig. 40 shows two views of part of a column to which an angle seat is welded. An *angle seat* is a short length of angle upon which the beam is to rest. Notice here the fillet welds along the sides of the angle and part way across the top. These welds fasten the angle to the column; they are made in the shop before the column is erected. The holes in the angle are for bolts to hold a beam on the angle.

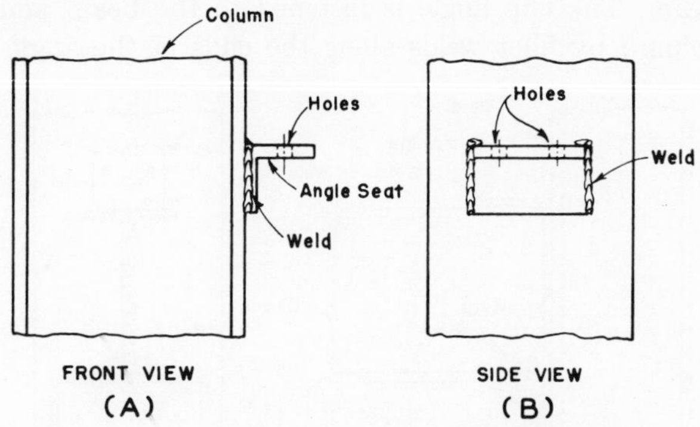

Fig. 40. An Angle Seat Welded to Column

The beam is bolted to the angle seat to hold the beam securely while it is being welded. There are several ways of bolting; Fig. 41 shows two of them. Fig. 41*A* shows the end of a beam with holes punched in the bottom flange for the bolts. Fig. 41*B* shows a method in which a plate is welded to the bottom flange of the beam and the holes are in the plate. The advantage of the second scheme is that it makes it unnecessary to punch holes in the beam. (This would require transporting the heavy beam to a punch.) However, the plate must be punched and then welded to the beam. Sometimes the method of Fig. 41*A* is better and sometimes the method of Fig. 41*B* is better. It depends upon the type of work and the equipment which the shop has.

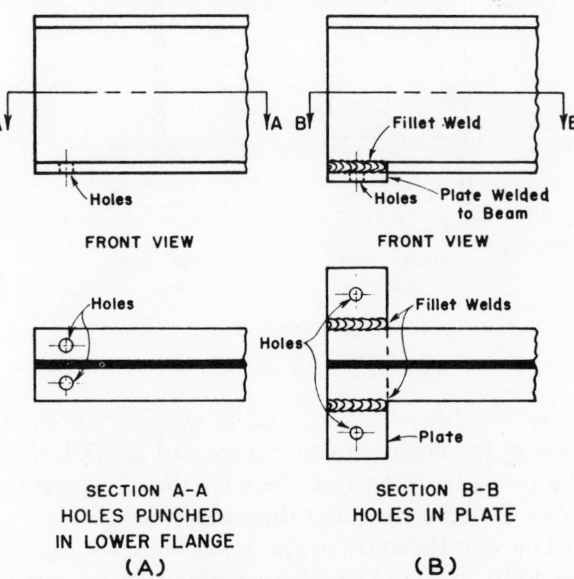

Fig. 41. End of Beam with Holes in Flange and Plate

Fig. 42 shows the finished connection. The beam is welded to the angle seat and, also, a clip angle is welded to the top of the beam and the column. The beam is fastened to the angle seat by means of fillet welds along the side of the lower flange of the beam. The clip angle is fastened to the beam and column by fillet welds along the ends of the angle.

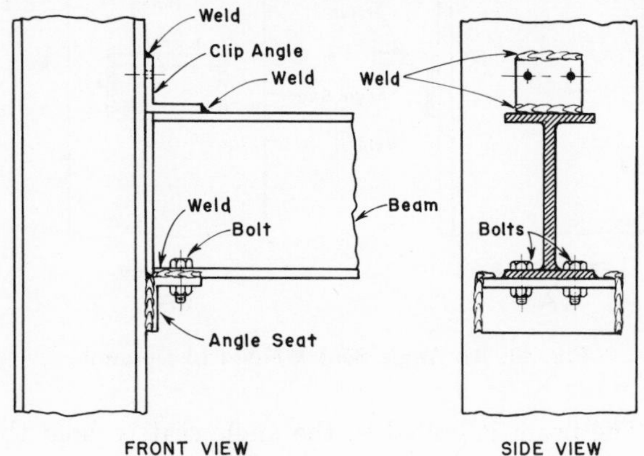

Fig. 42. Front and Side Views of Welded Connection of Beam to Column

You learned to design beams in Chapter VII and, as you remember, you had to find the reactions for the beam. Then, with the reaction at the end and the size of beam known, you are ready to design the connection.

The first step in designing a welded connection for a beam is to find the length of the outstanding leg of the angle seat; that is, the length L_2 in Fig.

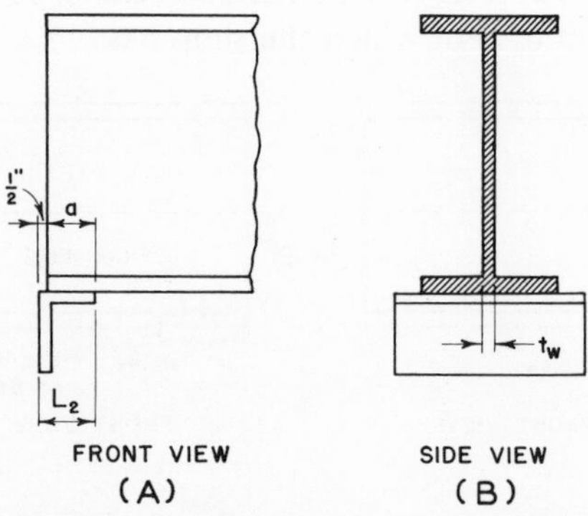

Fig. 43. Angle Seat and End View of Beam

43*A*. The beam is placed so its end is ½″ from the edge of the angle, as you can see in Fig. 43*A*. Then the beam bears against the angle for the length *a*. We will find *a* first, and then add ½″ to get L_2.

The web thickness of the beam is shown as t_w (*w* for web) in Fig. 43*B*. We can think of the web as bearing against the angle seat; the area in bearing is a rectangle of length *a* and width t_w, so the bearing area is

$$A_b = at_w$$

We will call the reaction on the beam *R*, and this reaction is developed by bearing stress between the angle seat and the web of the beam. The bearing stress is S_b, and the force *R* is equal to the bearing area times the bearing stress; that is

$$R = A_b S_b = at_w S_b$$

We want to find the length *a*, so we will solve this equation for *a* and write it as

$$a = \frac{R}{t_w S_b}$$

We know *R* and S_b, and we can look up t_w in Table I or II of Chapter VIII.

After we find *a*, we will take L_2 as

$$L_2 = a + \tfrac{1}{2}$$

which you can see is correct from Fig. 43*A*. The length L_2 will probably come out as something like 2.77″ or 3.42″, and we must pick a standard angle, so we increase L_2 to the next half inch, say, 3″, 3½″, or 4″. We will not select an angle seat with an outstanding leg of less than 3″ because we need room to bolt the beam to the angle.

Illustrative Example 1. A wide-flange beam, 10 WF 23, has an end reaction of 12,300 lbs. Take the bearing stress as 24,000 lbs. per sq. in. and find the length of the outstanding leg of the angle seat.

Solution:

1. The reaction *R* is 12,300 lbs.
2. From column 7, of Table I, the web thickness of the beam is $t_w = 0.240''$
3. The bearing stress S_b is 24,000 lbs. per sq. in.
4. The length *a* needed is

$$a = \frac{R}{t_w S_b} = \frac{12{,}300}{0.240 \times 24{,}000} = 2.14''$$

5. We add ½″ to *a* to find the length needed for L_2. This is

$$L_2 = a + \tfrac{1}{2} = 2.14 + 0.5 = 2.64''$$

We go up to the next half inch, which is 3″. $L_2 = 3''$.

Fig. 44 illustrates how long the angle seat should be; here *L* is the length of the angle. The angle is to be welded along the sides and for a ½″ length at each end on top. The angle must be long enough for the flange of the beam to fit between these welds; we will represent the width of the flange by w_f and you can look up w_f in Table I or II of Chapter VII.

The angle seat must be long enough for the flange of the beam and the weld at each end; this would give a minimum value of L as

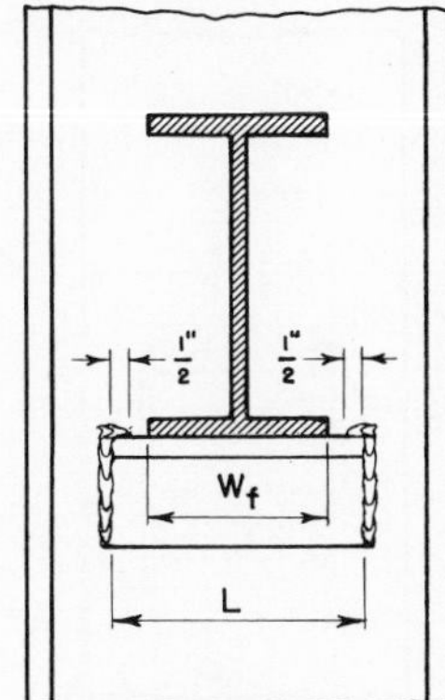

Fig. 44. Beam, Column, and Angle

$$L = w_f + \tfrac{1}{2} + \tfrac{1}{2} = w_f + 1$$

that is, L must be at least 1″ greater than the flange width of the beam. The length L will usually come out as some number such as 6.75″ or 7.34″, but measurements are not made to one-hundredth of an inch in fabricating shops, so we will increase this to the next larger inch. Thus, if we get 6.75″ for L, we will use a 7″ length of angle.

Illustrative Example 2. What length of seat angle should be used to support a wide-flange beam, 8 WF 27?

Solution:

1. The flange width (from column 5 of Table I, in Chapter VII) is $w_f = 6.53''$.

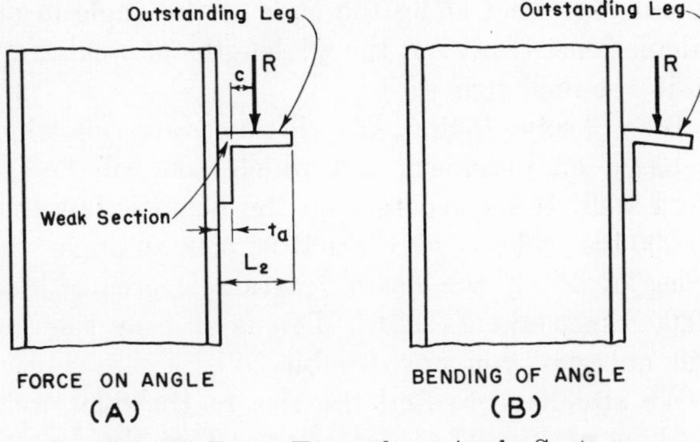

Fig. 45. Force Exerted on Angle Seat

2. We add 1″ to w_f to get

$$w_f + 1 = 6.53 + 1 = 7.53''$$

3. Then we increase this to the next larger inch which is 8″. $L = 8''$.

The next step is to find the thickness of the angle seat; the thickness is shown as t_a (the subscript *a* stands for angle.) in Fig. 45*A*. This figure shows the reaction R which the beam exerts on the angle. The beam is placed so its end is ½″ from the face of the column.

The force R bends the outstanding leg of the angle as shown in Fig. 45*B*. Looking at Fig. 45*A* you can see that the weak section of the angle (where it would fail) is where the outstanding leg joins the vertical leg. The outstanding leg of the angle acts as a beam and the moment arm of the force R is the distance of the force R from the weak section; this distance is shown as c in Fig. 45*A*, then the bending moment is

$$M = Rc$$

It is hard to estimate the distance c. However, a reasonable figure for beams of moderate size (from 8″ to 18″ in depth) would seem to be 1″. On this basis,

$$M = Rc = R \times 1 = R$$

The outstanding leg of the angle seat acts as a beam and has a rectangular cross section. Fig. 46

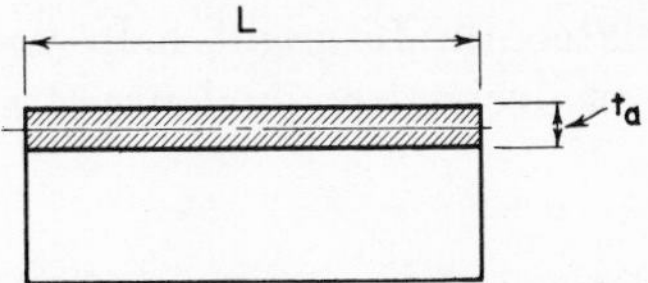

Fig. 46. Section through Outstanding Leg of Angle Seat

shows that the width of the rectangular beam is L (the length of the angle) and the depth is t_a (the thickness of the angle).

Remember the flexure formula which you studied in Chapter VI, and which you have used several times since. It is

$$M = \frac{SI}{c}$$

where M is bending moment, S is working stress in bending, I is moment of inertia and c is the distance from the neutral axis to the farthest point in the cross section. The moment of inertia of a rectangle is one-twelfth times the width, times the cube of the depth; this gives

$$I = \frac{1}{12} L t_a^3$$

for the rectangle in Fig. 46. The distance c is half the depth so $c = \frac{1}{2}t_a$. We had M as R, so we can write

$$M = \frac{SI}{c}$$

$$R = \frac{S \times \frac{1}{12} L t_a^3}{\frac{1}{2} t_a}$$

Now for an exercise in algebra. Suppose you see if you can work this out as

$$t_a^2 = \frac{6R}{SL}$$

which is correct. We could take the square root of this equation to get

$$t_a = \sqrt{\frac{6R}{SL}}$$

for the thickness of the angle. Here R is the beam reaction, S is the working stress in bending, and L is the length of the angle seat. (It is customary to use a high working stress in this type of problem.)

The answer for t_a will probably come out as something like 0.393″ and we will have to select a standard angle. These angles are made in thicknesses which go up by sixteenths of an inch, so we will take the next larger sixteenth. It might help you in this to have a table of decimal equivalents of sixteenths of an inch.

TABLE II. DECIMAL EQUIVALENTS OF SIXTEENTHS OF AN INCH

$\frac{1}{4} = \frac{4}{16} = 0.250$	$\frac{9}{16} = 0.5625$
$\frac{5}{16} = 0.3125$	$\frac{5}{8} = \frac{10}{16} = 0.625$
$\frac{3}{8} = \frac{6}{16} = 0.375$	$\frac{11}{16} = 0.6875$
$\frac{7}{16} = 0.4375$	$\frac{3}{4} = \frac{12}{16} = 0.750$
$\frac{1}{2} = \frac{8}{16} = 0.500$	

Illustrative Example 3. Find the thickness of the seat angle to carry an end reaction of 9,300 lbs. The length of the outstanding leg of the angle is 3″ and the length of the angle is 8″. Take a working stress in bending of 30,000 lbs. per sq. in.

Solution:

1. The reaction R is 9,300 lbs.
2. The working stress S is 30,000 lbs. per sq. in.
3. The length of the angle is $L = 8''$
4. Then, the thickness required is

$$t_a = \sqrt{\frac{6R}{SL}} = \sqrt{\frac{6 \times 9{,}300}{30{,}000 \times 8}} = \sqrt{0.233} = 0.482''$$

In Table II you can see that the next larger sixteenth is 0.5″ which is $\frac{1}{2}$″. So we take $t_a = \frac{1}{2}''$.

Now look at Fig. 47A and see how much we have done. We know how to find the length L of the angle seat, Fig. 47B, the length L_2 of the outstanding leg of the angle and the thickness t_a of the angle. Two items remain. We must find the length L_1 of the vertical leg of the angle seat and the size of the fillet weld along the ends of the angle. Fig. 47C shows a cross section of the fillet weld; here, t is the dimension.

We will not take account of the $\frac{1}{2}$″ lengths of weld at the top of the angle in Fig. 47B. We will only include the weld along the ends of the angle in our calculations. However, the $\frac{1}{2}$″ lengths of weld are to be in the final structure.

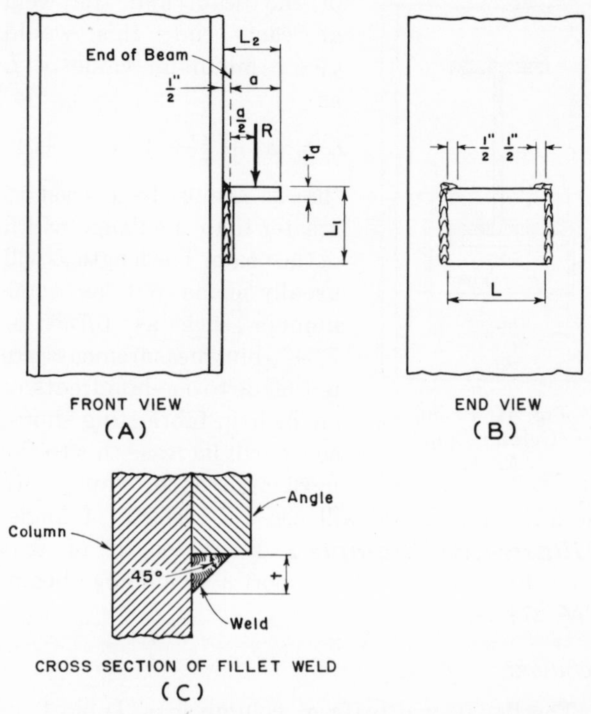

Fig. 47. Column, Angle Seat, and Fillet Weld

We will solve L_1 first. We will give you a rule which is based on judgment and which you will find to work well. If the reaction on the beam is less than 10,000 lbs., take L_1 as 4″; that is, pick an angle with a leg of 4″; if the beam reaction is greater than 10,000 lbs., take L_1 as 6″. This is an easy rule and will not give you any trouble.

We still have to find the size of the fillet weld. Looking at Fig. 47A, you can see that the force R is at some distance from the weld. (We could say that R is an eccentric load, as we did in Chapter XII.) The force will have a moment with respect to any point in the weld and will cause the weld to act similar to a beam.

The beam which rests on the angle seat in Fig. 47A is placed so its end is $\frac{1}{2}$″ from the face of the column. Then the beam is in contact with the angle over the length a (we saw this before). You can see that a is $\frac{1}{2}$″ less than L_2, so

$$a = L_2 - \tfrac{1}{2}$$

We can take the force R at the center of the length a and it is reasonable to take the moment arm of the force R with respect to the weld as $\frac{a}{2}$. Then the moment on the weld is

$$M = \frac{Ra}{2}$$

The force R in Fig. 47A is eccentric and, as we saw in Chapter XI, an eccentric load has two effects. First, is the effect of a vertical force on the centerline of the weld; second, there is the bending.

As we have been doing, we will continue to express the strength of a fillet weld as so many pounds per inch of length. We can find the effect of the vertical force on the weld by dividing the force R by two times the length L_1. (Because there are two welds, each of length L_1.) This will give the vertical force per inch of length of the weld. We will call it V and it will be

$$V = \frac{R}{2L_1}$$

Fig. 48A shows this force distributed over the length L_1.

The moment M causes a horizontal force at any point in the fillet weld, and the distribution is the same as the stress in a rectangular beam; that is,

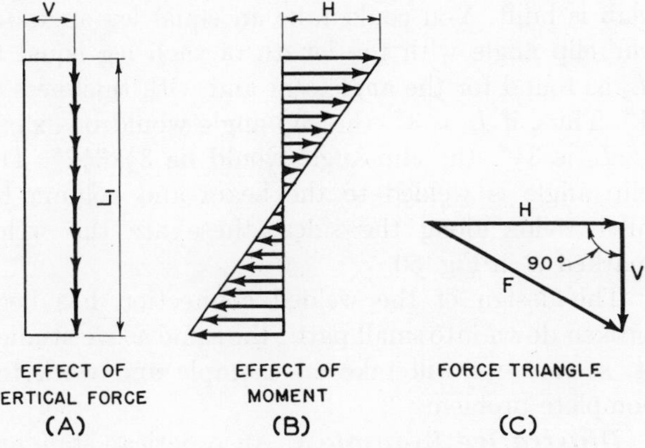

Fig. 48. Stresses in Weld

zero at the center, and maximum at the top and bottom, Fig. 48B. We will represent the maximum value by H, and give this formula for H

$$H = \frac{3M}{L_1^2}$$

where M is the moment and L_1 is the length of the vertical leg of the angle. If we take M as $\frac{Ra}{2}$, we get

$$H = \frac{3M}{L_1^2} = \frac{3\,\frac{Ra}{2}}{L_1^2} = \frac{3Ra}{2L_1^2}$$

At the top or bottom of the weld, we have a horizontal force H per unit length and a vertical force V per unit length. We could go back to Chapter I to recall force triangles which we used to find the resultant of two forces. The *resultant* is the single force which can replace two forces. We could use a force triangle to find the resultant of H and V. Fig. 48C shows how this is done. We draw a right triangle with the horizontal leg representing H and the vertical leg representing V. The hypotenuse of the triangle represents the single force F which can replace H and V; that is, F is the resultant of H and V.

The Pythagorean theorem gives

$$F = \sqrt{H^2 + V^2}$$

Then we can use

$$H = \frac{3Ra}{2L_1^2}; \quad \text{and} \quad V = \frac{R}{2L_1}$$

to get

$$F = \sqrt{\left(\frac{3Ra}{2L_1^2}\right)^2 + \left(\frac{R}{2L_1}\right)^2}$$

We could factor $\frac{R}{2}$ and L_1 from the right side of this equation to write it as

$$F = \frac{R}{2L_1}\sqrt{\left(\frac{3a}{L_1}\right)^2 + 1}$$

Here R is the reaction on the beam, L_1 is the length of the vertical leg of the angle seat and a is the length of bearing between the beam and angle seat. Now F is the force per inch of length on the fillet weld. We also had the force per inch of length as 8,000 t (remember?), so

$$F = 8{,}000\,t, \quad \text{or}$$

$$t = \frac{F}{8{,}000}$$

This gives us the thickness t required for the fillet weld. Increasing it to the next larger sixteenth of an inch, we get a standard size.

Illustrative Example 4. Find the length of the vertical leg and the size of the fillet weld for an angle seat which has an outstanding leg of 3″. The beam reaction is 8,700 lbs.

Solution:

Fig. 49 shows the angle seat.

1. The reaction R is 8,700 lbs. This is less than 10,000 lbs., so we will choose L_1 as 4″
2. The distance a is

$$a = L_2 - \tfrac{1}{2} = 3 - 0.5 = 2.5''$$

3. The force per unit length is

$$F = \frac{R}{2L_1}\sqrt{\left(\frac{3a}{L_1}\right)^2 + 1} = \frac{8{,}700}{2 \times 4}\sqrt{\left(\frac{3 \times 2.5}{4}\right)^2 + 1}$$

$$= 2{,}320 \text{ lbs. per in.}$$

4. The dimension t required for the fillet weld is

$$t = \frac{F}{8{,}000} = \frac{2{,}320}{8{,}000} = 0.289''$$

You could look in Table II (this chapter) to see that the next larger sixteenth of an inch is 0.3125″, which is $\frac{5}{16}''$. We will use a $\frac{5}{16}''$ fillet weld.

We have been calculating L_2 and L_1 (the lengths of the legs of the angle) separately; it might happen that we could not find an angle with the lengths we worked out. Standard angles are available in the following combinations of lengths of legs, among others,

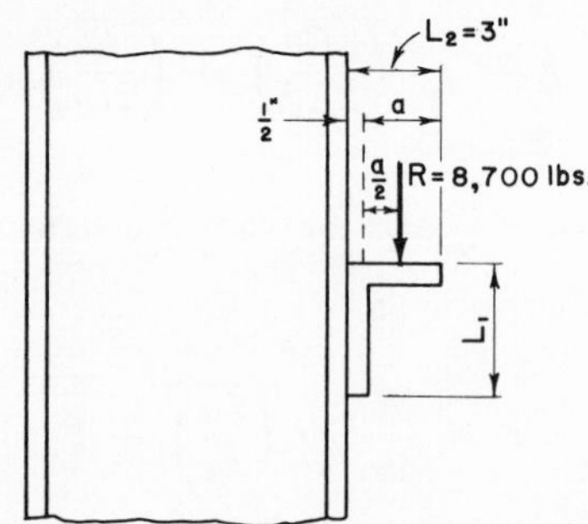

Fig. 49. Angle Seat for Example 4 (Art. 13-10)

4x3	6x3½
4x3½	6x4
4x4	

and in thicknesses from $\frac{1}{4}''$ to $\frac{3}{4}''$ by sixteenths. If you choose L_2 as $3\frac{1}{2}''$ or 4″, you can take either 4″ or 6″ for L_1. However, if you first take L_2 as 3″ and the reaction is so great that you want to take L_1 as 6″, you will have to raise L_2 to $3\frac{1}{2}''$ to get a standard angle.

Fig. 50 shows the complete beam and column connection. You know how to design the angle seat. The beam is fastened to the angle seat by means of fillet welds (marked A) along the sides of the lower flange of the beam. The clip angle, at the top of the beam, is not figured for strength. It is only there to keep the beam from moving sideways until the floor slab is built. You could take an equal leg angle for the clip angle with the length of each leg equal to L_2 as found for the angle seat and with thickness of $\frac{1}{4}''$. Thus, if L_2 is 3″, the clip angle would be 3x3x¼. If L_2 is $3\frac{1}{2}''$, the clip angle would be 3½x3½x¼. The clip angle is welded to the beam and column by fillet welds along the sides; these are the welds marked B in Fig. 50.

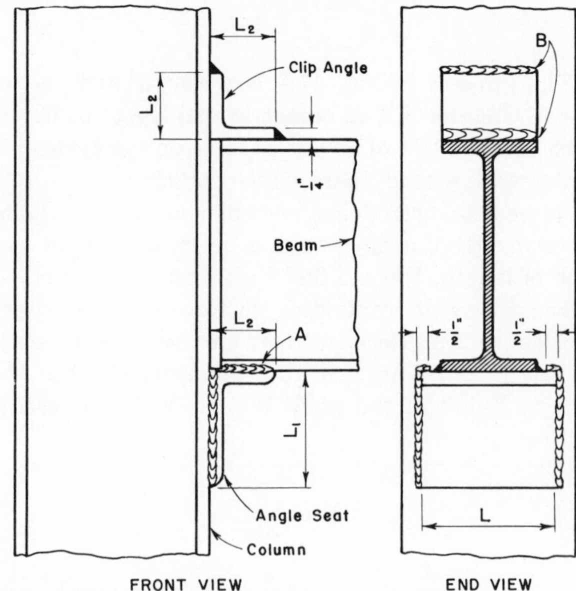

Fig. 50. Beam and Column Connection

The design of the welded connection has been broken down into small parts, the same as we studied it, so now we will take an example and work the complete problem.

Illustrative Example 5. An American standard beam, 12 **I** 35, is subjected to an end reaction of 13,900 lbs. Design a welded angle seat connection, using working stresses of 24,000 lbs. per sq. in. in bearing and 30,000 lbs. per sq. in. in bending of the angle seat.

Solution:

Fig. 51 shows the angle seat.

1. The length L_2 of the outstanding leg
   a) The reaction R is 13,900 lbs.

b) The web thickness of the beam is (from column 6 of Table II, in Chapter VII) $t_w = 0.428''$

c) The bearing stress S_b is 24,000 lbs. per sq. in.

d) The bearing length a needed is

$$a = \frac{R}{t_w S_b} = \frac{13{,}900}{0.428 \times 24{,}000} = 1.35''$$

e) We add $\frac{1}{2}''$ to a to get the length L_2 that is required,

$$L_2 = a + \tfrac{1}{2} = 1.35 + 0.5 = 1.85''$$

We do not want to use less than a 3″ angle, so we take $L_2 = 3''$.

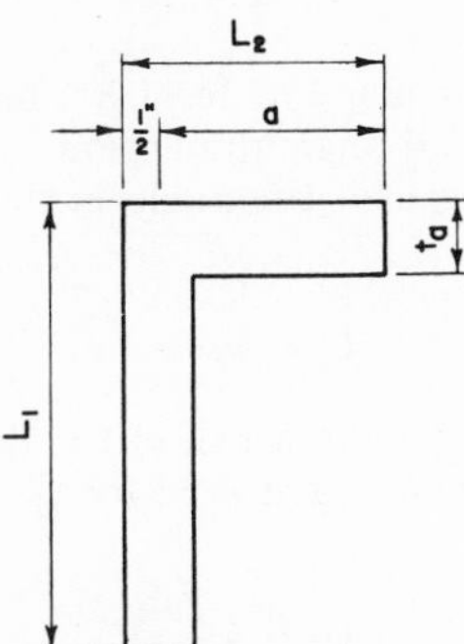

Fig. 51. Angle Seat for Example 5 (Art. 13-10)

2. Length of the angle
   a) The flange width of the beam is (from column 5 of Table II, in Chapter VII) $w_f = 5.08''$
   b) We add 1″ to w_f to get

$$5.08 + 1 = 6.08''$$

   c) Then we increase this to 7″, the next inch larger

$$L = 7''$$

3. The thickness of the seat angle
   a) The reaction R is 13,900 lbs.
   b) The working stress S is 30,000 lbs. per sq. in.
   c) The length L of the angle is 7″
   d) The thickness required is

$$t_a = \sqrt{\frac{6R}{SL}} = \sqrt{\frac{6 \times 13{,}900}{30{,}000 \times 7}} = \sqrt{0.398} = 0.631''$$

   We will raise this to 0.750″ which is $\frac{3}{4}$. $t_a = \frac{3}{4}''$ (see Table II, this chapter.)

4. The length L_1 of the vertical leg
   a) The reaction is greater than 10,000 lbs., so we will take L_1 as 6″
   b) To use a standard angle, raise L_2 to 4″
   c) The angle size is 6x4x$\frac{3}{4}$

5. The size of the fillet weld
   a) The reaction R is 13,900 lbs.
   b) The distance a is

$$a = L_2 - \tfrac{1}{2} = 4 - 0.5 = 3.5''$$

   c) The force per inch of length on the weld is

$$F = \frac{R}{2L_1}\sqrt{\left(\frac{3a}{L_1}\right)^2 + 1} = \frac{13{,}900}{2 \times 6}\sqrt{\left(\frac{3 \times 3.5}{6}\right)^2 + 1}$$

$$= 2{,}340 \text{ lbs. per in.}$$

   d) The required dimension t of the weld is

$$t = \frac{F}{8{,}000} = \frac{2{,}340}{8{,}000} = 0.292''$$

The next larger sixteenth is 0.3125″, which is $\frac{5}{16}''$. We will use $\frac{5}{16}''$ fillet welds.

Fig. 52 shows a welded connection of a beam to a girder.

The angle seat is designed in the same way for this as for a connection of a beam to a column.

Practice Problems (Art. 13-10). Now you can design welded angle seats. Take the data in the following problems given in table form.

Problem	Reaction in Lbs.	Size of Beam	Working Stresses	
			Bearing	Bending
1	6,200	6 I 12.5	30,000	32,000
2	11,400	12 WF 28	24,000	30,000
3	4,800	6 WF 20	24,000	28,000
4	17,500	12 WF 45	24,000	33,000

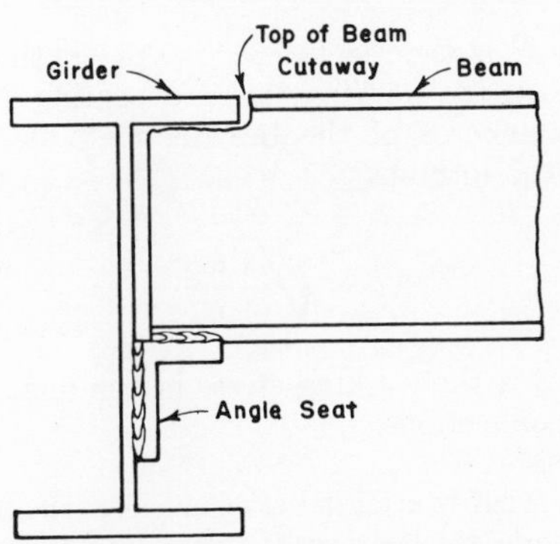

Fig. 52. Angle Seat for Welded Connection of Beam to Girder

SUMMARY OF CHAPTER XIII

Study the following summary carefully.

1. The fastening at the end of a beam must transfer the reactions from the support to the beam.
2. Connections of steel beams to steel columns or girders are usually riveted or welded, sometimes bolted.

3. Rivet connections.
   a) Rivets.
      (1) A rivet is a *round rod* with a head on one end.
      (2) A rivet is stressed in shear on its cross section. If there is shear on only one plane, the rivet is in single shear and the area is $\pi d^2/4$. If there is shear on two planes, the rivet is in double shear and the area is $2\pi d^2/4$.
      (3) A rivet is stressed in bearing on the surface between the rivet and the member it goes through. The area is equal to dt, where t is the thickness of the member.
      (4) The strength of one rivet in shear is the force required to develop working stress in shear.
      (5) The strength of one rivet in bearing is the force required to develop working stress in bearing.
      (6) The smaller of the strengths in shear and bearing is called the *strength of the rivet*.
   b) Connection angles.
      (1) Connection angles which fasten beams to columns or girders are standard. They are $4 \text{x} 3\frac{1}{2} \text{x} \frac{3}{8}$ when there are four or less rivets in the one vertical row, and $4 \text{x} 3\frac{1}{2} \text{x} \frac{7}{16}$ when there are more than four rivets in the one vertical row.
      (2) The number of rivets needed in the web legs of the connection angles is equal to the reaction R divided by the strength of one rivet.
      (3) There are *always* at least *two* rivets in the web legs of the angles.
      (4) The rivet spacing in the outstanding legs of the angles is the same as in the web legs.

4. Beam bearing plates.
   a) A steel bearing plate is used to distribute the reaction over a large area when a steel beam is supported on a masonry wall.
   b) The length of bearing C is determined by the space available.
   c) The width B of the plate is given by the formula,

$$B = \frac{R}{CS_b}$$

   where R is the reaction, C is the length of bearing, and S_b is the working stress in bearing.
   d) The thickness of the bearing plate is determined from the formula,

$$t = \sqrt{\frac{3}{4}\frac{RB}{Cs}}$$

   Here S is the working stress in bending.

5. Welded connections.
   a) Welds.
      (1) A weld is a joint between pieces of metal and is made by heating the metal to fusion, so that the pieces join as they solidify. Most structural welds are arc welds.
      (2) A fillet weld is a weld which is made in a corner between two pieces. The nominal shape of its cross section is a 45° right triangle.
      (3) The strength of a one-inch length of fillet weld is 8,000 t, where t is the length of the leg of the 45° right triangle.
   b) Angle seats.
      (1) An angle seat is a short length of steel angle which is welded to a column or girder. The end of the beam rests on the seat and is welded to the seat.
      (2) The length of bearing required for the beam on the angle seat is

$$a = \frac{R}{t_w S_b}$$

      Here, R is the reaction, t_w is the thickness of the web of the beam, and S_b is the working stress in bearing.
      (3) The length required for the outstanding leg of the angle seat is

$$L_2 = a + \tfrac{1}{2}$$

      but L_2 is made at least 3″, and, in any case, is a standard angle dimension.
      (4) The length of the angle is the next whole inch from

$$L = w_f + 1$$

      where w_f is the width of the flange of the beam.
      (5) The thickness required for the angle seat is

$$t_a = \sqrt{\frac{6R}{SL}}$$

      where S is the working stress in bending and is usually relatively high for this use. You must increase the calculated value of t_a to the next larger sixteenth of an inch. Table II gives decimal equivalents of sixteenths.
      (6) The length L_1 of the vertical leg of the angle seat can be taken as 4″ when the reaction is less than 10,000 lbs., and as 6″ when the reaction is greater than 10,000 lbs.
      (7) The dimensions L_1 and L_2 must be checked to be sure that they fit some standard size of angle.
      (8) The maximum force per inch of length on the fillet weld is

$$F = \frac{R}{2L_1}\sqrt{\left(\frac{3a}{L_1}\right)^2 + 1}$$

      (9) The thickness t required for the fillet welds is

$$t = \frac{F}{8{,}000}$$

      and the calculated result is increased to the next larger sixteenth of an inch.
   c) Beam welds. The beam is fastened to the angle seat by means of fillet welds along the sides of the lower flange of the beam.
   d) Clip angles.
      (1) A clip angle is welded to the column and the top of the beam by fillet welds along the sides of the angle.

(2) Clip angles are not designed for strength. They can be ¼″ thick and can have the lengths of the legs the same as L_2.

Review Questions

Answer all of the following questions.

1. What is the purpose of a beam connection?
2. What is a *rivet?*
3. How are rivets stressed?
4. What is *single shear?*
5. What is the *area of a rivet in single shear?*
6. What is *double shear?*
7. What is the *area of a rivet in double shear?*
8. What is *bearing stress?*
9. What is the *area of a rivet in bearing?*
10. What is the *strength of a rivet?*
11. What sizes of angles are used for riveted beam connections?
12. How do you determine the number of rivets needed to fasten a beam to a column?
13. What is a *beam bearing plate?*
14. Why is a bearing plate used?
15. What is *length of bearing* for a bearing plate?
16. What is the *width of a bearing plate?*
17. How do you find the thickness required for a bearing plate?
18. What is a *weld?*
19. What is a *fillet weld?*
20. What is the shape of the cross section of a fillet weld?
21. What is the *throat of a fillet weld?*
22. How do you state the size of a fillet weld?
23. How is the strength of a fillet weld given?
24. What is an *angle seat?*
25. What is the *length of bearing for an angle seat?*
26. What is the distance between the column and the end of the beam in a welded beam connection?
27. How do you find the length L_2 of the outstanding leg of the angle seat?
28. How do you find the thickness t_a of the angle seat?
29. How do you find the length L of the angle seat?
30. How do you determine the length of the vertical leg of the angle seat?
31. How do you find the size of the fillet weld between the angle seat and the column?
32. How is the beam fastened to the angle seat?
33. What is a *clip angle?*
34. What is the purpose of the clip angle?
35. Did you learn anything from this book?

Review Problems

Solve the following problems. Show each answer by a sketch.

1. Determine the number of rivets and select the connection angles for a wide-flange beam, 8 WF 27, with a reaction of 12,600 lbs. The rivet diameter is ¾″, and the working stresses are 10,000 lbs. per sq. in. in shear and 24,000 lbs. per sq. in. in bearing.
2. Find the number of rivets and choose the connection angles for an American standard beam, 15 **I** 50, with a reaction of 33,300 lbs. The rivets are ⅞″ in diameter, and the working stresses are 12,000 lbs. per sq. in. in shear and 30,000 lbs. per sq. in. in bearing.
3. Design a beam bearing plate for a steel beam which has a reaction of 21,600 lbs. The length of bearing is 6″; the working stress in bearing against the support is 500 lbs. per sq. in. and the working stress in bending for the plate is 16,000 lbs. per sq. in.
4. Design a beam bearing plate for a steel beam which has a reaction of 8,200 lbs. The length of bearing is 3″; the working stress in bearing against the support is 650 lbs. per sq. in. and the working stress for the plate in bending is 18,000 lbs. per sq. in.
5. Design an angle seat connection for a wide-flange beam, 10 WF 23, which has a reaction of 11,300 lbs. The working stress in bearing is 24,000 lbs. per sq. in. and the working stress in bending is 30,000 lbs. per sq. in.
6. Design an angle seat connection for an American standard beam, 8 **I** 18.4, which has a reaction of 6,400 lbs. Take the working stresses as 27,000 lbs. per sq. in. in bearing and 32,000 lbs. per sq. in. in bending.

ANSWERS TO PROBLEMS

Remember: Answers obtained on a slide rule give the accuracy required in these calculations. Don't consider it an error if the third digit, and in some cases the second digit, is at variance with your answer.

Page 5 (Art. 1-5)

1. F_x = 3,400 lbs.; F_y = 5,880 lbs. **2.** F_x = −261 lbs.; F_y = 290 lbs. **3.** F_x = −20,500 lbs.; F_y = 6,870 lbs. **4.** F_x = 952 lbs.; F_y = −1,343 lbs. **5.** F_x = 1,600 lbs.; F_y = −2,770 lbs. **6.** F_x = 0; F_y = 5,400 lbs. **7.** F_x = −2,080 lbs.; F_y = −1,200 lbs. **8.** F_x = − 1,125 lbs.; F_y = 4,210 lbs.

Page 6 (Art. 1-6)

1. 3,600 lb. ft. **2.** −10,500 lb. ft. **3.** −33,600 lb. ft. **4.** 38,500 lb. ft. **5.** −7,200 lb. ft. **6.** 25,200 lb. ft.

Page 8 (Art. 1-7)

1. 9,960 lb. ft.; **2.** −4,720 lb. ft. **3.** 2,690 lb. ft.; **4.** −8,320 lb. ft. **5.** −2,540 lb. ft.; **6.** 2,540 lb. ft. **7.** −7,200 lb. ft.; **8.** −12,000 lb. ft.

Page 9 (Review Problems)

1. F_x = 5,750 lbs.; F_y = 15,800 lbs. **2.** F_x = 797 lbs.; F_y = −537 lbs. **3.** 32,000 lb. ft. **4.** 66,000 lb. ft. **5.** −88,000 lb. ft. **6.** −80,300 lb. ft. **7.** −5,150 lb. ft. **8.** 76,500 lb. ft.

Page 14 (Art. 2-3)

1. R_1 = 3,400 lbs.; R_2 = 3,800 lbs. **2.** R_1 = 1,960 lbs.; R_2 = 440 lbs. **3.** R_1 = 6,400 lbs.; R_2 = 3,200 lbs. **4.** R_1 = 1,500 lbs.; R_2 = 4,500 lbs. **5.** R_1 = 1,930 lbs.; R_2 = 2,070 lbs. **6.** R_1 = 675 lbs.; R_2 = 525 lbs. **7.** R_1 = 4,460 lbs.; R_2 = 3,340 lbs. **8.** R_1 = 4,300 lbs.; R_2 = 3,700 lbs.

Page 17 (Art. 2-4)

1. R_1 = 1,850 lbs.; R_2 = 1,850 lbs. **2.** F_1 = 3,000 lbs.; F_2 = 3,000 lbs. **3.** R_1 = 1,634 lbs.; R_2=3,166 lbs. **4.** R_1 = 733 lbs.; R_2 = 518 lbs. **5.** No. **6.** R_1 = 954 lbs.; R_2 = 1,240 lbs.

Page 18 (Review Problems)

1. R_1 = 1,680 lbs.; R_{2x} = 1,450 lbs.; R_{2y} = 560 lbs. **2.** 424 lbs. **3.** A, 141 lbs.; B, 115 lbs. **4.** A, 2,240 lbs.; B, 2,160 lbs.

Page 22 (Art. 3-2)

1. $\bar{x}$ = −7″; $\bar{y}$ = 6.5″. **2.** $\bar{x}$ = 6.67″; $\bar{y}$ = 7″. **3.** $\bar{x}$ = −4.5″; $\bar{y}$ = −5″. **4.** $\bar{x}$ = 6.5″; $\bar{y}$ = −4″. **5.** $\bar{x}$ = 1″; $\bar{y}$ = 4″. **6.** $\bar{x}$ = −0.5″; $\bar{y}$ = −4.5″. **7.** $\bar{x}$ = −5.33″; $\bar{y}$ = 7.33″. **8.** $\bar{x}$ = 7.67″; $\bar{y}$ = −1″. **9.** $\bar{x}$ = −4.5″; $\bar{y}$ = −3″.

Page 23 (Art. 3-3)

1. M_x = 22.5 in.³; M_y = −13.8 in.³ **2.** M_x = 64 in.³; M_y = −112 in.³ **3.** M_x = −34 in.³; M_y = −42 in.³ **4.** M_x = −62.8 in.³; M_y = 25.1 in.³ **5.** M_x = −8.3 in.³; M_y = 33.3 in.³ **6.** M_x = 76.7 in.³; M_y = 6.7 in.³ **7.** M_x = 0; M_y = 311 in.³ **8.** M_x = −42 in.³; M_y = −28 in.³

Page 26 (Art. 3-4)

1. M_x = 39.5 in.³; M_y = 38.5 in.³ **2.** M_x = 112 in.³; M_y = 128 in.³ **3.** M_x = 284 in.³; M_y = 0. **4.** M_x = 32.5 in.³; M_y = 38.5 in.³ **5.** M_x = 0; M_y = 36 in.³ **6.** M_x = 371 in.³; M_y = 551 in.³ **7.** M_x = 105 in.³; M_y = 0. **8.** M_x = 0; M_y = 29 in.³

Page 27 (Art. 3-5)

1. $\bar{x}$ = 0.99″; $\bar{y}$ = 1.99″. **2.** $\bar{x}$ = 0; $\bar{y}$ = 2.64″ **3.** $\bar{x}$ = 0.932″; $\bar{y}$ = 0. **4.** $\bar{x}$ = 1.69″; $\bar{y}$ = 2.72″. **5.** $\bar{x}$ = 0; $\bar{y}$ = 3.13″. **6.** $\bar{x}$ = 0; $\bar{y}$ = 1.22″. **7.** $\bar{x}$ = 0; $\bar{y}$ = 2.25″. **8.** $\bar{x}$ = 0; $\bar{y}$ = 5.55″.

Page 29 (Review Problems)

1. $\bar{x}$ = 2.75″; $\bar{y}$ = 2.04″. **2.** $\bar{x}$ = 0; $\bar{y}$ = 2.33″. **3.** $\bar{x}$ = 0; $\bar{y}$ = 8.53″. **4.** $\bar{x}$ = 3.77″; $\bar{y}$ = 2.77″. **5.** $\bar{x}$ = 0.72″; $\bar{y}$ = 2.18″.

Page 32 (Art. 4-2)

1. 63.6 in.⁴ **2.** 667 in.⁴; 426 in.⁴ **3.** 8 in.⁴; 288 in.⁴ **4.** 8.88 in.⁴; 13.9 in.⁴ **5.** I_x = 9.5 in.⁴; I_y = 6.67 in.⁴ **6.** I_x = 25 in.⁴; I_y = 5.77 in.⁴ **7.** I_x = 0.563 in.⁴; I_y = 9.0 in.⁴ **8.** I_x = I_y = 8.67 in.⁴

Page 34 (Art. 4-3)

1. I_x=48.14 in.⁴; I_y = 32.3 in.⁴ **2.** I_x = 82.7 in.⁴; I_y = 130.7 in.⁴ **3.** I_x = 35.6 in.⁴; I_y = 45.3 in.⁴ **4.** I_x = 7.86 in.⁴; I_y = 1.57 in.⁴ **5.** I_x = 18 in.⁴; I_y = 72 in.⁴ **6.** I_x = 3.80 in.⁴; I_y = 11.40 in.⁴

Page 37 (Art. 4-4)

1. I_x = 428 in.⁴; I_y = 76 in.⁴ **2.** I_x = 329 in.⁴; I_y = 137.3 in.⁴ **3.** I_x=203 in.⁴; I_y=634 in.⁴ **4.** I_x=556 in.⁴; I_y=1,700 in.⁴ **5.** I_x=I_y=32.9 in.⁴ **6.** I_x=692 in.⁴; I_y=82.71 in.⁴

Page 38 (Review Problems)

1. I_x = 20 in.⁴; I_y = 56 in.⁴ **2.** I_x = 419 in.⁴; I_y = 459 in.⁴ **3.** I_x = 93.5 in.⁴; I_y = 4.28 in.⁴ **4.** I_x = 95.9 in.⁴; I_y = 315 in.⁴

Page 40 (Art. 5-1)

1. 1,390 #/in.² **2.** 7,523 #/in.² **3.** 10,736 #/in.² **4.** 25,100 lbs. **5.** 70,500 lbs. **6.** 19,200 lbs.

Page 42 (Art. 5-2)

1. 14,700 #/in.² **2.** 15,100 #/in.² **3.** 12,400 #/in.² **4.** 9,100 lbs. **5.** 44,900 lbs. **6.** 6,150 lbs.

Page 44 (Art. 5-3)

1. 855 #/in.² **2.** 6,270 #/in.² **3.** 11,200 #/in.² **4.** 11,800 lbs. **5.** 24,000 lbs. **6.** 2,280 lbs.

Page 45 (Arts. 5-4 and 5-5)

1. 0.00152. **2.** 0.00127. **3.** 0.209″. **4.** 0.000481. **5.** 0.000778.

Page 46 (Arts. 5-6 and 5-7)

1. 0.0603″. **2.** 0.0798″. **3.** 0.0444″. **4.** 0.0978″. **5.** 0.0478″.

Page 49 (Art. 5-10)

1. 21.4″. **2.** 6.88″. **3.** 0.923″. **4.** 1.23″. **5.** 15.4″. **6.** 8.8″ x 8.8″.

Page 50 (Review Problems)

1. 20,400 #/in.² **2.** 11,780 #/in.² **3.** 0.0853″. **4.** 0.0719″. **5.** 117,500 lbs. **6.** 14,430 lbs. **7.** (b). **8.** 3.

Page 53 (Art. 6-1)

1. R_1 = 6,450 lbs.; R_2 = 5,550 lbs. **2.** R_1 = 8,670 lbs.; R_2 = 4,330 lbs. **3.** R_1 = 2,340 lbs.; R_2 = 2,160 lbs. **4.** R_1 = 9,170 lbs.; R_2 = 9,430 lbs.

Page 55 (Art. 6-2)

1. $\bar{x}$ = 0; $\bar{y}$ = 2.71″. **2.** $\bar{x}$ = 0; $\bar{y}$ = 4.47″. **3.** $\bar{x}$ = 1.40″; $\bar{y}$ = 3.00″. **4.** $\bar{x}$ = 0; $\bar{y}$ = 1.73″.

Page 56 (Art. 6-3)

1. I_x = 613 in.⁴; I_y = 191 in.⁴ **2.** I_x = 136 in.⁴; I_y = 40 in.⁴ **3.** I_x=94.7 in⁴; I_y=50.7 in.⁴ **4.** I_x=192.3 in.⁴; I_y=746.8 in.⁴

Page 58 (Art. 6-4)

1. 3,500 lbs.; 1,400 lbs.; −2,800 lbs. **2.** 1,500 lbs.; 300 lbs.; −600 lbs.; −1,200 lbs. **3.** 6,400 lbs.; −5,200 lbs.; 4,000 lbs. **4.** 1,800 lbs.; −200 lbs.; −2,700 lbs.

Page 59 (Art. 6-5)

1. Fig. 33.

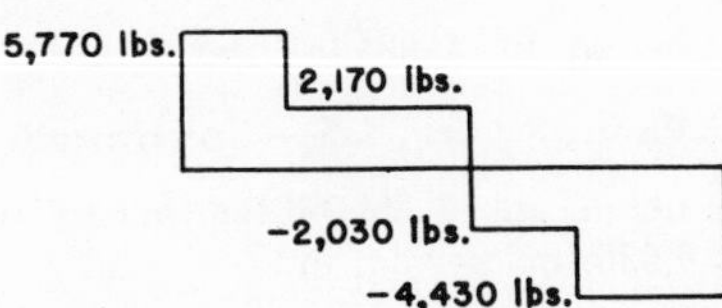

2. Fig. 34.

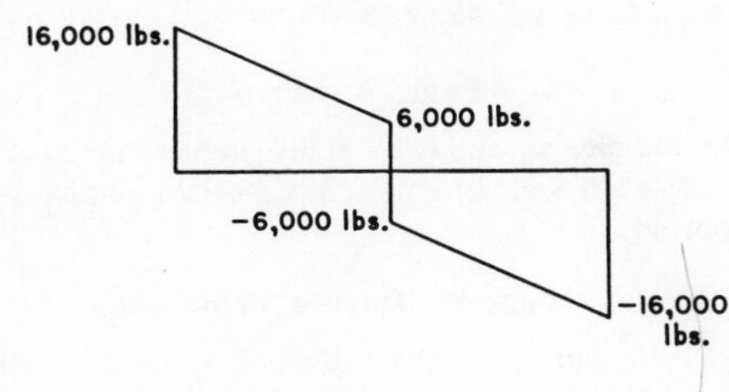

3. Fig. 35.

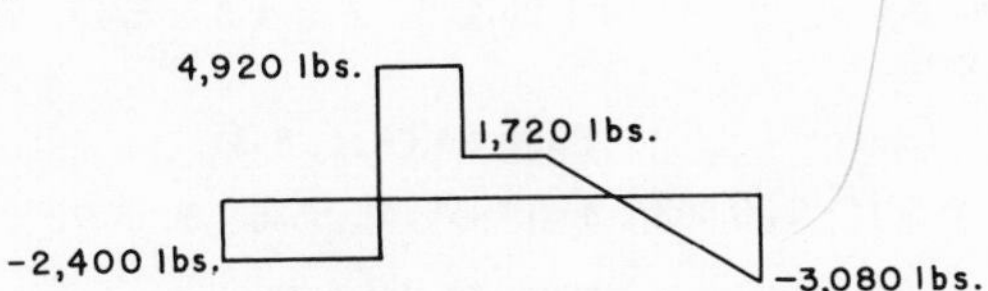

4. Fig. 36.

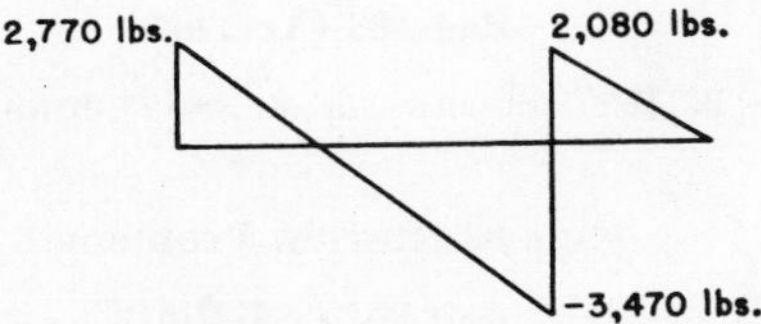

Page 61 (Art. 6-6)

1. 20,800 lb. ft.; 33,600 lb. ft.; 27,200 lb. ft. **2.** −6,400 lb. ft.; 2,700 lb. ft.; 11,800 lb. ft. **3.** 6,000 lb. ft.; 9,600 lb. ft.; 10,500 lb. ft. **4.** 32,500 lb. ft.; 35,400 lb. ft.; 34,500 lb. ft.

Page 63 (Art. 6-7)

1. Fig. 48.

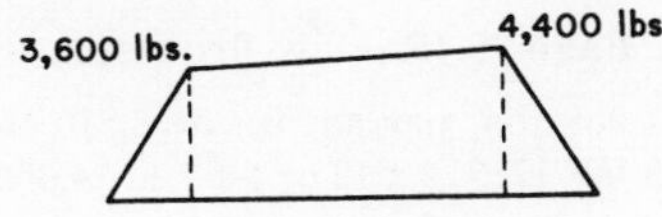

2. Fig. 49.

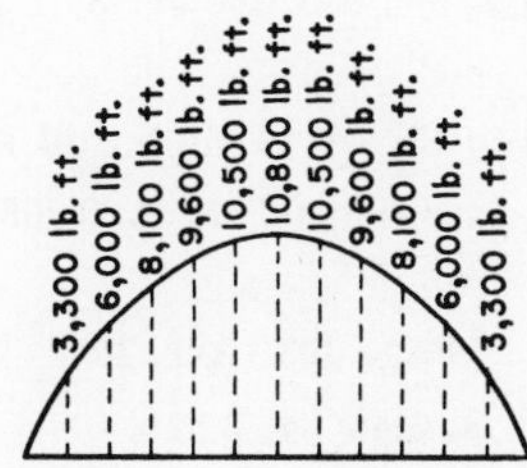

3. Fig. 50.

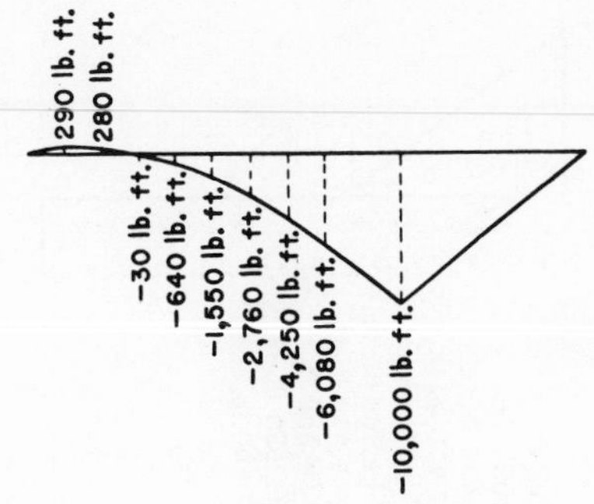

4. Fig. 51.

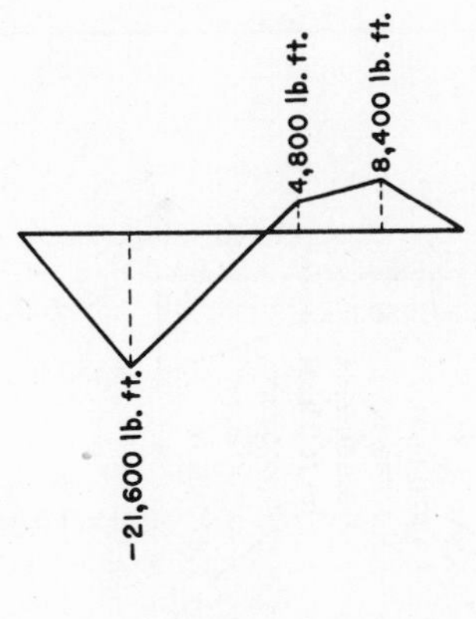

Page 65 (Art. 6-8)

1. 20,000 lb. ft. **2.** 10,513 lb. ft.; **3.** 23,600 lb. ft.; **4.** 9,500 lb. ft.

Page 68 (Art. 6-9)

1. 9,320 #/in.^{2} **2.** 25,200 #/in.^{2} **3.** 2,030 #/in.^{2} **4.** 1,980 #/in.^{2} **5.** 778 #/in.^{2} **6.** 900 #/in.^{2}

Page 69 (Art. 6-9)—*Continued*

7. 2,920 #/in.^{2} **8.** 1,473 #/in.^{2}

Page 70 (Art. 6-10)

1. 113 #/in.^{2} **2.** 116 #/in.^{2} **3.** 128 #/in.^{2} **4.** 150 #/in.^{2}

Page 71 (Review Problems)

1. Fig. 77.

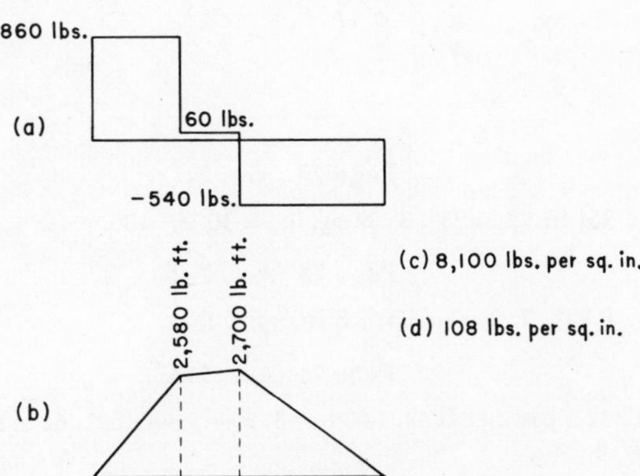

2. Fig. 78.

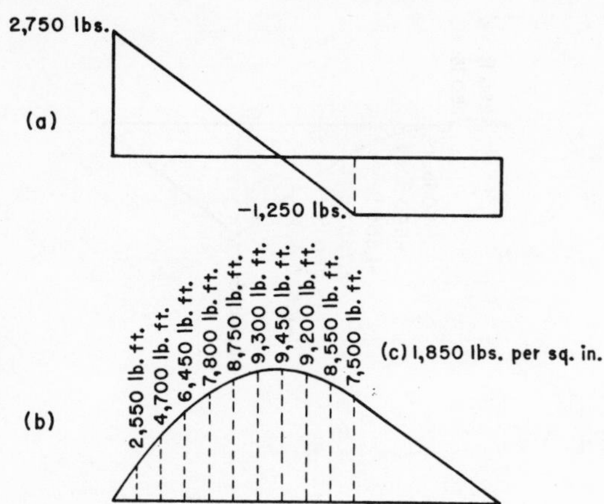

3. Fig. 79.

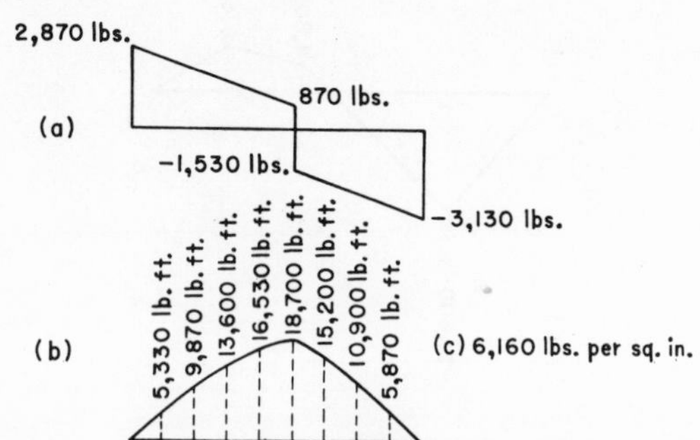

4. Fig. 80.

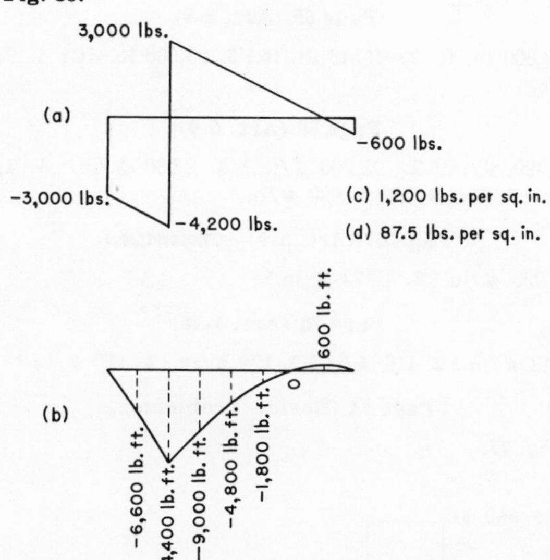

Page 73 (**Art. 7-1**)

1. 351 in.^{4} **2.** 5.25″. **3.** 20 sq. in. **4.** 10 WF 100.

Page 73 (**Art. 7-2**)

1. 6.39″. **2.** 269 in.^{4} **3.** 7.3 in.^{3}; 8 I 18.4.

Page 75 (**Art. 7-3**)

1. 17.1 lbs. per ft. **2.** 1.50 in.^{4} **3.** $\bar{x} = \bar{y} = 1.52''$. **4.** ∠3½ x 3½ x 9/16.

Page 75 (**Art. 7-3**)—***Continued***

1. 3.98 sq. in. **2.** 1.40 in.^{4} **3.** 4.20 in.^{3} **4.** ∠8 x 4 x 7/8.

Page 76 (**Art. 7-4**)

1. 9½ x 13½. **2.** 12.19 sq. in. **3.** 459 in.^{4} **4.** 47.8 in.^{3} **5.** 4 x 10. **6.** 6 x 8.

Page 77 (**Art. 7-5**)

1. 21,000 lbs. per sq. in. **2.** 884 lbs. per sq. in.

Page 78 (**Art. 7-5**)—***Continued***

3. 18,000 lbs. per sq. in. **4.** 22,500 lbs. per sq. in. **5.** 900 lbs. per sq. in. **6.** 9,930 lbs. per sq. in.

Page 79 (**Art. 7-6**)

1. 2 x 12. **2.** 16 WF 40. **3.** 12 I 35. **4.** 10 x 14 or 8 x 16. **5.** 12 I 40.8. **6.** 12 WF 45 or 16 WF 40.

Page 80 (**Art. 7-7**)

1. 113 lbs. per sq. in. **2.** 1,790 lbs. per sq. in. **3.** 124 lbs. per sq. in. **4.** 2,196 lbs. per sq. in. **5.** 1,480 lbs. per sq. in. **6.** 4,657 lbs. per sq. in.

Page 81 (Review Problems)

1. 1,235 lbs. per sq. in.; 38.7 lbs. per sq. in. **2.** 25,700 lbs. per sq. in.; 4,570 lbs. per sq. in. **3.** 15,000 lbs. per sq. in.; 2,840 lbs. per sq. in. **4.** 10 I 25.4. **5.** ∠ 3 x 3 x 5/16. **6.** 4 x 12 or 6 x 10.

Page 83 (**Art. 8-3**)

1. 0.561″. **2.** 0.303″. **3.** 0.789″. **4.** 0.536″. **5.** 0.272″.

Page 86 (**Art. 8-4**)

1. 0.122″; 0.163″. **2.** 0.827″; 0.234. **3.** 0.231″; 0.150″. **4.** 0.0336″; 0.0931″.

Page 88 (**Art. 8-5**)

1. 0.229″. **2.** .1527″ downward. **3.** .0617″ upward. **4.** 0.335″. **5.** 0.767″.

Page 88 (Review Problems)

1. 0.0627″. **2.** 0.167″. **3.** 0.9615″. **4.** 0.512″.

Page 93 (**Art. 9-2**)

1. 10,100 lbs. per sq. in. **2.** 948 lbs. per sq. in. **3.** 10 WF 23 or 8 WF 27. **4.** 2 x 8. **5.** 12 I 35. **6.** 6 I 12.5. **7.** 14,700 lbs. per sq. in.

Page 95 (**Art. 9-3**)

1. 18,900 lbs. per sq. in. **2.** 6 x 8 or 4 x 10. **3.** 12 WF 28. **4.** 15 I 50. **5.** 1,034 lbs. per sq. in.

Page 96 (Review Problems)

1. 7 I 15.3. **2.** 908 lbs. per sq. in. **3.** 5,210 lbs. per sq. in. **4.** 6 WF 20 or 8 WF 17. **5.** 2 x 12 or 4 x 8. **6.** 14,000 lbs. per sq. in.

Page 100 (**Art. 10-4**)

1. 1,860 lbs. ft. **2.** −1,630 lbs. ft. **3.** 1,330 lbs. ft. **4.** 684 lbs. ft.

Page 102 (**Arts. 10-5 and 10-6**)

1. 0.402; 0.866. **2.** 0.400; 0.867. **3.** 0.405; 0.865. **4.** 0.428; 0.857.

Page 103 (**Art. 10-7**)

1. 4.04″. **2.** 3.90″. **3.** 3.48″. **4.** 3.52″.

Page 104 (Art. 10-8)

1. 3″. **2.** 3.5″. **3.** 4.5″. **4.** 3.5″.

Page 105 (Art. 10-9)

1. *a.* 0.229 sq. in.; *b.* 0.367 sq. in.; *c.* 0.306 sq. in. **2.** *a.* 0.187 sq. in.; *b.* 0.299 sq. in.; *c.* 0.249 sq. in. **3.** *a.* 0.255 sq. in.; *b.* 0.408 sq. in.; *c.* 0.340 sq. in. **4.** *a.* 0.305 sq. in.; *b.* 0.487 sq. in.; *c.* 0.406 sq. in.

Page 106 (Art. 10-10)

1. ⅜″ round at 5″ or ½″ round at 9½″. **2.** ½″ round at 6″, ⅝″ round at 9½″ or ½″ square at 8″. **3.** ½″ round at 6½″ or ½″ square at 8½″. **4.** ⅜″ round at 4½″ or ½″ round at 8½″. **5.** ½″ round at 5″, ½″ square at 6½″ or ⅝″ round at 8″. **6.** ⅜″ round at 4″, ½″ round at 7½″ or ½″ sq. at 9½″.

Page 107 (Art. 10-10)—*Continued*

1. ½″ round; 6″; 7½″; 10″. **2.** 3/8″ round; 4½″; 5½″; 7½″. **3.** ½″ round; 5½″; 7″; 9″. **4.** 3/8″ round; 4″; 4½″; 6½″. **5.** 3/8″ round; 5½″; 6½″; 8½″.

Pages 108–109 (Art. 10-11)

Problem	*Total Depth*	*Rod Size*	*Spacings*
1.	3.5″	½″ round	7″; 8″; 10″
2.	3.5″	½″ round	6″; 7½″; 10″
3.	5″	½″ round	4½″; 5½″; 7½″
4.	3″	3/8″ round	4½″; 5½″; 7½″

Page 110 (Review Problems)

Problem	*Total Depth*	*Rod Size*	*Spacings*
1.	3.5″	3/8″ round	4½″; 5½″; 7½″
2.	3.5″	½″ round	6″; 7½″; 10″
3.	2.5″	3/8″ round	6½″; 8″; 10″
4.	5.5″	½″ round	4½″; 5½″; 7″

Page 113 (Art. 11-3)

1. 14,050 lbs. per sq. in. **2.** 15,650 lbs. per sq. in. **3.** 9,600 lbs. per sq. in. **4.** 3,330 lbs. per sq. in.

Page 114 (Art. 11-4)

1. 13,500 lbs. per sq. in. **2.** 18,900 lbs. per sq. in. **3.** 18,000 lbs. per sq. in. **4.** 3,110 lbs. per sq. in.

Page 116 (Art. 11-5)

1. 21,100 lbs. per sq. in. tension. **2.** 1,136 lbs. per sq. in. compression. **3.** 13,830 lbs. per sq. in. tension. **4.** 1,077 lbs. per sq. in. compression. **5.** 16,600 lbs. per sq. in. compression. **6.** 3,450 lbs. per sq. in. tension.

Page 118 (Art. 11-6)

1. 17,934 lbs. per sq. in. tension. **2.** 9,974 lbs. per sq. in. compression. **3.** 2,130 lbs. per sq. in. compression. **4.** 12,360 lbs. per sq. in. tension. **5.** 13,530 lbs. per sq. in. compression.

Page 120 (Review Problems)

1. 1,790 lbs. per sq. in. compression. **2.** 9,460 lbs. per sq. in. tension. **3.** 1,186 lbs. per sq. in. compression. **4.** 7,270 lbs. per sq. in. compression.

Page 123 (Art. 12-1)

1. r_x = 1.16″; r_y = 1.73″. **2.** r_x = 2.75″; r_y = 1.05″. **3.** r_x = 3.27″; r_y = 2.66″. **4.** r_x = 4.61″; r_y = 2.65″. **5.** 0.79″. **6.** 0.85″.

Page 124 (Art. 12-2)

1. 126. **2.** 153. **3.** 81.5. **4.** 12.3. **5.** 128. **6.** 108.

Page 126 (Art. 12-4)

1. 28,800 lbs. **2.** 96,000 lbs. **3.** 70,400 lbs. **4.** 212,000 lbs.

Page 127 (Art. 12-5)

1. 86,000 lbs. **2.** 47,000 lbs. **3.** 339,000 lbs. **4.** 18,500 lbs. **5.** 269,000 lbs. **6.** 106,000 lbs.

Page 128 (Art. 12-6)

1. 181,000 lbs. **2.** 33,500 lbs. **3.** 60,700 lbs. **4.** 40,700 lbs. **5.** 79,200 lbs. **6.** 118,000 lbs.

Page 129 (Art. 12-7)

1. 27,400 lbs. **2.** 96,800 lbs. **3.** 36,700 lbs. **4.** 54,200 lbs. **5.** 5,440 lbs.

Page 130 (Art. 12-8)

1. 12,600 lbs. **2.** 42,800 lbs. **3.** 149,500 lbs. **4.** 64,500 lbs.

Page 131 (Review Problems)

1. 335,000 lbs. **2.** 28,300 lbs. **3.** 67,900 lbs. **4.** 88,000 lbs.

Page 134 (Art. 13-2)

1. 12,000 lbs. per sq. in. **2.** 12,800 lbs. per sq. in. **3.** 9,150 lbs. per sq. in. **4.** 15,600 lbs. per sq. in.

Page 136 (Art. 13-3)

1. 20,500 lbs. per sq. in. **2.** 12,700 lbs. per sq. in. **3.** 20,800 lbs. per sq. in. **4.** 18,000 lbs. per sq. in. **5.** 32,300 lbs. per sq. in. **6.** 35,900 lbs. per sq. in.

Page 137 (Art. 13-4)

1. 18,000 lbs. **2.** 6,630 lbs. **3.** 10,800 lbs. **4.** 6,630 lbs.

Page 141 (Art. 13-6)

1. 4 rivets; 4 x 3½ x ⅜ angles. **2.** 2 rivets; 6 x 4 x ⅜ angles. **3.** 4 rivets; 4 x 3½ x ⅜ angles. **4.** 2 rivets; 6 x 4 x ⅜ angles. **5.** 2 rivets; 6 x 4 x ⅜ angles. **6.** 3 rivets; 4 x 3½ x ⅜ angles.

Page 142 (Art. 13-7)

1. B = 5″; t = ⅞″. **2.** B = 7″; t = 1″. **3.** B = 11″; t = 1½″. **4.** B = 5″; t = ⅞″.

Page 145 (Art. 13-9)

1. 2.15″. **2.** 1.75″. **3.** 3.5″. **4.** 3″.

Page 151 (Art. 13-10)

Problem	L_2	L	t_a	L_1	*Weld Size*
1	3	5	½	4	¼
2	3½	8	9/16	6	¼
3	3	8	⅜	4	3/16
4	3½	10	⅝	6	⅜

Page 153 (Review Problems)

1.

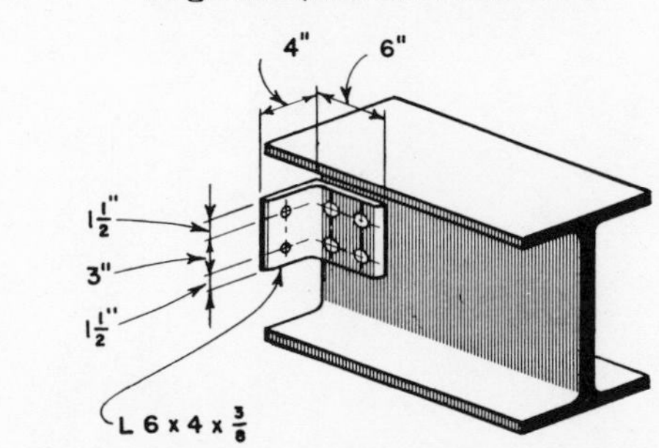

Page 153 (Review Problems)—*Continued*

2.

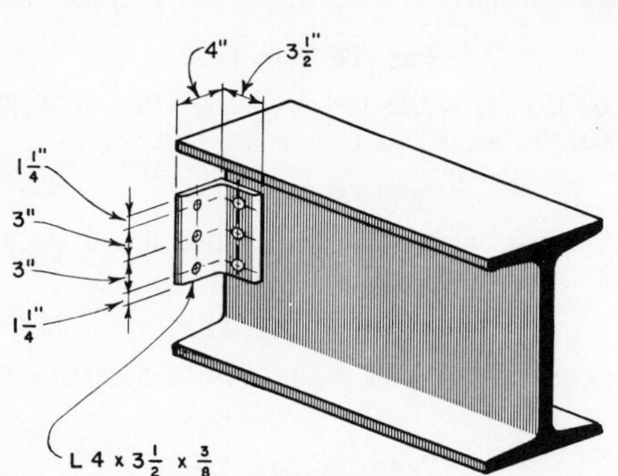

3.

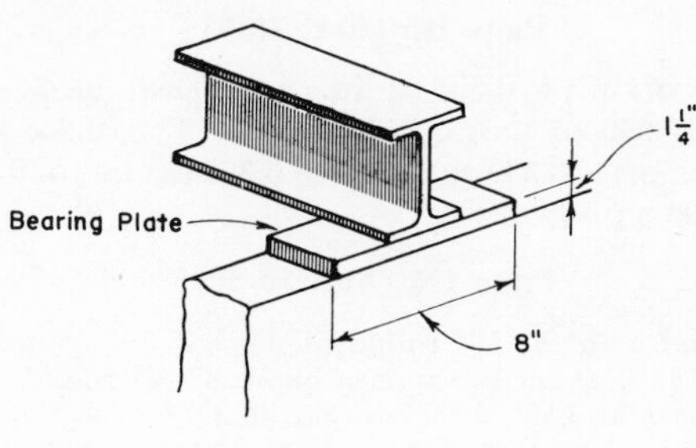

4.

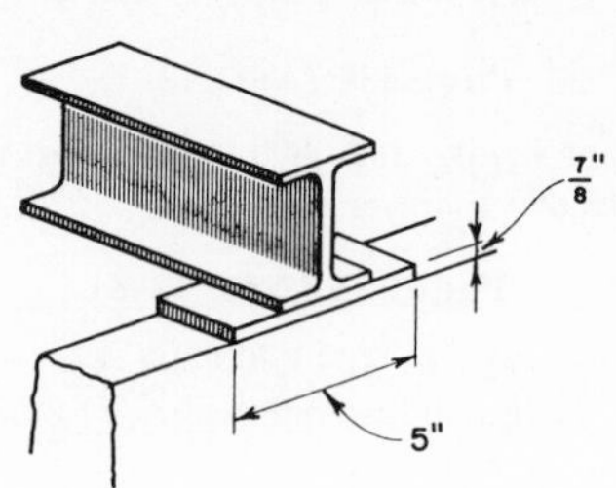

5.

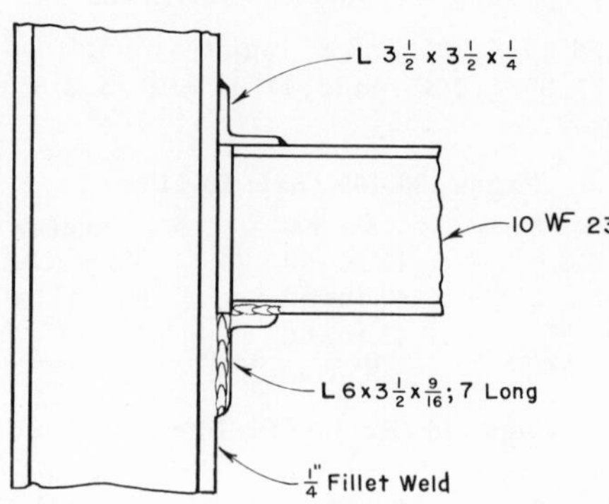

6.

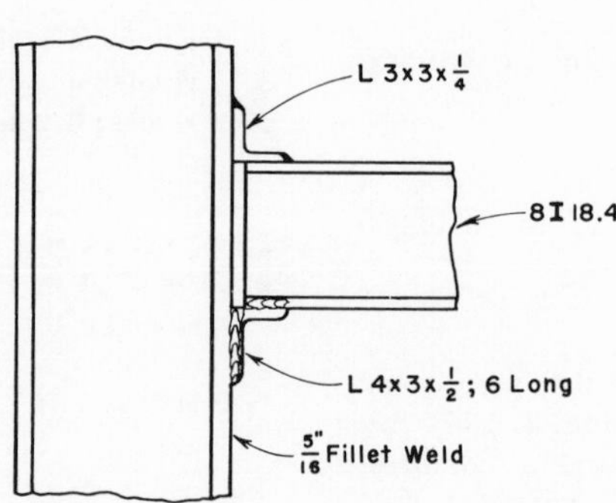

INDEX

FORMULES

$$\text{WATER CONTENT} = \frac{\text{WEIGHT OF WATER}}{\text{WEIGHT OF SOLIDS}}$$

$$\text{VOLUME OF SOLIDS} = \frac{\text{WT OF SOIL}}{G_s + \gamma w}$$

$\gamma w = 62.4$

VOLUME OF VOIDS = 1 - VOLUME OF S

$$\text{VOID RATIO} = \frac{\text{VOLUME OF VOIDS}}{\text{VOLUME OF SOLIDS}}$$

$$\text{PROSITY} = \frac{\text{VOLUME OF VOIDS}}{\text{TOTAL VOLUME} = 1}$$